SAM'S

A Cornish Schoolboy Sailor in World War 2

A true story
by
CYRIL HART

Foreword by EVThompson

Quelque chose de nouveau et de vrai; c'est la seule excuse d'un livre.
(Voltaire)

[The only reason for writing a book is that it is unique and true.]

First published 2004
by
LANDFALL PUBLICATIONS
Landfall, Penpol, Devoran, Truro, Cornwall TR3 6NR
Tel. 01872 862581

ISBN
1 873443 49 8

A CIP catalogue record for this book is available from the British Library.

The photograph on the back cover is by Dr David Hutson.

Printed by the Troutbeck Press
and bound by R.Booth Ltd., Antron Hill, Mabe, Penryn, Cornwall

For

Sally and Andrew

David and Marion

Jonathan, Sarah and Darcy

By the same author

Cornish Oasis
A Biographical Chronicle of the Fishing Village of
COVERACK
Cornwall

THANKS

I am most grateful for consultations held with my friend
Len Husband, former Lieutenant, R.N.V.R.,
to my good neighbours
Bridget and David Hutson
for their practical help with the photographs and encouragement
and to my former colleague and friend
Bob Acton
for his patience and good advice when proofreading the typescript.
Finally, my thanks to Cornish best-selling historical novelist
Ernest Thompson,
who also served in the Royal Navy, for reading the typescript,
suggesting improvements and writing a Foreword,
as he did for my first book, *Cornish Oasis*, in January 1991.

Cyril Hart

CONTENTS

PREFACE

Sam's War is a true account of a Cornish lad from Coverack, which is a fishing village on the Lizard peninsula. Sam Exelby leaves school in 1941 during his sixth form year in order to join the Royal Navy as an Ordinary Seaman. The narrator describes Sam's experiences on the destroyer HMS *Pathfinder* during convoys to West Africa, the Caribbean and the Mediterranean. Eventually the former Grammar School boy becomes a Midshipman and joins a Combined Operations Scout Unit which takes part in the invasion of Normandy, by creating a successful diversion in the Pas de Calais area. After a brief rest, Sam goes on to land Canadian infantry on Juno Beach. He slowly changes into manhood, having the confidence of untried youth, but at the same time is aware of his inadequacies when he has to assume responsibilities beyond his tender years. His quiet Cornish sense of humour, though tinged at times with inherited Celtic gloom, helps him keep a sense of proportion while coping with periods of boredom punctuated by moments of sheer fright and excitement. After D Day he is sent to the Far East and eventually lands in Singapore when the Japanese surrender.

Sam's War emulates, to a certain degree, the genre of writer Charles Lee, who wrote the story of *Paul Carah, Cornishman*. The name was a pseudonym for a real person who lived in Coverack, which Lee called Porthvean. Sam Exelby, his relations and fellow villagers, have also been given pseudonyms, but most of the other people in this war story retain their own names or naval nicknames.

Cyril Hart
Falmouth, March 2004

FOREWORD

In his preface to *Sam's War*, Cyril Hart describes the book as a story of a Cornish boy going to war. It is, indeed, the tale of a young man from a small fishing community who is taken from a close, insular environment and thrust into a world at war.

But there is much more to this fascinating book than the record of one man. *Sam's War* draws the reader into a world full of interest and excitement and is written with the authority of an author who has lived his story, and relates it with an astonishing eye for detail.

It is a record of a world at war from a man who saw it at first hand and with him we share the bewilderment of a recruit encountering the seemingly senseless rules and regulations of naval discipline, and actions at sea when such discipline ensures that a ship is a super-efficient fighting machine.

The reader shares the tragedies encountered by one of the most famous convoys of the war when, despite constant attack from German and Italian warships, submarines and aircraft, and after suffering appalling losses, the Royal Navy escorts the surviving merchant ships into Malta, enabling the island to survive and fight on with such determination that the tiny island community is awarded a George Cross.

Cyril Hart gives us an insight into life on the lower deck of a warship before going on to offer an enthralling glimpse of wardroom life when he becomes an officer in the Royal Navy. It is now that he enters the world of Combined Operations, serving in a unit whose whole *raison d'être* is to deceive the enemy.

The unit moves from Europe to the Far East where the author - Sam - is deeply moved by the sad plight of those men who survived the horrors of Japanese prisoner-of-war camps.

This book is not only a moving and detailed narrative of one man's experience of war, I consider it to be an important and valuable addition to our knowledge of World War II itself.

EVThompson
Pentewan, September 2004

NAVAL TERMINOLOGY

There are many naval terms used in this book. The opening words, for example, "Heave Ho! Heave Ho! Lash up and stow!" are the traditional way of telling sailors to get out of their hammocks, tie them up and put them in the rack provided.

The meaning of such terms will become evident from the context.

By the time you have finished reading the book you will have gleaned that the sailor's slang word for the Royal Navy is the Andrew, Guz is the name given to Devonport, a battlewagon is a battleship, ticklers are cigarettes rolled by hand from tobacco supplied to sailors by Jack Dusty, - the unofficial title of the rating responsible for issuing naval stores - nutty is chocolate, kye is cocoa, a buzz is an unconfirmed rumour, a pipe is an announcement made on board ship, a stone frigate is a shore establishment, and so on.

Happy reading!

Cyril Hart

Sam is in the final March Past before HM Queen Elizabeth II on the 60th anniversary of D Day at Arromanches, 6th June 2004

CHAPTER ONE

SIERRA LEONE

"Heave Ho! Heave Ho! Lash up and stow!" Sam Exelby was sleeping sweatily in his hammock. Gradually the import of the pipe dawned, causing him to peer cautiously in the direction from which the sound of the voice was coming. Had someone taken over his job as Bosun's Mate? To his astonishment, he could see a grinning black face blocking the open porthole. For a moment he panicked. Why wasn't the deadlight covering the porthole? The ship would be seen for miles in the dark and before long a torpedo would come crashing into the thin hull of the destroyer *Pathfinder* and he would be to blame! Before he could decide what to do, the familiar voice of the killick boomed out, "F... off, you noisy bastard." The black face disappeared and peace reigned.

Sam settled down in his hammock, adjusting the towel covering his middle which was doing service as pyjamas. He closed his eyes, relishing the feeling of being able to "crash" for a while longer. His hammock was slung over the mess table. The cook arrived with a fanny of tea and thumping Sam's bottom said, "Hey, Jan, I thought you had the forenoon watch. It's turned half past seven." Sam was proud of being a Janner. That was the name given to all westcountry sailors by those who came from "up the line". However, without more ado, Sam swung his legs over the side of the hammock, stepping on the mess table as he did so, then he quickly lashed up his hammock, undid the clews and removed it from the hooks in the deck head and stowed it away. He grabbed his toilet gear from the locker and ran to the heads, washed and shaved in a couple of minutes, dashed back to the mess, put on his white shorts and cotton "flannel", long blue knee-high stockings and white topee, swallowed his daily dose of quinine, washing it down with a swig of tea made with condensed milk, and raced from the fo'c'sle to the Quarter Deck where the Quartermaster, Alan Emmett, was already on duty.

Alan, who came from Penzance, greeted him with, "Where 'ee been boy? Thought you'd fallen in the hoggin." Sam mumbled his apologies from beneath his topee which had nearly dropped in the hoggin when he tripped up on the Iron Deck, pointing out it was the first time he'd slept in his hammock since leaving the Clyde. At sea when he was off watch he turned in all standing, if that is the correct expression - with his clothes on and lifebelt half inflated. He slept on a mess deck form with one arm curled round a stanchion so that he wouldn't fall off when the ship rolled more violently than usual. Last night, the first time he had been able to sleep more than three and a half hours for a couple of weeks, he had slung his hammock and had a wonderful sleep.

Slowly Sam began to realise where he was as he stood at ease on the Quarter Deck beside Alan. The big adventure of arriving in Africa was unfolding before him. The *Pathfinder* was lying at anchor off Freetown. The destroyer was surrounded by a group of dugout canoes, each one handled by a young West African boy and laden with bananas. Every time a canoe got close to the Quarter Deck, Alan waved it away. The Quarter Deck was the preserve of the officers and they were not to be bothered, but some trade was being carried on from nearer the bow of the ship. Matelots were bargaining with the boys for bunches of green bananas. There were no bananas available in the U.K. in early 1942 and the sailors were keen to take some back on the next convoy, assuming of course that they were going to return. The natives' command of English was confined to what they had picked up from sailors calling at the port. The boys had no idea what they were saying, except that when they raised a laugh from their prospective buyers they knew it was good for trade. "Bananas Sir? No f...ing good." That opening gambit was certain to provoke a bawdy retort from Jack and the bargaining would begin. The local lads were not necessarily interested in money. The sailors had all kinds of interesting gadgets and articles of clothing which were coveted by the boys. Later, Sam was to get a huge bunch of bananas in exchange for an old black cap. Once the bananas were obtained, the trick was to wrap the coveted fruit in a naval black silk scarf and stow it in a cool locker. By the time the ship was back in the U.K. the bananas would be ripe and the sailor the envy of the civvies who could not offer a girl such luxuries.

As the forenoon watch wore on, the *Pathfinder* was visited by various port officials and Sam was kept busy making fast the painters and piping aboard Captains of sister destroyers who had come to see Commander E.A. Gibbs, D.S.O., R.N., Captain of the *Pathfinder* and Half Leader, or second in command of the destroyer flotilla. The Engineer Officer went ashore and came back an hour later looking none too pleased. Shortly afterwards the "buzz" indicated that they were to have a boiler clean in Freetown before setting out with the next convoy. The rumour initiated by the stokers proved to be correct and a large tender came alongside bearing a couple of dozen local dockies. As Sam went about his duties he met his first "real" Africans. They were somewhat different from what he expected. His notion of an African was influenced by what he had been told by visiting missionaries toting for funds in the Wesleyan Sunday School he had attended in Coverack. These men were lean, tough characters dressed in rags. They looked as if they would steal the shirt off your back - as indeed they probably would for they were desperately poor. Sam was told to keep an eye open for petty pilfering. When he had piped "Cooks to the galley" he noticed a stir of interest in the dock gang who were on deck. "Cooks to the galley" meant that the mess cooks of the day had to go to the ship's galley to collect the meal which they had prepared after breakfast for the twenty-or-so men in the mess. The job of the chef was to cook the meals and have them ready in time for the pipe "Cooks to the galley".

When the meal was over the mess cooks cleared up and took the waste "gash" along to the bins on the Iron Deck. In the interests of port hygiene, waste food had to be stored ready for collection by gash barges which called on the ships at anchor every day. To Sam's astonishment, when the bins had been filled with the waste from two hundred crew members, the dockies gathered round the bins, dipped their meal tins into the revolting mess and began eating with evident relish. Sam's education in colonial concerns was proceeding apace.

After lunch, Sam got ready to go ashore with his mate Dick Davies. The liberty men were inspected by the Officer of the Watch and they all went ashore in a large cutter sent from the Naval Base. As they approached the jetty they could see the huge NAAFI beer marquee with several brawny Naval Police lounging outside in case of trouble. Dick and Sam were thirsty but decided NAAFI beer was probably even worse in Freetown than it was in the U.K. and kept to their original plan which was to make their way to the beach for their first swim in tropical seas.

On their way to Lumley Beach they went along Wilberforce Street, which was a colonial replica of almost any High Street back home. The traffic was mainly two-wheeled, apart from commercial lorries and service vehicles. It was controlled by a khaki-uniformed policeman wearing snow-white cuffs and obviously relishing every moment of his power over lesser mortals travelling along his patch.

On their way down to the beach they passed several bare-breasted women carrying bundles on their heads. Neither Sam nor Dick had seen women in this state of undress before but they tried to look as if they were seasoned sailors and continued on their way. It was almost a relief when they were able to run into the sea and dive into the surf. The presence of shark nets beyond the breaking waves was a little disconcerting but the lure of the warm sea was such that the sharks were soon put out of their minds as they frolicked in the surf. All too soon it was time to come out of the water and wend their way to the jetty where they had landed.

This time the lads were ready for the disturbing sight of the black mamas swinging along and stared unabashed at the sight. Before long they had invented an amended drill for the buxom ladies: "Ladies, by the left, quick march! Left tittie, right tittie, left tittie, right tittie. Come on, ladies, head up, chest out, chin in - left tittie, right tittie, left tittie, right tittie, swing those arms. Left tittie, right tittie!' The ladies in question seemed to divine what the lads were saying and passed with broad grins and a provocative swing of the hips.

All too soon they had passed the NAAFI tent and caught up some of the crew who had drunk well but not wisely and were staggering towards the returning liberty boats. Sam and Dick helped a couple along the dusty road and steadied them as they climbed down the ladder to the cutter going to the *Pathfinder*. They headed into the wind and as the cutter gathered speed, warm spray came over the bows and drenched those who had to sit for'ard. By the time they were alongside, the NAAFI-frequenting sailors had sobered up enough to manage a fair semblance of a salute as they stepped on the quarter deck and made their way for'ard to collect their station card to prove they had returned on board.

There was no dusk. Darkness descended swiftly with little warning. Freetown was in no danger of bombing raids or shelling from the sea so all the ships were lit up and Sam found it difficult to turn in. He had the Middle Watch from midnight to 4 a.m. and needed to sleep. His disappointment was short-lived because when he woke up and went along to relieve his opposite number, not only were the ships still illuminated but lightning was playing on the aerials and rigging. The electrical discharge was not sudden like one sees in Europe: it ran gently along the wires, rippling like wavelets on a calm day. There was no thunder, just blue flashes everywhere. No one had told him about "St. Elmo's Fire" and he stood, fascinated, throughout the watch, almost forgetting that he had to rouse the next batch of duty men. Unlike Dylan Thomas' exhortation, it was the custom to "go gentle into that good night" when rousing men at such an hour. They were advised to "Heave ho! Heave ho!" but that was all. They could not disturb everyone and lash up and stow their hammocks. Like Sam, most of them slept "all standing" at sea to avoid having to spend time dressing up to go on deck but in port it was different, especially on that night in Freetown when many had turned in late as they could not bear to leave nature's display in the harbour. On the second day in Freetown harbour the mail arrived. After the excitement of clamouring to collect the letters a silence descended on the mess deck as the sailors began to read their letters from home. Some of the men on board were from the base at Guz, the sailors' name for Devonport. It became apparent that there had not been many raids since the ship had left the U.K. and the men were soon exchanging gossip about happenings at home. Sam saved the parcel he received until he had read all his letters. The parcel was from his mother. He opened it and immediately a horrible smell pervaded the mess. His doting mother had decided Sam ought to have a few eggs from their own hens, not knowing, of course, that the *Pathfinder* was going to West Africa, because she had been at Scapa Flow for some time doing torpedo trials. Censorship would not allow sailors to say where they were, but Sam and his Mum had a code. Sam would ask how Mr. Combes was getting on. That meant he was in Scotland as their neighbour, Mr. Combes, the former station Officer of Coastguards in Coverack, had moved to Aberdeen. It was a rough and ready code but it worked quite well as they knew village people who had connections all over the world due to emigration from the village in the 19th and early 20th centuries. The trouble was that Sam did not know they were going to West Africa after the work-up in Scapa Flow. As the smell of rotten eggs spread, Sam left Mess No. 3 hurriedly and dumped the offending parcel in the nearest gash bin. It took him many moons to live that down. Most of the comments were unprintable, but Sam's next letter home convinced his mother that he was not starving and there was absolutely no need to send any food at all as they were living like fighting cocks in the "Andrew", which was the sailors' name for the Royal Navy. An exaggeration, of course, but it did the trick. Sam's father had spent four years in the trenches during the Great War and his mother used to send him home-made cakes whenever she could, so she was only continuing the family tradition.

CHAPTER TWO

COVERACK

The arrival of the mail caused Sam to think about his present position. From an early age he had wanted to join the Navy. It was inevitable really because he could throw a stone into the bay from the front of the family cottage in Coverack. Sam's Grandfather Trengilly was a fisherman, his own father George Exelby a lifeboatman, and his uncles and cousins were all seamen of one sort or another.

The house in Sunny Cove, Coverack, was all that a Cornish boy could wish for. It was on the top of a low cliff with a garden in front belonging to the thatched cottage just below. The properties were separated by a path which led to the point opposite the row of houses, which was known as Mears Point. In winter months, Sam slept in a tiny bedroom at the front of the house. From there he could see ships going up- and down-Channel. Those close in were making for Falmouth when they went up Channel and those on the horizon were bound for Plymouth or Southampton and beyond. Ships going down-Channel were going to round the Lizard and Land's End or if they were out deep they were on their way to America or Africa, depending on the course being steered. Sometimes Sam would sneak his father's telescope up to the bedroom and take a look at close quarters. This led to his speculating what it would be like to be aboard one of the ocean-going ships, bound for foreign shores. How he would love to go on a long voyage and return up-Channel and spy at his beloved Coverack on the way. He was destined to pass up-Channel only once during his naval career and then he was asleep as he had to take the Middle Watch from midnight to four in the morning. It so happened that he was not terribly disappointed because it was the occasion of returning to the U.K. from the Far East at the end of the war and he was too excited to bother about his childhood dream. Besides, on that occasion he had other matters on his mind such as a reunion with the girl he hadn't seen for nearly two years, and another dream - about the possibility of sudden wealth. The crew of the Indomitable had organised a sweepstake concerning the time of passing Nab Tower on the way into Portsmouth Harbour. Sam had never won anything before and he felt that this time he might be lucky and have a substantial sum to add to his gratuity when he was demobbed. He didn't win and he didn't see Coverack from out to sea but the thought of starting a new life tempered his disappointment.

Sunny Cove was at the western end of Coverack. Sam's cottage was an old Coastguard House which had been sold by the Admiralty when the government of the day introduced a cut in personnel. Coastguards still lived in the remainder of the small row of cottages. This meant that there were always plenty of children with whom he could play. The Coastguards came and went at regular intervals so his friends were constantly changing. It was not a very satisfactory state of affairs but it was inflexible. Of course, the native village lads were always there, so when changes came about on the Coastguard station the sense of loss was not too great and there was always the anticipation of making new acquaintances when the replacement officers arrived with their families.

Sam was born five years after the end of the Great War. He was aware that something momentous happened which had changed village life dramatically. The men who marched to the War Memorial on Remembrance Sunday were something special. Sam didn't have to be told, it was a fact of village life. When he was five years old the village hall was completed and the ex-servicemen had a billiard room of their own at the back of the building. Sam's father was the Secretary of the British Legion and Sam was privileged to go down and try his hand at potting balls while his father tidied the room and got the hall ready for whist drives and meetings. Each year in November there was a lesson devoted to the Great War in school and gradually the significance of that event became apparent to Sam, but his father rarely mentioned it and his mother always looked as if she were about to cry when the subject was brought up in conversation. By the time Sam realised the magnitude of what had taken place during the Great War, the newspapers had begun mentioning the real possibility of another world-wide conflict.

School proved to be a period of almost pure enjoyment for Sam. Of course, he did not realise this until he had left but he rarely hated the thought of having to walk up the steep hill behind his house to the Council School at the top. School was an extension of village life. All his friends were there in the two rooms which held around forty pupils from five to fourteen. Miss Corlyon was his first teacher. She was a kindly person and taught the three Rs in such a way that no one seemed to think she was asking them to achieve the impossible. There were one or two children who found it difficult but when they were promoted to the "big room" they could usually read, if somewhat hesitantly. Sam found reading easy but when it came to writing, the pen would never do what he wanted it to do and his writing was to remain a scrawl despite the beautiful copperplate examples of his teacher.

Life out of school was not a problem. Once he was released, Sam would run down the hill with his mates. Sometimes they trundled an iron hoop in the middle of the road and let it run on until it hit the Chapel wall and jumped over into the clump of pampas grass which appeared to the boys to have been planted in that very spot to cushion the blow of being hurled over the barrier. Sometimes it was a boy on a bike without brakes who had been dared to ride it down the steep slope. The trick was to put the foot against the back wheel and slow down the bike but this was impossible after gaining a certain speed, so when the hapless boy hit the wall and flew into the Chapel garden he was glad of the relative softness of the spiky leaves even if they did scratch him badly.

Sam's mother, Mary Exelby, insisted that Sam report home before going to play in the village. She was very protective because Sam had a "tricky" stomach and Mary made sure he was well wrapped up before he left Sunny Cove and went down to the harbour. Sam hated this maternal concern and tried to conceal it from the other boys by telling them he would catch them up. Unfortunately from time to time he did catch cold. It would go straight to his stomach, and that meant a few days in bed to get his temperature down. The only consolation in that was that he was able to read in bed. He always finished any book he had been given in a few days so when he was ill he borrowed his parents' books from the cupboard on the landing. When he was about ten his mother and father decided to buy a set of Arthur Mee's *Children's Encyclopedia*s on the "never never" after being persuaded by a travelling salesman that all households should have a set. The villagers were not in favour of hire purchase, their philosophy being that if you haven't got the money, you do not buy the goods. However, Sam's parents made an exception, knowing the value of education. From then on, Sam unconsciously began to assimilate a fair fund of knowledge but despite that he had failed to get into the local secondary school. It didn't bother him greatly. Coverack was all he wanted at that stage in his development. The great wide world did not beckon at the tender age of eleven.

When the depression began to be felt in Coverack, Sam was quite unaware of the belt-tightening that came about. There were chickens in the back garden and plenty of vegetables. Fish were plentiful. Clothes were of no concern to the village lads. And why buy football boots when hobnailers struck terrror into your opponents? His Uncle Alexander Trengilly was a Bosun in British Tankers. When he came back to Falmouth after a trip to Abadan he told his sister Mary, Sam's mother, that he had three Master Mariners in the fo'c'sle, serving as Able Bodied Seamen. The significance of this did not strike Sam. After all, on another occasion he remembered Uncle Alexander telling his mother that the skipper of his tanker had asked him if he would teach him to sail. Uncle Alexander had taught Sam and his cousin Horace to sail in the *Rosemary* so why shouldn't he teach his skipper? There was nothing remarkable in that. One consequence of the depression did make Sam stop and think, although he did not realise it was the depression which was changing his life style. His father decided to build a tea room. He even invited Sam to draw a plan but he did not tell him work was scarce and the family needed more money to survive. George Exelby had managed to rent a plot of land and the room was going to be built in such a way that if the landlord gave notice the café could be dismantled and assembled somewhere else. This was exciting. Sam always like helping his father, who was the local builder. In due course the café was ready and the first customers had a taste of his mother's cream teas which were to become well known far and wide. Sam was recruited as messenger boy and he cycled to the farm every day to fetch the clotted cream. He was also needed for washing up and other chores. That sort of work was not very interesting. Sam began to realise that he was no longer able to go down to the quay and mess about in boats as often as he would like.

When he got a bit older he persuaded his mother to allow him to camp in Mr. Reseigh's field during the summer months. Cousin Horace shared the tent (eight shillings and sixpence plus postage from the Gamages catalogue) and the two boys soon devised ways of having a rare old time in the village when they were ostensibly fast asleep in the field behind the row of Coastguard houses. The boys' parents did not check up too closely on the camping lark. Their absence from home meant their rooms could be let to summer visitors and that supplemented the family income in lean times. Sam was to look back on those halcyon days with great affection. Sometimes, during the long summer holidays, Horace and Sam would get up early and go out in the *Isis*, Uncle Alexander's rowing boat. They would catch a couple of mackerel or if the tide was right spear an unsuspecting plaice lurking on the sandy bottom behind the quay wall. The spear was a bamboo with a sharp nail bound to the end by a whipping. They learned all about refraction before doing it in Science lessons. If you didn't know about it, and aimed the spear from the perpendicular, you didn't get the fish.Then they would go back up to Mr. Reseigh's field and fry the fish over a wood fire. The smell of the frying and the taste of the smoky fish signalled the beginning of another perfect day in Coverack.

Sam as a schoolboy

CHAPTER THREE

HAPPY DAYS

After the fuss of failing to win a place in the secondary school at Helston had died down, Sam steeped himself in the life of the village. He did his chores with good grace as he loved his family and wanted to pull his weight. He took pride in being one of the village boys but found that he needed space and time to himself, so he would go off on long bike rides and explore the nearby villages. When he got thirsty he found that if he stopped in front of a roadside farm there was the possibility that if the farmer's wife spotted him she would offer him a glass of water, or sometimes a delicious drink of fresh milk. Sam didn't stop to consider if it had been pasteurised. He knew nothing of such things but he did enjoy quenching his thirst while telling the farmer's wife who he was and where he had come from. Sam's grandfather, Henry Exelby, was a Wesleyan local preacher, and sometimes when Sam stopped at a farm it so happened that his grandfather had spent a Sunday there when preaching in the local chapel. On one occasion he was taken to see the well his grandfather had dug for the farmer. Henry was a renowned dowser and would dig a well for £5 on the proviso that if water was not found he would charge nothing for his work. Later, when they had a chance to go ashore on one of the Scottish islands from the *Pathfinder*, Sam and Dick Davies would hire bikes and go on a tour. Being in Naval uniform, they found they were welcome at any croft where they happened to stop and were regaled with home cooking and a warm by the fire, thus exploding the myth about the mean streak in the Scots.

Another enjoyable lone activity was to go for long cliff walks. Sam's father, George Exelby, used to take him when he was a small lad and tell him stories about the village as they climbed the cliffs and gathered wreck wood for burning in the open grate of the cottage. Sam loved these tales, especially about the wrecks which occurred in the early part of the century. George had been a member of the crew of the Coverack lifeboat, the *Constance M.,* but he left the village to try his luck in Canada when a young man. He returned to Coverack and went into the army during the Great War. When he came home he went on a few call-outs in the pulling and sailing boat and then was asked if he would become head launcher. He held that position for thirty years until he retired.

Summers seemed endless in Coverack. They took a long time in coming, but there were plenty of activities in winter to keep the village children happy. The school only had about forty children, including infants, so there were not many girls to choose from. The only opportunity to kiss a girl was when playing "Postman's Knock" at a Sunday School party. That was a matter of luck as a girl would go into the kitchen behind the school room and whisper a boy's name to the door keeper. The name would be announced in a loud voice to the expectant scholars and the blushing boy would stumble to the kitchen amid cheers and jeers to receive his kiss in the darkened kitchen. It was then his turn to choose a girl. Usually he was afraid to ask for the one he really wanted because he would be the butt of jokes in the playground the following day. As Sam grew older he grew bolder and finally managed to ask a girl to go for a walk. A meeting place away from the tiny village had to be arranged. Even then, someone was bound to put two and two together if a boy and a girl were seen making their separate ways to a rendezvous. Sam's favourite ploy was to go down a cliff and then make his way along the rocks as if looking for wreck wood. Then he would climb up a cleft unseen and make his way to the appointed spot.A quick stroll hand in hand out of sight of prying eyes and a hasty kiss on parting had to do until he was old and bold enough to be seen in public with someone. That, plus reading answers to letters asking for advice in the *Woman's Weekly,* had to do for Sam's sex education until his world extended beyond Coverack.

Sam's clandestine walks were most enjoyable, perhaps all the more so because he thought no one knew about his assignations with Elsie Barker. She was younger than he was, typically Cornish in appearance. She had a pretty face, was dark-haired, short and plump but with all the curves in the right places. They walked and talked and kissed and cuddled and spent much of their time arranging the next meeting. They were both happy in their innocence. Elsie's father was a strict disciplinarian although he was known to be the type who bent the rules to suit himself, especially if there was any financial gain to be had from his activities. This state of affairs made the meetings all the more enjoyable because of the hint of danger attached to them. Joseph Barker was not a violent man but like all fathers he was very protective of his only daughter. He himself had been a chaser of anything in skirts in his day and he naturally assumed all young males in the village were keen to deflower his daughter. Imagine Sam's consternation when a farmer's daughter told him on one of her regular Saturday visits to the village to deliver cream and butter and eggs that he and Elsie had been observed canoodling on the cliffs. How on earth did she know? She laughed when he asked and confided that she often spent an afternoon sitting in the sycamore tree behind the farm house, peering through her father's binoculars. Sam was mortified but Millie Martin assured him his secret was safe with her and confided that she used to do the same with Elsie's father when they were young! Later, when Sam had joined the navy, he and Elsie corresponded, and when he came home on leave he was invited to tea at Elsie's house. Joe seemed pleased to see him but hinted that after being educated at the Grammar School he had not expected Sam to be wearing bell bottoms. That rather unfortunate remark stayed with Sam and when in due course he and Elsie went their separate ways, Sam thought it was just as well because he did not want to be judged by his progress in the navy. He wanted to be appreciated for being just Sam.

CHAPTER FOUR

HELSTON

Sam's first acquaintance with Helston Secondary School was at the age of 10 when he went to take the Minor Scholarship, or "Examination for Special Places" as the exam paper was headed. He had already passed the "Prelim.", which he sat in Coverack Council School, and was looking forward to seeing what he hoped would be his new place of learning. He was unprepared for the ordeal.

The candidates were ushered into what Sam subsequently identified as the Detention Room. The master was Mr. Manks, a formidable character, who commanded instant obedience and seemed to instill a feeling of guilt in the most innocent of boys! This was due partly to the fact that he was cross-eyed and when he addressed the class it was never certain if he was looking directly at one particularly frightened boy or at some other poor wretch. He was wearing his academic gown. Sam had never seen one before and felt intimidated. It gave him a feeling of inferiority and made him wish he had never embarked on this great adventure. He longed for the friendly security of the litttle school in Coverack.

English Part 1 invited Sam to write a composition about a country he would like to live in should he be forced to leave England. The examiner was clearly unaware that many Cornish people considered they were not living in England - or perhaps, as it was 1933, he or she may have wanted the candidates to compare their situation with the plight of the non-Aryans in Germany who were faced with the dilemma of where they would go if they had to leave Germany. In fact, the children were also asked to state what they would expect to find in their chosen country so probably the aim of the question was to find out if they were capable of writing well about a subject which interested them, as the alternative subject was to describe the greatest surprise ever experienced.

Arithmetic Part 2 instructed them to do as many of the eight questions as possible during one hour. They were advised to do the easiest first. The first question was a bill:

15 lemons at 10d. a dozen
168 lbs. of potatoes at 7d. per 14 lbs.
3½ dozen oranges at 14 a shilling
2 bags of apples containing 28 lbs. each, at 3d. per lb.

It was all too much for Sam. In due course his failure was notified and he settled down once more to life in Coverack Council School. There were compensations. After the age of 11 he was allowed to go to St Keverne once a week to learn woodwork. It was a wonderful experience. The master was Mr. Walters, who taught the subject in Helston County School. Mr. Walters could be a hard taskmaster at times but Sam enjoyed being on his own in St Keverne Parish Hall and got into the habit of visiting his friend Mr. Toms, the local Headmaster. The boys soon had a system of lookouts arranged and enjoyed themselves during his absence but they didn't go too far as they knew retribution would be swift and terrible and it wasn't worth the risk. When the boys had been good during these absences they were sometimes rewarded with a bag of Mickey Mouse toffees which cost one penny for two ounces. It was a treat to eat the sweets while they went home through the fields to Coverack.

This idyllic existence was shortlived. Sam's mother began dropping heavy hints about the advantages of a secondary education. She told him about her experiences in Helston Secondary School when she won a scholarship in 1903. In those days it was not possible to return home at night so she stayed in lodgings during the week and came home on the horse bus on Saturdays. She got back to Helston on Sunday by riding with the local preacher or she came late on the horse bus which brought the farmers to market on Monday mornings. Sam was regaled with stories about her teachers, most of whom she thought were demigods, and he was told that if he were to follow in her footsteps his future was assured. There was much unemployment at that time in Coverack.

Sam was blissfully unaware that he had already been entered for the local "charity" exam because of his parents' financial circumstances but he was taken to St Keverne one fine Saturday morning and he sat the exam. He was pleased when the result came out a few weeks later and found he had been awarded the sum of £15 per annum. This was enough to pay the fees of £3+ per term with about £6 left over to pay for books, uniform, P.E. equipment, and travel etc. The £6 paid for the books which could be bought secondhand at school or at Bert Gill's Bookshop, but the money for the other things had to be found by his parents. The bus fare was 10 pence return. Sam tried to help by cycling the ten miles to school in fine weather and he also cycled when he was chosen to play for the school on Saturdays. Quite a number of boys did this so it was no wonder the team got beaten when the opposing team arrived fresh after riding in a bus from Redruth or wherever.

After a fortnight's work in the new school the pupils were given a report to take home. There were almost as many children in Sam's class as there were in the whole of Coverack School. Due to his late start, Sam was a year or so older than most of the children in his class. He had enjoyed being "a big fish in a little sea" but soon realised he had to work hard to keep up with the rest of the class. It seemed to pay off as he was awarded three books at the end of the year for coming first in the class. They were *Kenilworth*, *The Last of the Mohicans* and *The Last Days of Pompeii.* Each one was embossed in gold leaf with the school name and badge together with the school motto - "Humiles Consilium Servat!" Pride comes before a fall! The next year he was third and by the time he took Cambridge School Certificate he was 7th. It did him good: he worked hard at the last moment and managed to get Matriculation. He blamed his duties as messenger in the Home Guard for his fall from grace - France had fallen and Cornwall was now in the front line - but he had little sympathy from those who thought he could have done better.

In spite of Sam's miserable performance in Mathematics in the Minor Scholarship, the intervening years in Coverack had enabled him to improve enough to be able to enjoy Mr. Lesley's Maths lessons. He was firm but fair and consequently well-liked by most pupils. He had an unerring aim with a piece of chalk which would land on any hapless pupil not paying attention. Anyone venturing to speak while his back was turned when he was writing on the blackboard was called by name. At first Sam thought Mr. Lesley had supernatural hearing and eyes in the back of his head but later discovered that the teacher used his rimless spectacles as a mirror and watched the class while he was writing. It was a trick Sam was to adopt later in life with some success. Mr. Johns introduced Sam to Science. Like Mr. Lesley, he did not suffer fools gladly but did his job competently and with humour. When he hadn't prepared the compulsory Science homework, he would give the pupils a string of temperatures to convert from Centigrade (it was not called Celsius in those days) to Fahrenheit. After sweating over the sums by the light of an oil lamp Sam was always faintly disappointed that they were called upon to mark their own work when he called out the answers. "Johnny" as they called him behind his back had one favourite experiment which he repeated frequently when they were old enough to understand what he was doing. He would say, "Now we are going to revise the theory of convection currents," and with a broad smile on his face he would say, "Take a piece of smouldering paper and place it at the bottom of the fume chamber." While talking he would take a cigarette from his cigarette case and light it, blowing the smoke in the right direction so that it would go up and round the cupboard. Everyone knew he was dying for a puff and enjoyed the conspiracy.

Both Mr. Lesley and Mr. Johns played football with the school team when they were having a practice for a match so in a sense the masters became the boys' team mates and they respected the teachers for giving up their time to provide some stiff opposition.

From the second year onwards Mr. Archer took Geography. He was young and enthusiastic and the boys played him up gently while the girls fell in love with his wavy hair. He introduced Sam to elementary Geology and when Sam told him about the rocks in Coverack he took the trouble to come out and explain the formations. He took away some examples of igneous rock found at the Black Head to add to his collection. When the fall of France came about he would begin each lesson with a description of what was happening and update the position of the coloured flags he used to indicate the advance of the German army. The children learned much from this incidental method of studying Geography. The background knowledge concerning the terrain over which the German troops were advancing and the importance of the industrial strength of the towns they were capturing enabled them to discuss the gravity of the situation with some authority. Not long after the fall of France Mr. Archer left to join the Royal Navy where he became a Navigating Officer on a cruiser. Quite by accident, Sam and he were to meet again in Lancashire when they were both on demobilisation leave after the end of the war in the Far East.

Headmaster Mr. Stanley himself was Sam's Latin teacher. Some of the pages of Kennedy's Latin Primer became etched on his mind. What on earth was the point of saying "O table!" in the vocative case? In the end he accepted his mother's word that it would be "useful" one day and used the time on the bus to learn the declensions and conjugations by heart. Before long the pupils were making up imaginary Latin verbs, which when recited aloud on the bus sounded faintly obscene. If passengers enquired what they were doing, they were assured,as innocently as teeenaged boys knew how, that they were preparing their Latin homework. However, School Certificate was a serious business and the Head was intent that his pupils should be well prepared. They worked hard and with the aid of some cribs bought from the obliging Bert Gill, unravelled *Aeneid* Book IX etc. and emerged triumphant after a long struggle. It was not until Sam took up Latin again after the war that he began to enjoy what had almost literally been knocked into him. It says something for being made to learn a subject you don't like.

To return to Mr. Stanley. He was an imposing, all-powerful figure, held in awe by the pupils. Although he was unable to run, due, it was thought, to a war injury, he was a good cricketer, as most Yorkshiremen seem to be. In the Staff versus Pupils matches the balls were soon flying all over the ground when he went into bat with a small pupil as his runner. Having witnessed the power of his broad shoulders, not many were likely to risk having the cane from him. He seemed to have an all-seeing eye and would know if a boy walked up the school drive without his school cap on. He also became aware of anyone eating fish and chips in the street and made the culprit aware that he knew. The school was well run under his leadership and the pupils were proud of it. Speech Days in the Town Hall showed off the school to the locality. After much practising under Miss Porkellis, known to the pupils as Cap'n Wesley, as she was a local preacher, they would sing "Forty Years On" with great gusto at the end of the afternoon and mean every word, if only temporarily. Sam was blissfully unaware that the song had been borrowed from Eton, or was it Harrow? He never found out which.

Sam had not been enthusiastic about going to Helston. It meant being separated from friends whom he had known all his short life, and setting about making new ones. The old friends remained friends but his new "status" caused some problems. In Coverack it was considered to be "stuck up" to wear a cap, especially a "secatary" cap so Sam calculated that Mr. Stanley's all-seeing eye did not extend as far as the village and he would stuff his cap in his satchel when he walked through the cove. The satchel, or rather its contents, was another bone of contention. After tea, friends would call round to see if he would go out with them. He often had to refuse because of the homework which had to be done. The boys were unaware of the trouble he would be in if he arrived in school the next morning, unable to give the monitor the work which had been set the previous day. The problem was exacerbated by the fact that the Coverack boys would tell him that his cousin Horace Trengilly, a fee-paying pupil, was going out, so why couldn't he? Horace was in the same class and a past master at what we would now call brinkmanship. He had sufficient daring to leave everything to the last moment and if all else was lost, he knew cousin Sam could probably help by lending his work for him to adapt on the bus the following morning. His capacity for taking a calculated risk was to earn him, in later years, a R.N.L.I. Silver Medal as Coxswain of Sennen Lifeboat.

Miss Stephens introduced Sam to French. He had already made an attempt to teach himself by following the lessons in *The Children's Encyclopedia* and attempting to join in the conversations his mother had when the Breton onion seller came to the door. Miss Stephens made the language come alive. Sam was fascinated by the quaint illustrations in Collins' French Course. Miss Oliver followed Miss Stephens and she often illustrated the point she was trying to make by referring to episodes she had experienced when abroad. This was an opportunity for Sam and his friends to sidetrack her intentions and allow her to go on about her last holiday. One day she revealed that she had met a handsome S.S. man when in Germany but at that point the S.S. did not have the unsavoury reputation they were to gain in Britain after the outbreak of war and the pupils just enjoyed the diversion from a formal lesson.

Miss Naytor, the Senior Mistress, took over English from Miss Porkellis in readiness for the School Certificate. She was in despair sometimes of ever getting her pupils to appreciate the finer points of Jane Austen's writing but they managed to muddle through. An Air Raid Siren had been installed on the Town Hall, and Horace Trengilly discovered he could make a passable imitation of the Raid Warning signal. When English lessons became seemingly unending he would be encouraged by the rest of the Form to make the signal and Miss Naytor would order the pupils down to the shelter, which was in the reinforced corridor outside the Head's room . Of course, the class was soon sent packing, but the diversion was enjoyed by all except Miss Naytor. To her credit she showed no resentment and carried on gently trying to teach the ungrateful Philistines of Form 5A.

In later years Sam often tried to discover the secret ingredient which has bound the pupils of Helston together. Sir Arthur Quiller Couch, or "Q" as he is known to all Cornish people, resorted to a poetic description of the phenomenon, and wrote, "It is a spirit which, like the wind, blows where it lists." This indefinable "spirit" was to stand Sam in good stead throughout the war years and the friends he made in school remained his friends throughout his life. Sometimes there was a gap of twenty or thirty years when he did not meet them but he found that within minutes almost, the magic of the spirit returned and they were at home with one another and talking as if school were only yesterday.

CHAPTER FIVE

GROWING UP

"Q"'s "spirit" must have acted rather like the slow-release pain-relieving capsule of modern times in that its influence acted gently on Sam over a fair period of time. When he found his name in the *West Briton*'s pass list of School Certificate candidates, Sam was delighted, especially as he had been awarded Matriculation for good measure. Somehow or other a miracle had been performed. His pre-exam report was a gloomy one and he had been full of foreboding ever since. Now he could get on with his life.

It was not to be. Mary Exelby had already decided her son was to go into the 6th Form. Sam was bitterly disappointed but his mother would brook no argument. Sam consoled himself in the fact that being a 6th Former carried a lot of kudos in Helston Secondary. You were almost certain to be appointed Prefect and you had the privilege of being able to boss the little tiddlers about because you had already got School Cert. under your belt and were destined theoretically for even greater academic distinction. The teachers treated you as if you were a young adult and you had free time in which you could do private study in school hours. When Sam gained his Certificate it was only some forty years since children in his situation had first been able to get access to secondary education, and the Certificate was regarded as a significant milestone. Little did he know at that stage that he was to spend over a quarter of a century encouraging, cajoling, exhorting and even bullying those who, like himself, did not pass the scholarship, but were just as good as those who "on the day" had managed to get enough marks to be accepted for a more advanced type of education. The war had already affected life in Coverack. Sam was doing his bit with cousin Horace in the Home Guard. They were messengers and had a rare old time, being on call and sleeping under the table in the Guard Room, which by day was the Reseighs' kitchen next to the shop and Post Office. The guard commander was a local "lad" who had made good and retired early to Coverack. He had been a Civil Engineer, working in one of the oil Emirates since the end of World War One, and had doubled up as the Middle East correspondent for a national newspaper. Harry Ford was called Harry Hippo behind his back as his rotund figure resembled that of the hippopotamus in a cartoon serial story of a popular boys' comic. As a result of his war service, Harry was made the C.O. of the Local Defence Volunteers and was given a captaincy when it was transformed into the Home Guard. Harry soon had the village men organised into a passable infantry platoon although some were only armed with staves and various fearsome agricultural implements. When a heterogeneous collection of old rifles arrived in Coverack, Sam and Horace were put on parade and were soon forming fours almost as well as the veterans who had responded to the call to arms. Sam was given a rifle dated 1870. It had been brought across the Channel in a French fishing boat after the fall of France. He only had 30 bullets but he felt proud that he was allowed to have a gun, much to his mother's disgust, as she was afraid of firearms and insisted on the rifle being kept in the cowshed at the back of the house. The two lads were destined to be disillusioned when later on they joined the navy and had to learn to drill in threes. They had hoped the experience would enable them to steal a march on their fellow recruits. Instead, they had to unlearn all that had been taught in the village hall at Coverack.

The boy messengers were not called out very often. It was just as well because they had to go to school after being on stand-by all night. When given a job to do, Sam enjoyed riding through the countryside at night without lights, never knowing when he was going to be challenged by a roving foot patrol lurking behind a thick Cornish hedge. Of course, he was known to all the volunteers. Perhaps volunteers is not the correct term: let's just say that some were more volunteer than others! When he replied to the challenge, "Halt! Who goes there?" frequently one of the patrol would add, "Don't worry boy, we 'abn got nothing up the spout." When this happened, Sam wisely decided that it would not be diplomatic to explain that a double negative was actually a positive, in case the next time he was challenged some joker gave him a fright by loosing off a round of .303 just to show who was boss and to put the uppity "secatary" kid in his place.

During their hours of duty the cousins could not resist getting up to the sort of pranks all village boys get up to. If they were both called out in the small hours, on their return to Coverack they would stop outside the house of the War Reserve Special Constable and throw handfuls of gravel at his bedroom window. When the unfortunate "Rick" Rickard awoke he would slide down the sash window - it's curious how country people who work in the open air invariably sleep with the bedroom windows shut tight - and call out, "What do 'ee want now un?" Horace was a good mimic and would ask in a very refined voice, "Excuse me constable, could you possibly tell me the time, please?" The reply was usually quite unprintable but served to add to the boys' store of expletives which they were to use to good effect when the occasion demanded while they were serving in the Andrew.

On one memorable occasion when the boys were ostensibly sleeping while on "stand-by" under the table in the Reseigh's kitchen, it was observed that Harry Hippo had loosened his boot laces and was softly snoring. Carefully, from his vantage point under the table, Horace tied one of Harry's right-foot laces to one of the left. Meanwhile Sam crept out to a nearby telephone kiosk and rang the guard commander. The telephone was situated in the room Mr. Reseigh used as an office for his business transactions. Harry woke up with a start when the bell rang and made for the telephone, only to fall flat on his face. The cousins had not expected such a dramatic outcome of their prank and made themselves scarce, spending the rest of their guard in front of the fire in the Fishermen's Club which had been commandeered as as a Home Guard rest room for the village foot patrols. It was a very popular rendezvous, especially when an easterly gale was blowing and the locals knew no self-respecting German would attempt a landing at Coverack in such weather.

To his credit, Harry Hippo didn't take direct action against the pranksters. He adopted a more subtle method of getting his own back. He took to rousing the boys just after midnight when they were sleeping soundly and sending them with non-urgent, routine messages to the pill boxes which were situated at strategic points near the likely landing places in and around Coverack. On these occasions he would say, with a twinkle in his eye, "Now, Sam and Horace, I have to stay awake in case the phone rings, so will you deliver these messages and get a signature for each one. I shall expect you back before the hour is up. Good soldiers can estimate the passing of time, so don't ask anyone the time, will you?" No more needed to be said. The boys knew that Harry knew and they knew he knew about the Rick Rickard episodes as well. After a few call outs, Harry deemed the boys had learned their lesson and the mysterious messages ceased to be sent.

Sam entered the 6th Form after the long harvest holiday. He enjoyed his new-found prestige and, to his surprise, the challenge of learning spherical trigonometry and advanced physics. These subjects did not involve a great deal of swotting so in his free periods he took to lending the school groundsman a hand by driving the motor mower round the sports field. Sometimes, when he was feeling particularly energetic, he joined the volunteer pupils digging for victory on a spare patch of land which was being used to grow vegetables for the canteen.

Due to his new-found knowledge, Sam decided he would like to join the RAF as aircrew. He was bitterly disappointed when he applied to learn that as he had a dental plate he could not be accepted. School began to pall. Sam could not envisage two whole years in the 6th Form, followed by three years in college, so on the spur of the moment he answered a naval recruiting advertisement in the *News Chronicle* and within a week he had been invited to Bristol for an interview. He was sent a railway warrant and promised subsistence pay at the end of the interview, which was to take place in Whiteladies Road. There was no turning back. He plucked up courage and told his parents what he had done. After a good scolding from his mother and a disapproving look from his father, Sam thought he had got away with it. Then to his horror his mother announced she was coming with him. Sam was mortified, but had to concede. He did get his mother to agree to go and visit a friend who lived in Bristol while he attended the interview. What would the authorities think if a would-be sailor turned up with his mother in tow?

Arrangements were hastily made and the pair arrived in Bristol. It was the first time either had crossed the Tamar. Sam found Whiteladies Road and presented himself for the medical examination. Surely the navy didn't mind if he had a few false teeth? No mention was made by the doctor and after a test for colour blindness Sam was ushered into a tiny office where a very-much-retired Rear Admiral sat glaring at him. The Admiral's first salvo was a question involving a simultaneous quadratic equation. That held no terrors for Sam. Six years of Maths with Mr. Leslie had prepared him well for any trick question the old boy could throw at him. Sam's answer set the seal of approval in the Admiral's mind and the rest of the questions were answered with growing confidence. Sam even managed to steer the conversation into a discussion about the origins of the Helston Flora Dance and the interview ended with the old gent telling him he was now an Ordinary Seaman in the Royal Naval Volunteer Reserve and that he would be hearing from the Lords Commissioners of the Admiralty in due course.

CHAPTER SIX

RALEIGH

Sam was puzzled that an aspiring Ordinary Seaman should have the undivided attention of a Rear Admiral. Later, a Petty Officer Writer in the know told him he had been entered under the "Y" scheme and selected for possible "officer material". A village lad from Coverack who had failed the Minor Scholarship? "No", said Sam,"pull the other one - it's got bells on it." But the P.O. was right. Sam thought the Royal Navy must be getting pretty desperate. Senior officers had always selected a few Upper Yard men for advancement to commissioned rank, but these ratings had proved themselves during years of service. Sam had only just left school.

With good grace Mary Exelby accepted the inevitable and began to steel herself for the anxiety which her third child would cause when he left home. Mary herself was active in the Coverack Red Cross. Her husband George was the village ARP Warden and her elder children Alex and Emily were Territorials in the Royal Artillery and stationed on anti-aircraft gun sites around Plymouth, which had already suffered a devastating blitz. Sam loved to tease his mother, so copying the black humour of those wartime days he consoled his mother when she mentioned his approaching departure by saying, "It's all right, Mum, you join the navy to see the world and the Air Force to see the next." Casualties in the RAF were mounting in 1941.

Fortunately, Singapore was still being fêted as an impregnable fortress in the Far East so Mary had no qualms about her baby boy being drafted to that part of the world. One would have thought *someone* would have pointed out to the powers that be that a determined enemy would only have to approach the base from the virtually undefended rear in order to capture it. After all, the Germans went round the back of the unassailable Maginot Line via the lightly-defended Ardennes mountains of Belgium in 1940. Sam had met an Army type who told him he was enjoying a drink in a café when he saw a German soldier walking up the street outside. Fortunately he was able to go out of the back door and make good his escape. In the same tone, it seemed, with hindsight, equally incredible that the battle wagons *Repulse* and *Prince of Wales* were operating at sea within easy distance of a Japanese bomber base without even requesting air cover. The two ships were sunk for the loss of only eight Japanese aircraft. That happened on the very day Sam reported to HMS *Raleigh* - the 10th December, 1941. Pearl Harbour had been attacked by the Japs three days before. The day of the battleship was over and their lordships recognised in due season that air power was vital in modern warfare at sea as well as on land. Of course, Sam was too preoccupied with the dramatic changes in his own life at the time to give the matter much thought, but later on he reflected with a wry grin that perhaps the old Admiral was in effect a far-seeing individual who really was seeking new blood to groom for a leadership which would eventually replace the dyed-in-the-wool types occupying positions of power in a navy that was slipping behind the times. It was certainly the right moment to do it as the emergency of the situation precluded debate on the subject. Sam had no illusions about his own ability and sensed he was not destined for great things but he was pleased to be part of the "spring cleaning" of the Andrew. In the same way that being part of the team in Helston Secondary School meant belonging to an élite band of people, it did not take long for Sam to become imbued with the spirit of comradeship which convinced him that the Senior Service was infinitely superior to the brown jobs and the Brylcreem Boys as the army and airforce were dubbed in wartime Britain.

Sam duly received the promised subsistence allowance. It came in the form of a cheque made out to Ordinary Seaman Exelby, D/JX 304736. His father, the ever practical George Exelby, told him to start a bank account with it. Shortly afterwards Sam received a railway warrant and orders to report to HMS *Raleigh* at Torpoint to begin his training. He was advised to bring the minimum of clothing as it would have to be sent home by post when he received his uniform.

After a slow wartime journey by bus and train from Coverack Sam found himself lined up with a motley bunch of "civvies" outside the Regulating Office of the "stone frigate" known as HMS *Raleigh*. Squads of rookie sailors marching by jeered and cheered when they spotted the new recruits. Sam began to wonder if he had done the right thing. They seemed a strange lot of sailors. What had happened to the Silent Service?

Sam's musings were interrupted by the arrival of a grey-haired Petty Officer with three good-conduct stripes below the crossed anchors on his arm and wearing green gaiters which came to just below the knee. "Right, you lot," he growled. "When I call your name, get fell in over 'ere." Life in the Royal Navy had begun! After much shouting and repetition of names called out in a strong Cornish accent which Sam identified as one from Penwith, the class was marched off in a shambles to the clothing store by Petty Officer Bob Matthews from Penzance. He was a reservist who had been called back to instruct new recruits. Sam felt he had got off to a good start as at least he could understand what the PO was saying, which was more than he could say about his classmates. They all lined up at the counter in Jack Dusty's store - Jack Dusty is the name given to all Supply ratings in the Navy - and each man was given a pile of clothing. Sam's cap was two sizes too small and he had to resort to wearing the chinstrap to keep it on his head. The stores didn't find the right size for two weeks, by which time every one good-naturedly called Sam "bighead". The bell bottoms were intriguing. The recruits were shown how to fold the legs into seven sections to represent the seven seas. There was no fly front: a central flap had to be unbuttoned on each side of the centre. This provoked a number of ribald jokes among the recruits but they were soon silenced by the PO who had heard them all before and was anxious to get the class settled in so that he could go to the POs' mess and have his tea. The purse on the regulation belt was welcomed by everyone as the PO had warned them at the start of the presence of thieves and had advised them to nail everything down if they didn't want to lose it! No one expected to get rich in the navy on two bob a day but every man had a secure place for his cash. At least, that is what they thought, but some weeks later when Sam was drafted to HMS *Drake*, the naval base in Plymouth, a great hullabaloo erupted one morning when a matelot discovered someone had skilfully sliced through his hammock with a cut-throat razor (standard issue also!) and removed the portion of the belt he was wearing which contained the purse. The unfortunate chap was going on leave that very day and had been paid up to date and given his subsistence allowance. Of course, someone had been watching what he did with his money and relieved him of it during the night. The culprit was never found but the messmates chipped in with a few coins each to help the victim on his way home.

It was fortunate that PO Bob Matthews hailed from Penzance. The rest of the class were Glaswegians, including twenty-year-old identical twins, with the exception of two Welsh boys - Bevan and Griffiths - and a Gaelic-speaking McDonald from Stornaway. Sam found it convenient to call everyone Jock, except the two Taffies. It went without saying that Sam was dubbed Jan, in true naval tradition. His mates teased him gently because of his accent and his naievety in comparison with what would now be called the "streetwise" Glasgow boys. They pretended never to have heard of Cornwall and would ask Sam where it was. Sam was ready

Seamanship Class, HMS *Raleigh*, Torpoint, Cornwall, 1941
Sam is 4th from right, second row down

for that question and repeated what he had heard a fellow Cornishman say - "It's a craggy peninsula held together by seagull droppings on the end of England"! Sam was continuing to grow up fast.

The class was housed in a Nissen hut which was connected to an ablution block. There were half a dozen huts radiating from the "heads" as the toilets now had to be called. Every morning there was a panic to get washed and shaved and into the dining hall on time so that they could "stoke up!" in readiness for a hard morning's drill on the parade ground under the watchful eye of the untiring Bob Matthews. At the tender age of eighteen Sam didn't need to shave every morning so he usually managed to have a good breakfast in time for work.

Everyone grumbled about the food. Sam was always ravenous - his gastric stomach forgotten - and he ate whatever he was given without considering its culinary quality. He had a sneaking suspicion that it was de rigueur to grumble so he joined in with the uncomplimentary comments regarding the cooking and the ancestry of the cooks. On being given a plate of stodge which he couldn't eat, some joker could always be relied on to call out in a menacing tone, "Who called the cook a clot?" The stock reply always came in a chorus, "Who called the clot a cook?" It became apparent that the schoolboy type of humour Sam was used to had spilled over into the Andrew.

Nevertheless, in his first few weeks as a sailor, Sam did long for his mother's home cooking. She was renowned in Coverack for her prowess at pasty making and Sam was the envy of many of the village boys, most of whose mothers folded the skirt (thin, lean steak which produces good gravy), potatoes, "turmot" (swede), and onion into a pastry envelope which was so thick and strong that one had to have exceptionally strong teeth to be able to penetrate the crimping (a folded seam of pastry) in order to get at the succulent beef and vegetables within. Perhaps this tough pastry was traditional because of the rumours that a pasty should be strong enough to be able to be dropped down a mine shaft without breaking! By contrast, Mary Exelby's pasties almost melted in the mouth. Her method of "painting" the pastry with milk ensured the pasties came out of the coal-fired oven a rich golden brown and they were invariably done to a turn, except, that is, when it was east wind and the draught went up the chimney, making the oven too hot. Before serving the pasties Mary invariably covered them with a clean cloth for a few minutes. This ensured the shortcrust pasty pastry was just the right consistency for consumption by George Exelby and the children. Mary's pasties were much in demand by the visitors who came to Sunny Cove Café in the summer months. Now and again a group of people who had been recommended to try her pasties would arrive late, when there were none left. The up-country folk would then plead with Mary, saying how much they had looked forward to a real Cornish pasty. In order to please her customers, Mary had been known to dash into the cottage kitchen and swoop up the pasties waiting to be eaten by her brood. It was a family custom to sit for a few minutes and contemplate the favourite meal of the week while father arrived home from work and went into the back room known as the cows' house to wash his hands before sitting down at the table. Then, when father sat down they would all begin their meal together. Grace was not said, but the children were frequently reminded by their parents that they should be thankful for the good food set before them.

Of course, George and the children were not as eager to please Mary's customers as she was, especially after losing their meals a few times in the manner just described, so they formed a habit of cutting their pasties in half as soon as they were placed on the plate before them so that they would not be hijacked for the latecomers to the café. Bitter experience taught them this, having had to eat cold corned beef and bread and butter in lieu of a pasty on a number of occasions.

Sam was rash enough when home on a short leave to tell his mother how much he loved her cooking, and that led to the fresh eggs episode on board the *Pathfinder* in Freetown harbour. Henceforth he steadfastly refused to allow himself to indulge in nostalgia. Like most young, healthy lads, he ate whatever he was given with gusto, not pausing to make comparisons. He never ceased to be thankful that his tricky gastric stomach was no longer a problem after he reached puberty. He could eat whatever he liked whenever he liked without unpleasant consequences. Added to that, he was only seasick once during five years in the Andrew and that was triggered by breathing in the oil fumes from the funnel when he was a lookout in the crow's nest during a prolonged period at action stations. Seasickness is a curse but Sam always smiled when he thought of that evening when they were escorting a convoy through the Bay of Biscay. Action Stations was sounded and Sam raced up the rigging to the crow's nest. He had just unhooked the binoculars when he knew he was going to be sick. He had recently had a meal of baked beans and bacon and had eaten too many beans. Up they came and Sam had the doubtful satisfaction of seeing a shower of barely digested beans go cascading towards the deck below. The Officer of the Watch was on the starboard wing of the bridge holding a cup of cocoa while he handed over to his relief before leaving for his action station. Out of the corner of his eye Sam saw a solitary bean drop with a plop right in the cup. It went unnoticed by Lieutenant Smythe, who was renowned for his caustic comments when talking to ratings. He swigged down his drink and left the bridge. Meanwhile Sam, feeling somewhat empty, continued his sweep of the horizon with what one might call a sickly grin on his face!

To return to *Raleigh*. Having come straight from school, Sam did not find the training particularly arduous. He was reasonably fit and managed the physical training without too much difficulty. He had to admire the super-fitness of the instructors and knew he would never be able to emulate the way in which they did their long fly and aerial somersault over the box. Now and again he performed a passable imitation, more by luck than good management. He was grateful for being taught the correct way to climb a rope without exhausting himself and was eventually able to hang upside down from parallel ropes without holding on with his hands. His new-found agility was to stand him in good stead when he was sent for Combined Ops. training before D Day.

By contrast, Sam found the method of discovering who were the non-swimmers in his class rather primitive to say the least. The recruits were lined up at the deep end of the swimming bath. A couple of PTIs emerged from behind the line of men. They held a long pole at each end. At a given signal from the PTI in charge at the other end of the pool, the two PTIs walked forward with their pole and pushed the line of men into the water. The non-swimmers among them soon became apparent and were fished out by the two instructors who had pushed them in the water. Sam had no problem, having learned to swim at an early age in the harbour at Coverack. The unfortunate non-swimmers, having been frightened out of their lives by the brutal introduction to the water, were then told they would have to report to the swimming instructor at the bath every lunch hour until they could swim a length. There was no argument. No shop steward to protest about the inhumane treatment. You never question an order in the navy. Sam wondered how his Coverack fisherman friends would fare if they were drafted to *Raleigh*. Quite a number of them were unable to swim, including his cousin James Rickard. The non-swimmers' philosophy was that if you fall overboard and start swimming, the chances are that you will not be picked up, so you will get colder and colder and weaker and weaker until finally you sink beneath the waves. The Coverack men declared that if you've got to go, you might as well go quickly, rather than die a lingering death. The non-swimmers refused to consider the argument that it is possible to go in the hoggin close to shore or within easy swimming distance of another boat, in which case being a swimmer gives you another chance. Nor did these gentlemen agree that swimming is an agreeable pastime. Being stubborn and Cornish, or perhaps being Cornish and stubborn, they were not going to listen to any old tale from "up-country". They were going to do what they always "belong" to do and to hell with the consequences (perhaps literally!). The PE dept. of HMS *Raleigh* were not interested in old fishermen's tales. They knew that a non-swimmer on a warship is a liability to his shipmates. They took pride in the fact that no one left the stone frigate without being able to swim at least a hundred yards. Of course, some of the older recruits grumbled about the amount of exercise they were forced to endure. They had become soft since leaving school and developed unsightly beer bellies. Their complaints fell on deaf ears. One day a seaman Petty Officer heard the men muttering among themselves and rounded on them. He was a survivor of a torpedoing and told the hapless mumblers that if he had not been fit he would not have survived three days in an open boat in freezing weather. Later, Sam was to question that statement. One of the lookouts on HMS *Pathfinder* sighted a drifting lifeboat in the Atlantic. It contained a score of survivors from the MS *Cortona* which had been torpedoed by a U boat some eleven days earlier. The only merchant seaman able to climb unaided up the scrambling net which had been lowered over the destroyer's side was a man in his sixties. The other younger, and to all intents and purposes stronger and fitter, seamen were all too weak to climb aboard and had to be lifted out of the ship's boat. One of the few good outcomes of the war at sea was that a series of in-depth studies of survivors' experiences was made. This work is on-going some fifty years later and is so advanced that the general public is no longer surprised when told of the survival of adventurers who have been up against seemingly impossible odds. Much of the success is due to innovations such as thermal clothing, enclosed life rafts and EPIRBs (Emergency Position-Indicating Radio Beacons).

In contrast to the relatively short training in swimming - most of it in the trainees' spare time, as described above - an inordinate amount of time was devoted to "square bashing". The civilian sailors could see the point but it appeared to the more thoughtful recruits that some senior officers still had the "big ship mentality". They were dreaming of squads of sailors performing intricate drill patterns on the upper decks of huge Leviathans lined up for some post-war Spithead review. Sam himself was neutral concerning rifle drill and marching. Once he had mastered the art of slinging his rifle about in the approved manner he quite enjoyed showing off his skill and listening to the ribald comments of the drill instructor when a seaman dropped a clanger. Most of the "asides" bellowed by the GI at the top of his voice were unprintable and frequently unintelligible as they often contained sexual overtones beyond Sam's limited knowledge of such things. In time he discovered what was meant by listening to his mates.

The navy had a language all of its own. Almost every word uttered was preceded or followed by a swearword. For example if you asked someone the time, you were liable to be told, "Half past f.....g three, mate". Sometimes a word was split into two with a swearword in the middle, as in "im *b....y* possible". In spite of his Wesleyan upbringing, Sam found it all-too-easy to slip into the vernacular. Most of the men were quite unaware of the nature of the offensive words they were uttering and were genuinely dismayed when called to book by some well-meaning person who castigated them for their coarse language.

Sam's swift immersion as it were into lower-deck language was to cause him to hurt deeply the person he loved most of all. Following a particularly tedious spell of convoy work, Sam arrived home on leave in a state of near exhaustion, having had little sleep for a number of weeks and on top of that a long train journey from Girvan on the Firth of Clyde. After one of Mary's meals, Sam fell into bed at 9 p.m. and within seconds was fast asleep. Mary let Sam sleep on in the morning but by the evening he still hadn't stirred so she went to wake up her sailor son. His reactions were still geared to life on board ship so when Mary shook him gently he told her to "f..k off". Mary gasped, Sam opened his eyes, saw his beloved mother's shocked face and wished the floor would open and swallow him up. Without a word, Mary turned and left the bedroom before Sam could begin to stutter an apology. Nothing was ever mentioned about that incident. Sam did not know how to even begin to prepare an apology. When he summoned up the courage to come down to tea, how Mary would have loved to hear him quote Euripides in mitigation. -*"'Twas but my tongue,'twas not my soul that swore."* But Sam knew nothing of such things. He shamefacedly entered the kitchen and regarded the Cornish tea which Mary had lovingly prepared. Mary avoided looking him in the eye and for the first time in his life, Sam didn't want to tuck in to "thunder and lightning" - splits spread with thick clotted cream with a spoonful of golden syrup glistening on the top and beginning to to creep down to the blue and white Cornishware plate. To make things worse, there were saffron buns and heavy cake to follow - all a rare treat in wartime Cornwall. It was forbidden to make clotted cream because of the shortage of milk, but Mary had told her close friend Ann Reseigh, who was married to a farmer, that Sam had come home unexpectedly, and after dinner that very day Ann's son Bill arrived with a quarter of cream in a shiny tin of the type that was used before the war to post cream to people up-country.

When George came home from work he sensed the atmosphere was rather strained but said nothing. He sat at the tea table and while tucking in to the special treat began asking his son what he had been up to. Sam assumed his father was referring to life on board ship so he gradually revealed that he had had a rough trip escorting tankers across the Atlantic. George didn't probe about losses and Sam didn't mention them. Mary sat quite still, eating very little. After tea Sam and George did the washing up while Mary began darning the navy blue socks Sam had brought home with him. There were none of the usual jokes about "holy" socks. When the chores were finished, George went into the parlour to record the day's work in his journal.

Sam went behind his mother's chair, put his arms around her and mumbled, "Thanks, Mum, that was some handsome tea but I'm a bit upset and couldn't do it justice. I'll make up for it tomorrow." "That's all right dear," murmured Mary, with tears in her eyes. "I understand. You'll be all right after a few days in Coverack. We still do things proper down here." Sam heaved a sigh of relief. His mother had rebuked him gently in her inimitable fashion, but he knew she had forgiven him, as mothers always do. The swearing incident had become one of those close secrets shared only between mother and son.

In *Raleigh* there was barely time to assimilate one new skill before PO Matthews started on another. Gas drill was an eye-opener for the raw sailors. Perhaps one should say an "eye-stinger" because they were all sat wearing gas masks in a long trailer which was parked behind the gymnasium. The instructor released some tear gas from a small canister and enquired if anyone could smell it. They all shook their heads. "Right ho lads," he said, with relish. "Now take off your respirators." By now the members of the class were accustomed to instant obedience to a command and they did so without hesitation. Of course, they all began spluttering, coughing and retching. After about thirty seconds, which seemed an age to the men, Bob Matthews opened the door of the trailer and told them to file out quickly. "Now then lads," he said with a twinkle in his eye, "you know the value of a respirator, I'm sure. Don't let me hear you call it a gas mask and never go anywhere without it - and make sure it never gets damaged." There followed the first of a short series of lectures on poison gas. It is doubtful if any of Bob's class ever grumbled about having to carry a respirator when going ashore after that. When talking about the deadly properties of chlorine, Bob related a story about an instructor who had been testing the efficacy of a respirator in a compartment filled with the gas. Some days later, the man decided to take his dog for a walk. The pet bounded up to him as dogs do when excited at the prospect of a run. The animal sniffed at his master's trousers, began choking and eventually had to be put down. Some of the gas had remained in the uniform trousers of the PO and the dog was poisoned. This demonstrated vividly the need for protective clothing and the importance of wearing the eye shields which were provided for every man. There is no doubt that Bob was a natural teacher. His class realised at the end of their course how lucky they were to have benefited from his vast experience.

An old naval cutter was resting on stocks in a corner of the parade ground. One morning PO Matthews marched his class to the spot, stood them easy and proceeded to indicate the names of the parts of the boat, followed by a demonstration of how to handle an oar. The PO then chose four of the lads to sit on the thwarts. After removing the poppets which revealed a built-in rowlock, the four were invited to row. They thought it a huge joke, rowing on dry land, but they entered into the spirit of the lesson and dipped the oars into an imaginary ocean flooding the parade ground. It was hilarious. It became obvious to Sam that very few of the would-be sailors had ever been in a boat, let alone rowed one. There was not enough time for everyone to have a go as other classes were already assembling prior to going in for lunch.

The next day the class was on the march again. This time they went down to a jetty where a trot of grey-painted naval cutters bobbed at their moorings. Sam was in the first crew to man the boat. After a few mishaps they got under way and moved off at a fair pace, due to an offshore wind rather than the prowess of the rowers. When they had gone a couple of cables (400 yards) Bob Matthews wisely decided to make for the jetty again. It was hopeless. With the boat going into the wind, the rowers began catching crabs (missing the water altogether when they attempted a stroke). When one did manage to get his blade into the water the oar took charge because of the pressure and the boat then began going round in circles. The class of onlookers raised a cheer which sounded suspiciously like a jeer. After a few minutes it became apparent that the boat was drifting further from the jetty. In exasperation the PO shouted, "Is there anyone on board who can really row?" - the last two words were pronounced "reely raw" - Sam was disappointed. He had hoped his prowess at rowing was being noted. Nevertheless he said, "Yes, Sir." "Right boy," said Bob. "You and me are going to get this lot back to the jetty." Bob took the place of the man rowing stroke, Sam stayed where he was and the two Cornishmen set to, keeping the bow into the wind and feathering their oars to reduce the effect of the wind on the wide-bladed oars. The rest of the crew sat quietly while the cuttter was brought back to the jetty. True to type, apart from saying, "Proper job, boy," when they got alongside, PO Matthews didn't mention the incident again, but whenever they passed one another in the course of their duties, Bob would acknowledge Sam by smiling and saying, "All right un boy?" "Ess," Sam would reply. That was all the conversation necessary between the two Cornish sailors.

Every man in the class had been issued with a copy of the *Manual of Seamanship*, Volume 1, on joining *Raleigh*. The book was a veritable mine of information. The class was exhorted to read the *Manual* whenever they had a few spare moments. It was hinted that if they did they would find the end of training exams a "piece of cake". In fact, a full-page diagram was devoted to "The correct method of pulling an oar". A stroke was divided into ten sections with dotted lines indicating the position of the blade in each section of the stroke. Sam had looked at it but decided it was too complicated, resigning himself to the fact that he had managed all right in Coverack so he probably would when called upon to row in *Raleigh*. He was right, fortunately. There was a whole page listing "Faults to guard against when rowing". Sam read these because he thought he might pick up some useful tips. He was right. He did wonder at the regulation regarding saluting in boats which stated that "boat keepers waiting for their officer are to stand up and salute officers passing their boats." Sam could envisage a boat tossing about on the end of a painter and the keeper being tossed into the sea by standing up to salute. Of course, PO Matthews should not have taken a cutter of untrained sailors out in the estuary but it was that or nothing so he took the risk. At least he had demonstrated the importance of the art of rowing if you want to be a sailor!

When it was deemed the class could handle rifles on the parade ground with reasonable ease - Sam had discovered his Home Guard training did not serve him particularly well - PO Matthews took the class to the rifle range and handed it over to a grizzled Chief Petty Officer. He was about the same age as Sam's father and wore First World War medal ribbons on his chest. CPO Parrish had long been retired but was recalled to the colours. He wore thick, pebble-like spectacles and looked as if he really ought to be putting his feet up in front of the fire at home. His appearance was deceptive and once again Sam was to be amazed at the skill of a naval instructor. Mr. Parrish went through the range drill patiently, getting three of the class, chosen at random, to copy his movements with their rifles.

When he was satisfied, the CPO got the three learners to load live ammunition and take aim. He advised them to hold their breath when aiming at the bull's eye on the range targets so that the rifles did not waver due to the movement of their chests. At a given signal the rifles were fired. One sailor got an outer. The others missed their targets completely and were rewarded by the range attendants waving a dirty piece of sacking on a stick. This signified a "washout". The old CPO was sympathetic and announced he would have a go, advising the class to observe carefully every movement he made. By way of conversation Parrish explained that his eyesight was no longer what it had been but that he would try his best. He then proceeded to score a bull and two inners, saying laconically, "I know you boys can do better than that." Of course they could not, but as each sailor went through the drill and fired, Parrish knew that secretly he would be trying to do better than the instructor. On subsequent visits to the range everyone remembered the standard which was required of them and CPO Parrish produced a class of fairly competent rifle men - considering they were sailors and were not expected to be as good as the army at shooting.

When the weather was bad, PO Matthews would take the class under cover and teach them how to tie knots, semaphore, the rules of the road at sea, the method of anchoring and mooring a ship and so on. The instructor was in fact working his way through the *Manual of Seamanship* and at each session he exhorted his class to read the relevant chapter in the evening as he would be asking questions the next day. Most of this instruction was meat and drink to Sam. He had obtained his Coastwatcher's Badge in the Scouts and could do knots and splices as well as semaphore. They did not have to learn morse at *Raleigh*, apart from a few letters used in rules of the road at sea. He also had a smattering of the other subjects. In the evenings small groups of trainees used to go through the *Manual of Seamanship* together, testing each other and trying to understand the rather pompous language in which some parts were written. They were amused by the Gieves advertisement on the front end-paper which had a Lieutenant Commander's uniform illustrated. The lowly sailors did not aspire to such heights nor did they think they would wish to buy any Hyland Hydraulic Machinery which was also illustrated. By making sarcastic, amusing comments about the *Manual* the lads were in fact unconsciously assimilating useful scraps of knowledge. One had only to turn to the glossary of Sea Terms in order to baffle one's listeners by asking them to explain such matters as a lazy painter, which turned out to be an extra piece of rope for making fast a ship's boat and not an unwilling worker. Gripes were not unpleasant pains in the bowels but pieces of matting fitted into thimbles (which were not thimbles at all) and lanyards to secure a boat when hoisted at the davits. A horse was a bar of iron across the stern of a boat for the sheet (rope attached to a sail) to travel on. A holiday was a space left bare when painting. Springs were ropes led from the bow or quarter when making a ship fast. Purchase was power gained in a tackle. Tackle was an arrangement of pulleys and rope. It was possible to get thoroughly confused when learning the rules of the road at sea. For example, there were aids to memory such as when two ships were passing:

Green to Green - or Red to Red -
Perfect safety. Go ahead.

The green referred to the right hand or starboard side of the ship which burned a green light at night, and the red was the port or left hand side which burned a red light. Of course it was not long before some wag was reciting:

Red to Red - or Green to Green -
Perfect safety. Go between!

One can imagine the terrible consequences of reciting the wrong version and taking action on it.

After the war, Sam used to go and see Dolph Hocking in Coverack. He lived in the house on the hill behind Sam's back garden. Dolph was ill, in fact he was dying slowly. He had lost the use of his legs following an action when he was a Chief Petty Officer. In the course of conversation one evening, Sam discovered to his delight that it was Dolph who had made the model of the arrangement of cable leads on a modern ship which had been used to instruct him when in HMS *Raleigh*. Dolph was so pleased when Sam told him how the model had clarified the way in which a ship came to anchor and how it made fast to a buoy using the anchor cable. It reinforced Sam's notion that the navy was really one big family. You are not a nonentity when serving on a ship, you are part of a crew, a family in fact. Sam was to find fifty years after the war ended that it was easy to relate to shipmates he had known.

The ten weeks of intensive training at *Raleigh* passed quickly. The duty Chief Petty Officer had been right when he told the raw recruits on entering the establishment, "In 'ere you you don't walk, you don't run, when you're given an order, you f.....g well fly!" Time had indeed flown, even if the recruits themselves had not mastered the art of flying. Although many of the lads were homesick, most were pleasantly surprised when they were informed by PO Matthews that they were to take exams prior to being sent home on leave and drafted to their first ship. Of course, no one was remotely ready for what was to come but the fear of the unknown paled into insignificance before the thought of swaggering along in uniform on home territory. A few of the extroverts began practising the sailor's characteristic roll when they walked.

Before the delights of home leave could be sampled, the exams had to be faced. Most of the tests such as parade ground drill were taken en bloc as it were and caused no problems. The class worked as a team and each man was conscious of the need to do his best so as not to let down his mates. No one was asked to read or send a message by semaphore, which left Sam feeling faintly disappointed. A few were called on to tie simple knots in front of the assembled class and in response to the question, "Can you lot do that?" the class shouted "Yes, Chief." They were then all deemed to have passed the test. Elementary questions concerning naval customs, discipline, KR & AIs - King's Regulations and Admiralty Instructions - were called out and the answers, mainly one word, were written down. The recruits had been advised to study certain sections of the *Manual of Seamanship* and so in theory were prepared for the questions. The examiner did all he could to help. As he asked how many compartments there are in a torpedo, he held up an open hand indicating the number five. One or two were not looking so he said, "Look at me lad. Pay attention" and there was no longer any doubt about the answer! On asking how one recognised a British mine, he undid his jacket and tucked his thumbs under his belt - British mines had a distinctive raised metal band or belt around the centre of the mine.

It was necessary that everyone should pass. The examiners made sure they did. After all, there was a war on. That phrase was trotted out as the stock excuse for anything which was not exactly as it should be in those heady days. No one, including Sam of course, seemed concerned about the ethics involved. No one apparently worried unduly about sending unseasoned men to sea where they could become a liability. The Petty Officers knew that on board ship each new man would probably acquire a "sea daddy" who would literally show him the ropes, thus salving their consciences. At least it was an improvement on the methods of the Press Gangs during the Napoleonic Wars, little more than a century previously!

As the day of the passing-out parade drew near, the class of seamen - if they could be called that - got excited at the thought of pastures new.

Perhaps it was mainly the thought of going back to their homes for a while. For Sam it was a mixture of both. He longed to see his beloved Coverack again, though like him, most of his contemporaries were no longer resident there due to the demands of the war coupled with the need to find employment. Most Cornishmen had to leave home when they reached their teens because of the chronic shortage of work in the county. While he had been at *Raleigh* Sam had been writing to Elsie and he was looking forward to seeing her again as well. The envelopes he had bought in the canteen had the *Raleigh* crest and motto on the back - "Amore et virtute" - Sam thought that rather a nice touch when writing to a girlfriend. In addition he was impatient to become a "proper" seaman and not be regarded as a "rookie". The professional sailors or Active Service ratings as they were officially called often treated the Hostilities Only ratings with disdain. They seemed to regard them as interlopers. Before the war was over their attitude was to change. Of course, many of the HOs like Sam were volunteers and would probably have become Active Service ratings anyway if there hadn't been a war. On reflection it occurred to Sam that some of the conscripts - a pejorative word rarely heard in the service - did not take kindly to being forced to join the navy and consequently their attitude was not exactly co-operative. They seemed sullen and resentful. Not without good reason. They did not all feel their country needed them. It has to be remembered they had lived through the depression as youngsters and probably found it difficult to equate a personal impression of their homeland with the description of the green and pleasant land, now being threatened by a foreign foe, being spread about by propagandists paid to drum up a sentimental feeling of patriotism. In later years many of the wartime unwilling sailors became proud members of organisations such as the Royal Naval Association and the Royal British Legion. Their initial rancour was forgotten, submerged by pride in wartime achievements, reinforcing what was to become one of Sam's favourite homilies - that it is often a good thing to be made to do something you do not want to do. He had learned that rather painfully in Helston and was to bore his own family by repeating it when he could think of no other answer when trying to make them do something they could see no point in doing.

The final parade was quite a grand affair. PO Matthews saw to it that his class was the smartest, best co-ordinated, most seaman-like body of men about to leave the training establishment. Before Bob was satisfied his men would pass muster he sent not a few back to the hut to give boots a final polish, to cut off a persistent wisp of hair protruding beneath a forage cap, to "take off that fancy collar and put on your pusser's issue!" and so on. All the new sailors wanted their collars to look as if they had been well dhobied, giving the impression the collars had faded because the wearer had been in the navy for a considerable period of time. It was possible to buy collars in shops ashore which were Mediterranean blue in colour and not navy blue as issued by Jack Dusty. PO Matthews was having none of that. Everyone had to look the same - or else!

It was a cold spring morning and the men on parade were made to stand for some time before the Captain arrived to give his final address. In fact it was his only address because it was the first time the men had seen him. His words were standard and not memorable. They were a fine bunch of ratings and must remember that the honour of HMS *Raleigh* was at stake so they were expected to uphold the traditions of the "ship" wherever they might find themselves at the end of their first leave in the navy. And so on and so on. After joining all the other newly qualified Ordinary Seamen in a grand march past the saluting base the class returned to their hut where PO Matthews gave details of their first draft. Greatcoats were put on, respirators slung, kitbags locked and shouldered, hammocks tucked under arms and they all trooped to the Regulating Office to collect travel warrants, ration cards, pay and subsistence and the all-important drafting instructions. Sam was to report to HMS *Drake* at Devonport at the end of his leave to go into a "pool" to await being sent to a ship.

CHAPTER SEVEN

GUZ

The *Raleigh* class went to Plymouth North Road Station in a three-ton lorry. There was a carnival atmosphere, a feeling of release, freedom, rejoicing. No one to bark orders at them for ten whole days. They sang on the ferry from Torpoint and continued chanting until they arrived at the station, where a couple of Naval Police appeared, to find out what all the noise was about. Their presence quietened the sailors down. The ex-*Raleigh* boys didn't want to miss their trains by having a confrontation. When the kit was unloaded they all went to the "up" platform. Sam went to the "down". He was on his way. The Penzance train appeared after a short wait during which he stoked up on station tea and a wad, as he had learned to call a bun.

The train was still quite full, although it had disgorged a crowd of sailors and Royal Marines at North Road. Sam heaved his kit on board, stacking it in the corridor while he found a seat. Carriages were not designed to cope with hammocks so he left his at the end of the corridor, rightly judging that no one would want to be burdened with such a cumbersome object. Sam had been told that Christopher Columbus saw the natives of San Salvador sleeping in netted "hamaca" and adopted the idea, realising the potential for saving valuable space on board ship. He had also been informed that that they had been in use in the Royal Navy since the end of the 16th century but that didn't really impress Sam. In fact he was to discover later that although hammocks were comfortable they were not practical in the cramped conditions on board small ships. While waiting for the train to start, Sam's mind wandered from the problems of travelling with an oversized "banana" in the form of a hammock, to the history lessons he had at school. He was never very good at dates. Was it 1492 when Columbus sailed the ocean blue or was it 1493 when he sailed the bright blue sea? His daydreaming was interrupted by the staccato slamming of carriage doors. The GWR Guard, resplendent in a gold-braided peaked cap reminiscent of a naval Commander, imperiously blew his whistle, waved his green flag, and they were off.

From the carriage window Sam could see the devastation wrought by the German bombers. The train went slowly along the back of Stuart

Road, through Keyham and Devonport on to the Brunel Bridge. The bombed buildings along the way resembled discarded dolls' houses, the ones which have removable roofs so that little girls can lift them off and rearrange the furniture or do imaginary housework. These had been people's homes. Some had been sliced as if by a giant knife. Pictures still hung crazily on leaning walls. Beds were hanging down from the joists. A bath, miraculously retained by the piping, hung vertically like a hollowed segment of white orange. Walls were blackened by fire. Windows were dark, gaping holes. Here and there a carpet had been lifted bodily by an explosion and deposited on a heap of rubble in front of the house. Scattered all round were household articles - kitchen utensils, an armchair with its upholstery in tatters, a buckled bicycle wheel, a doll, a child's scooter. The occupants of the carriage fell silent in sympathy as the train rumbled on. Conversation didn't begin again until they were crossing the Tamar, when someone drawled, "'Ere, got your passports 'ave 'ee?" The light-hearted remark relieved the tension and soon there was an animated buzz of conversation as passengers began questioning one another about their destinations. Cornwall was working its old magic. Before long people were swapping life histories and discovering they had something in common. The frosty English reserve which had prevailed as far as Plymouth melted away and Cornish curiosity took over.

Sam sat quietly in the corner of the carriage. It transpired that no one else was getting off at Gwinear Road and when in response to a friendly question regarding his destination he revealed he was going to Coverack, no one in the compartment had ever heard of it, so Sam was left alone with his thoughts and daydreams. The journey seemed endless. It was a stopping train. The driver seemed to think it was a good idea to halt for a while between stops as well. It was getting dark. All the blinds had to be drawn in case the lights of the train attracted the attention of a passing Luftwaffe pilot. At each stop the blinds were lifted a fraction in order to read the name of the station. No one wanted to miss getting off at the right place and the porters didn't always pass every carriage when calling out the name of the station.

After what seemed an age the train reached Gwinear Road and Sam got off, not forgetting to retrieve his hammock. He crossed to the branch line for Helston and sat waiting for the last leg of the train journey to begin. A large lady got in the carriage and immediately struck up a conversation. She was bound for Porthallow and straight away launched into a series of searching questions regarding Sam, his family and the navy. It transpired that Mrs. Trevail was a friend of Sam's great aunt Bertha. Sam and his cousin Horace used to visit her from time to time. She was a replica of Sam's travelling companion, fat, jolly, bearded - in a discreet sort of way - and insatiable in her quest for information about the people with whom she came into contact.

When visiting Bertha, Sam and Horace got into the habit of telling her all the latest gossip about the more colourful characters of Coverack in return for a glass of lemonade made from crystals, plus a bun or perhaps a corner of a pasty. They needed this sustenance to gather strength for cycling up the hill out of Porthallow and back to Coverack, so they saw to it that the tales they told were interesting enough to warrant a generous offering of food, even if it meant embroidering them somewhat to satisfy their aunt's need for news. So Sam found himself making up tales just to hear Mrs. Trevail's expletives. "Oh! fancy that." "Mind you, I always thought she was a bit of a fast one." "He'll come to no good, you mark my words." Sam enjoyed his stratagems, reasoning that he would be far away on the high seas before it became known he had been spreading tales and hoping that by the time he returned to Coverack his inventive fabrications would be forgotten. He looked forward to meeting Horace and telling him what he had done, knowing that Horace would continue the fictional account to lend a sort of false credibility to it when he got the ear of a gullible listener.

Sam hurriedly got off the train at Helston. He did not want to miss the bus at that late hour and he wanted to find a seat as far from Mrs. Trevail as possible. The bus would go on to Porthallow after calling at Coverack and Sam had run out of ideas to keep Mrs. Trevail interested. He reflected wryly that all he had managed to glean about her was her name and that she knew great aunt Bertha. Besides, he was nearly home, he was tired, and he was wondering what his beloved Mary had got for his tea. He need not have worried. By the time he had stowed all his kit Mrs. Trevail had already cornered another victim, so he was left in peace.

George Exelby was waiting for his son at the bus stop. His greeting was traditional. "All right, boy?" "Ess," replied Sam. No more needed to be said for the time being. They were together again. Sam shouldered his kit-bag and his father picked up the hammock. As they walked along by the beach, George could not resist commenting, "You're some lucky to have a hammock, boy. We didn't have beds in the trenches." "I know, Dad," replied Sam. "I'm some glad you told me not to join the army." George had never said much about his four years in France. Sam knew it must have been absolute hell and sensed it was not something he could tease his father about, so he set about asking what had been going on in the village while he had been away. Before long they were home and a smiling, red-faced Mary hugged Sam as he came through the doorway. "You've lost weight," she said accusingly. "Never mind my 'an'some, we'll soon fatten you up. We've got pasties for tea." Sam sat down to the finest meal he had had in three months. He was home. He was happy. His first leave saw the start of what became a tradition. Every time he came home, Mary always said he had lost weight and to start the fattening up process anew, she always had a proper pasty waiting. What more could a Cornishman ask?

Sam's leave, in common with all service leave, went by in a twinkling. He enjoyed going down to the Fishermen's Club for a game of billiards and to catch up on recent events in Coverack. When there was no one of his age there he went to Henry Mundy's shoemaker's shop and sat listening to the conversation. It was the custom of villagers to gather there, have a game of darts and discuss world events, beginning with Coverack and going on to the war. While all this was going on, Henry Mundy kept working away and added his comments to the conversation, usually through clenched teeth as he had the habit of holding spare nails in his mouth when hammering new soles to old boots. The wireless was on all the time, so up-to-the-minute news received attention straight away, including Lord Haw Haw, for the set was tuned in to him when it was time for his nightly propaganda broadcast. His statements were always good for a laugh except when he mentioned the loss of a ship. He kept the whole village on tenterhooks when he announced the loss of the submarine Sea Horse. Jack Selsey from Coverack was a member of the crew and William Joyce cruelly promised to give names of survivors, reading a few at a time. Jack's name was never included. Meanwhile the family went through agonies. Jack's younger brothers went to school with Sam and they too were in the forces. Of course, Sam was asked about his new life in the Andrew. He had his leg gently pulled about being careful not to get his feet wet. Everyone in the village had fallen in at some time or other and there was always someone who remembered a personal embarrassing moment. Sam was no exception but it was all light-hearted fun. Sam's "audience" wanted to know about air raids so he told them about having to race to the shelters at night when the bombers were overhead. They were amused when he explained that when the bugle sounded to take cover they had to drop flat wherever they happened to be. He recounted with feeling that it was not amusing to throw yourself down on wet ground when in night clothes, and listen to the hot shrapnel hissing as it landed with a plop in the grass, even if you were wearing a tin hat and had remembered to put on your greatcoat. Someone said, "You ought to keep on running, boy. Don't take no notice of un." At that point Sam realised that the navy had got to him. It hadn't occurred to him to disobey. Orders were made to be obeyed. Questions can be asked afterwards - but who dared do that?

Before going back Sam arranged a meeting with Elsie. He was an official boyfriend now so they went quite openly for a walk along the cliffs and back to her home for tea. They had a lovely afternoon and Sam enjoyed the special spread laid on in his honour, in spite of being nervous about talking to Elsie's parents. Her father, Joseph Barker, had served in the Royal Navy and questioned Sam closely about his training. He was faintly disappointed when Sam said he couldn't recite the names of the sails of a square-rigged ship, as he hadn't had to learn them, although he did remember there was a diagram in the *Manual of Seamanship* giving the names of the sails. Joseph then proceeded to recite all twenty-eight names beginning with the flying jib and ending with the mizzen t'gallant stay-sail. Sam was suitably impressed but secretly glad he didn't have to know much about sailing ships. He had already been told that in the days of sail the ships were made of wood and the men of iron. He had also heard the jibe that in his generation the ships were made of iron and the men of wood but he wisely refrained from discussing the matter with his host.

The days had flown by. Suddenly it was time to say goodbye. His Granny, Ann Trengilly, presented him with a shilling to buy something to eat on the train. She was so proud of her old-age pension money and gave everyone the impression that she was well off. Sam knew she wasn't but accepted the money to please her. Granny Exelby had wrapped a piece of seed cake in paper for him to eat when he got back to the barracks. This he also accepted with thanks, although he couldn't bear caraway seeds. Granny Exelby's three sons had served in the Great War and they had all liked caraway seeds so she assumed Sam did as well! Elsie gave him a photo of herself and promised to write as often as she could. His father, George, gave him the hussive he was issued with in 1914. It was a leather roll lined with silky material, used for carrying pins and needles, thread etc. Sam was delighted. He used it all through the war and right up to the time when his bachelor days were over and Bronwen took over his mending. Mary presented him with a large packet of sandwiches which would last a couple of days. She knew her son was only going as far as Plymouth but it was her way of showing how much she cared for him.

At eight o'clock on the last morning of his leave, George Exelby accompanied his son to the bus stop, carrying the "luxurious" hammock. Sam had demonstrated to his parents how to sling it, using the substantial knobs on the kitchen cupboards in lieu of hooks. They were fascinated by the fact that when lashed, the hammock had to have seven equidistant turns, called marline hitches, with the end ones stopping the blanket from protruding. The name SAM EXELBY D/JX 304736 had had to be painted in one-inch letters exactly twenty-one inches from the head of the hammock. Wisely, Sam did not demonstrate how to get in the hammock because he wasn't sure he could do it and in any case he would probably have pulled the cupboard doors off their hinges. George was wearing his overalls as he walked beside his son. He was a stickler for punctuality and always started his day's work at precisely 8 a.m., but today was an exception. Mrs. Bowden's chimney would have to wait until Sam was safely on the bus.

Mary had pleaded with Sam to allow her to accompany him to Helston, saying she needed to go and get a new pair of shoes. Sam knew it was a ploy. Mary, in common with the other village ladies, used to get three or four pairs sent out on the bus so that she could try them on in the comfort of her home. There was no sense in spending money on a bus fare to Helston when the obliging Mr. Walters was prepared to pack a parcel of shoes and have it delivered to the door. Sam was adamant he didn't want Mary weeping as she waved good-bye at Helston station. He compensated by turning round several times, blowing kisses and waving as Mary stood at the door until he turned the corner and began the next stage of his career in the Andrew.

Thus the journey to Gwinear Road was accomplished without undue stress. Sam knew some of the people travelling on the bus to Helston and he chatted with them as if he were just going to town for a day's outing. Jack, the station porter, helped him stow his kit on the train. He had known Sam ever since he had started going to the Secondary School and Sam thought Jack wouldn't consider him as a tipping traveller. Nevertheless, he had no hesitation in accepting the threepenny bit Sam pressed in his hand as they bade farewell.

At Gwinear Road Sam struggled across the track to the "up" line and when the train came in he had to walk the length of the platform, seeking a carriage with a spare seat. The train was already packed so he resigned himself to sitting on his kit-bag in the corridor, feeling glad that he was only going as far as Plymouth. In fact, after crossing the Tamar the train stopped at Keyham. Dozens of sailors got off and Sam joined them, sensing there might be transport laid on to the barracks known as HMS *Drake*. He was right and a few minutes later found himself reporting to the Regulating Office. He was given a card which indicated where he was to sleep and eat, also that he was part of a "Pool".

Drake was a shock. Sailors were milling about all over the place. It didn't even give the impression of ordered confusion as one might expect. Aimless confusion would be a more appropriate description. However, Sam found his sleeping quarters and stowed his gear. He didn't put any of his belongings in the locker provided, mindful of the admonition of the *Raleigh* PO regarding thieves. The sailor using the space next to Sam's advised him to sling his hammock or he might find himself having to sleep on the "deck", such was the state of overcrowding. Sam followed his advice and asked the friendly matelot about the work he had to do and what the food was like. Sam was advised to get to Jago's, the euphemistic name given to the dining hall, as early as possible, because latecomers were often given semi-warm, inedible meals that even the shitehawks refused to eat. Shitehawk is the sailors' name for seagull. Regarding work, Sam learned that the best thing to do in the forenoon watch from eight to twelve midday was to stand at the end of the line furthest away from the duty PO. There were so many sailors in Guz, apparently, that two men were being sent to do one man's job and even then the Petty Officers couldn't find enough for everyone to do. Those at the end of the line were usually told to "get lost" and come back after dinner. Mind you, these men were also told by the PO that if they quoted him when caught skiving, he would deny he ever said it. Sam's education was proceeding apace!

On his first morning in HMS *Drake*, Sam discovered that his barrack-room companion had not exaggerated but as he would rather do something positive he did get "told off" for a job. He had to collect a broom and sweep the road leading to the galley. When he had finished he returned to the starting place and did it all over again. Another rating was sweeping the other side of the road so Sam began sweeping in time with him. They grinned at each other and went along doing a sort of slow-brush-ballet step. They kept this up until "stand easy" when they were allowed to stop work for ten minutes and have a cup of char. Sam contented himself with a nibble at the bar of chocolate he had bought with the money Granny Trengilly had given him.

After "stand easy" it was brooms to the ready and off again, sweeping non-existent rubbish from the road. There were a few fresh fag ends dropped by passers by during the break but that was all. A quarter of an hour before dinner Sam took a cue from his opposite number, so sloping brooms as if they were rifles, they went off at a funereal pace to return them to the store. They then sauntered towards the much-vaunted Jago's. They were by no means first in the queue for a meal but they didn't have to wait long. The food was just about edible, the noise horrendous and the tables in need of a really good scrub. Apparently the sailors working there were nearly all "skates", that is they were made to work there because they had committed some sort of petty crime and this was part of their punishment. They took no pride in their work and those in charge seemed to have lost heart because of the sheer weight of numbers being fed there.

When they fell in again after dinner, Sam was sent down to a jetty to load stores on to a lorry. When that was finished he was told quietly to "get lost" again. He decided to wander along the jetty, to look at the ships in the "Grey Funnel Line". He wondered if he would ever get a draft to one. As he looked across the water Sam spied the shape of the *Paris*, an old French battleship. He was fascinated to note the large clock-like dial on the platform of the mainmast. He assumed it was to do with gunnery but he hadn't been told about it during gunnery instruction in *Raleigh*. If it were that, it seemed odd to advertise what was happening to any enemy approaching the ship. He decided not to pursue the matter. Thinking about the *Paris*, he remembered being somewhat confused the previous year when the French signed an armistice with Germany and shortly afterwards in July, 1940 the Royal Navy was ordered to seize all French warships in port for fear that they would obey the German order to return to France. Local people in Plymouth were scandalised when the French sailors resisted, especially after two Royal Navy Officers and a rating were killed in a struggle to seize the *Surcouf*, the largest submarine in the world at the time. Sam, in his ignorance of politics, had assumed the French would automatically continue the fight against the Germans, but a thousand French sailors were killed at the naval base near Oran when Admiral Somerville had to attack the French fleet to prevent it returning to occupied France.

Despite the problem of the Vichy French, there were a number of Free French sailors in the barracks and they could be seen enthusiastically trying to assimilate the techniques of the Royal Navy so that they could become an effective force. There were also a number of Norwegian sailors being trained. Most of the allied personnel were "bunting tossers" or signallers and they spent long hours on the parade ground moving in formation in response to flag hoists just as ships do when in company at sea. It was a fascinating sight to see the signalmen responding with affirmative flags when given an executive command. It goes without saying that the manoeuvring of the "bunting tossers" attracted quite a lot of attention from the matelots who had been told to "get lost". While watching the foreign seamen at work one day, Sam fell into conversation with another "lost" soul who informed him that he had devised a system of wandering about HMS *Drake* in working hours without fear of being put on a charge for loafing. The trick was to purloin a blank sheet of signal pad from the Regulating Office, write a fictitious name of an allied sailor on it and when challenged claim to have been sent to find the individual who obviously not heard the "pipe" ordering him to report to the Officer of the Watch. A "pipe" is a message relayed all round the ship or in this case barracks. Sam agreed his new-found friend seemed to have hit upon a pretty foolproof system. He had obtained a Credit in School Certificate French so he would be able to demonstrate to any inquisitive Petty Officer that in theory he would be able to communicate with the man when found. French sailors were easy to spot as they had red pom-poms in the middle of their caps. The friendly sailor gave Sam a couple of spare sheets of signal pad before moving on. Sam pocketed them, wondering if he would ever have the nerve to try out such an ingenious idea.

One morning Sam found himself a member of a working party detailed to clear debris from a bombed building. It was hard, dusty, thirsty work but all the sailors felt it was something positive and well worth doing. They went at it with a will. Little did Sam think that his rather sketchy knowledge of Latin would come in handy in such a situation. A Latin scholar had daubed the word "Resurgam" on the lintel of a doorway. After due thought, Sam remembered it was the future tense of "resurgere" and meant "I shall rise again" - the words of Jesus recalled by the Chief Priests and Pharisees when they were trying to persuade Pontius Pilate to keep the tomb of Jesus secure for three days to prevent a resurrection. Mr. Stanley would have been proud of Sam, who shared his knowledge of Latin with his mates who had been trying to discover the meaning.

For twenty-four hours every week, Sam was a member of the Duty Watch. He was usually assigned one of two jobs, either firewatching or galley work at Jago's. He preferred firewatching. That entailed slinging his hammock in the church tower and being on hand should incendiary bombs be dropped during the night. Sam enjoyed sleeping high up in the tower. It was relatively quiet and if the sirens did sound he and his mate had a good view of the "fireworks". They were never called upon to extinguish a firebomb and were rather disappointed about this as they had been trained to use the long shovels to scoop them up and deposit them away from the main fabric of the building before smothering them with sand. Each night they also laid out the hoses in readiness and made sure the key was in position to turn on the water. In the morning, they had to "knock off and make up" in the approved manner, i.e. disconnect the hose with a sharp tap on each clip and roll it up neatly before hanging it on the wall of the church. The less agreeable job was peeling potatoes for Jago's. The job was usually done by sailors on "Number Elevens" - that is doing punishment for some minor misdemeanour such as smoking while working, being improperly dressed, arriving back "on board" late after an evening's liberty and so on. If there were not enough miscreants to do the necessary work in the galley, some of the Duty Watch were assigned to it. Every sailor is given a "pusser's" knife on joining. It has a sturdy blade and a marline spike and should be attached to a lanyard. The knives were not ideal for peeling spuds: the blade was thick and furthermore often stained with tar or some other unpleasant substance. Nevertheless it was decreed that sailors should use their knives for peeling potatoes. There was usually a huge mound to be done, with huge baths of water placed nearby for washing them. On the first occasion when he had to peel potatoes, Sam set to and laboriously removed the skin as he had been taught at home. He was soon told that they would be there all night at the rate he was going on and was promptly shown the quickest way to prepare a spud for cooking. All you did was to slice down the two "flat" sides and the two ends, producing in four deft strokes an oblong potato which was then tossed peremptorily into the waiting bath. Sam had been brought up never to waste anything and found it hard to be a party to such a crude way of working but he knew there was no point in making a stand. These men were his shipmates and wise in the ways of the world! Besides, if they finished early they would probably be able to get into the cinema. That was a form of public entertainment that didn't exist in Coverack but Sam had seen a few films on Saturday evenings after playing football in Helston. Cinema-going had developed into quite a cult in HMS *Drake*. The films were up to date and usually of the adventure or romantic type. If the film depicted anything to do with the sea, the sailors voiced their opinions loudly when technical details were incorrect. Likewise in romantic sequences cries of encouragement and advice could be heard and bawdy comments came fast and furious. There were always one or two wags who competed with the film for laughs and sometimes two particularly witty matelots vied with each other in trying to draw the biggest laughs. The film script was largely ignored by the audience, indeed it often could not be heard because of the noise from the cinema goers. When the noise became quite unbearable the lights would go on in an attempt to expose the culprits. The audience would then stamp and cheer until the film continued. No one seemed to consider the Wren cinematograph operators listening to the hullabaloo. Presumably it was assumed they were accustomed to hearing such language. Thinking about it reminded Sam of an incident on Coverack quay when a visitor remonstrated with a swearing fisherman, reminding him there were ladies present. "They aren't ladies, Cap'n," said the man, unabashed. "They're Coastguards' wives!"

After he had been in HMS *Drake* a couple of weeks, Sam found himself in a squad chosen to represent the Royal Navy at a "Warships' Week". It was part of a National Savings drive to encourage people to use their spare money to promote the war effort and make a modest amount of interest at the same time. The sailors were drilled relentlessly until the GI (Gunnery Instructor) was satisfied they were fit to perform in public. He added a bit of bayonet fighting practice as well for good measure, explaining that in some towns the Royal Navy had the freedom to march with bands playing, flags flying and bayonets fixed. He reasoned that since they had to know how to fix bayonets they might as well know how to use them in a combat situation. It proved a welcome change from parade ground drill pure and simple. The practices were indeed an improvement on boring barrack duties. The squad began to look forward to trips through the Devon countryside and seeing towns they had not visited before.

Sam was in the squad that went to Honiton. They were cheered and clapped as they marched through the streets. Afterwards they were entertained to a scrumptious Devonshire tea. The sailors tucked in to the home-made fare with a will and didn't worry a jot about missing Jago's mucky mash. After tea the sailors were invited to join in the Flora Dance before going back to barracks. It didn't quite come up to the Helston standard but it was good to be in the company of young females, albeit they were closely chaperoned by ladies who had heard all about randy sailors from Guz.

There was method in the "madness" of the GI responsible for the smartness of the "Warships' Week" company. After a couple more visits to local towns he announced with a grin that they had been chosen to be the Guard of Honour for King Peter II of Yugoslavia. The sailors groaned inwardly. They knew they would be submitted to more hours of parade ground drill in preparation for the event. The big day arrived. On a cold, frosty morning they were lined up in the drill shed in their Number Ones (best uniforms) and issued with some very clean-looking rifles and bayonets for the occasion. They did a couple of manoeuvres just as a warmer and then they were marched outside to await the arrival of the King. His appearance was a bit of an anticlimax. Sam had never seen a King before. He had a gorgeous uniform but not the figure to fill it out. He looked pale and forlorn. In fact he was the same age as Sam. He had been King since his father was assassinated in Marseilles in 1934 when he was only ten years old. His uncle was one of the Regents appointed to look after affairs of state until he came of age. In turn his uncle was overthrown but by then Peter was old enough to take over. He ruled for three weeks, then the Germans invaded and he had to go into exile and eventually made his way to London via the Middle East. The young man hastened along the ranks of sailors awaiting his inspection and after shaking hands with the Officer in Charge, got into his Bentley and was driven away. Sam never did find out the purpose of the King's visit to HMS *Drake*. The sailors were not very pleased after all the effort they had made but they were given a "make and mend" by way of compensation which meant they could loaf legitimately in the barrack room for the whole afternoon and go ashore at 1600 if they wished. The term "make and mend" came from sailing-ship days when crews were allowed time to mend their clothes and sew new ones. Sam's contemporaries were like him, just about able to thread a needle and darn a sock or put a button on - not that there were many buttons on a seaman's rig, because they have a habit of getting tangled in rope which could put a sailor's life in danger when working on deck.

Sam began to settle down to a routine, punctuating spells of actual work with wandering about, ostensibly searching for a non-existent French sailor. As he did so, his thoughts turned to his pen friend Pierre Dorsemaine who was almost certainly in occupied France. The two boys had been corresponding for about three years when the Germans began their blitzkrieg. Sam had heard no news since early 1940. In fact he had written Pierre's name on the signal pad as it had a "genuine" ring about it. It was to be 1945 before Sam got in contact again when Pierre gave a letter to an American soldier to post to Coverack. By then Sam was in Singapore but the letter arrived in due course.

In spite of a reasonably comfortable, if not fulfilling existence, Sam reasoned that it would be better if he moved on. He had learned that some men had been in HMS *Drake* since the beginning of the war. They were known as "barrack stanchions". Sam also discovered that if you could play rugby or soccer and get in the barracks team it was unlikely that you would be sent to sea. He did not aspire to such sporting heights and decided he had to get out of Guz and see the world. He went to the Drafting Office and asked the Chief Petty Officer in charge if he could be sent to sea. The Chief stared in disbelief for a moment or two, thinking that Sam was having him on. After asking a few questions he concluded that Sam was in earnest and told him he would see what he could do. A week went by. During "stand easy" one morning Sam heard his name being piped, telling him to report to the Drafting Office. There he learned that he would be going to South Shields the following morning to join HMS *Pathfinder*, which was about to be commissioned.

At last the sailor was going to sea.

HMS *Pathfinder* 1942-1948

First Captain: Commander E.A.Gibbs, DSO and 4 Bars, DSC and Bar
G10 is flying the black contact flag indicating that she is hunting a U-boat. She was credited with sinking six, possibly seven German submarines.

CHAPTER EIGHT

PATHFINDER

On leaving the Drafting Office Sam went back to work. After dinner he was told he could have the afternoon off to get ready for sea. There were only a few people in the barrack room so he decided to do the job properly and began to lay out his kit in the approved fashion. He started with the two towels, folded so that the name SAM EXELBY was in view, then his blue jean collar, underclothes, socks, ducks - white cotton-type jumper and trousers for warmer climates - sundries such as handkerchiefs, knife with codline lanyard, white dress lanyard and silk. This was a black silk scarf which sailors wear, supposedly in memory of Admiral Lord Nelson. It is tied in a reef knot under the collar and held by tapes situated at the bottom of the open "V" of the jumper. His toilet gear and what he needed for travelling was packed in a small brown attaché case which was issued in lieu of the "ditty box" used in the old days for small personal items. Next came shoe-cleaning gear, greatcoat, shiny black oilskin, blue overalls, best number-one jumper and trousers and boots, plus, of course, the all-important *Manual of Seamanship*. Finally there was the hammock. It was slung ready for use that night so Sam left it where it was to be dealt with in the morning. While he was laying out his kit Sam brushed and polished and made sure his name was visible on each item. Fortunately there was no mending to be done. When he was satisfied, the lot was repacked in his kitbag and locked up, with the exception of his greatcoat, steel helmet and respirator. For some reason or other, the helmet and respirator were not counted as "kit" and did not feature in the illustration in the "book of words" but Sam knew he wouldn't be allowed to leave the barracks without them. Indeed, he didn't want to. It went without saying that the greatcoat was essential to anyone travelling north.

The next morning Sam lined up at the dockyard siding with a hundred or so other members of the new crew of the new ship and after a roll call they boarded the reserved carriages which were shunted the short distance to Plymouth North Road Station and coupled to the train for York via Bristol.

The previous evening Sam had managed to phone his parents in Coverack and tell them his news. They in turn contacted his sister Emily who was stationed on a gun site at Pilning just outside Bristol. She was waiting on the platform at Temple Meads and got Sam a hot cup of tea from the station buffet. No sooner had she passed it to him than the train began moving out of the station. Sam learned later that Emily had prepared a packet of ham sandwiches for him, courtesy of the Royal Artillery in which she was a Sergeant Cook. She had them in her haversack and didn't have time to hand them over. It was just as well Sam knew nothing of it for it was to be twenty-four hours before he had anything substantial to eat, apart from a station bun at York and a bit of "nutty" he had in his greatcoat pocket. Nutty is a sailor's blanket term for all kinds of chocolate. In fact, this one was a penny Nestlé's bar which Sam had got from a machine on Helston Station - he had heard on the local grapevine that despite rationing, the tea-room staff had a secret hoard of penny bars and were determined to keep on filling up the machine until there were no more, or some nosy Ministry Of Food Official put a stop to it - so Sam had bought a few on his way to Guz. After all, he had been a good customer when attending school in Helston, so as a good Cornishman he took a delight in getting one over on the English!

The train rumbled on. Sam started to get to know his new shipmates, chatting about this and that. He dozed, came awake, continued the chat, dozed off again. The pattern was repeated, seemingly endlessly, against the background noise of the slow double beat of the train wheels, going thumpthump, thumpthump, thumpthump, thumpthump as if saying, "Blowthis, blowthis, blowthis, blowthis". During his many train journeys, including two across India, Sam invented a game to pass the time when he became impatient. He pretended the train was tapping out a message to him. This one was definitely "Blowthis" repeated ad infinitum. The "troop" train carriages, being tacked on to the civilian passenger section, did not always come up to the station platform when the train stopped. Consequently there was no opportunity to sprint to the canteen and buy refreshments before the train started off again.

Darkness descended. Blackout blinds were pulled down. The train rumbled on through the night. "Blowthis, blowthis, blowthis, blowthis." By now the sailors were getting bored and impatient. Idle chat had ceased. They had stopped playing cards. They had consumed all the food they had brought with them. From time to time someone would announce to no one in particular that he was "chokka" - fed up - and wished the f.....g driver would pull his f.....g finger out and get them to their f.....g destination. These statements were met with general approval to start with, but as their progress became slower than ever, the self-appointed commentators were told to stop "dripping" - complaining - by the senior sailors in the compartment and an eerie silence descended.

The reading lights were switched off and the occupants of Sam's carriage slowly slumped into a somnolent state, those in the centre seats leaning sideways on to their neighbours' shoulders, with those lucky enough to have corner seats taking all the strain. Abruptly, the train came to a shuddering halt, escaping steam hissing noisily. Above the sound coming from the locomotive, the unmistakable droning beat of the engines of a German bomber could be heard, then another, then another until the sky above appeared to contain squadrons of them. The hissing stopped. The droning reached a climax when the bombers were directly overhead, then slowly died away. Then came the distant thud of exploding bombs and the sharp crack of ack-ack fire. Nothing was said but they all knew some poor souls were copping it. They remained stationary in uneasy silence for an hour or perhaps two or more. It was as if they were in limbo, waiting for their fate to be decided by some ethereal sentinel on the borders of hell. Suddenly there was an almighty jolt. The train began moving again. Desultory discussion resumed. Everyone avoided mentioning the bombing. The train proceeded at a snail's pace for about half an hour, then pulled slowly into York station. It was two in the morning. Everyone was at his lowest ebb.

Word was passed that they could get out and go to the station buffet. All was confusion. Broken glass everywhere. The smoky sky could be seen through holes in the roof. Bleary-eyed civilians stood in a daze beside their luggage, waiting for a train that would probably never come. First Aiders were patching up walking wounded who had been cut by flying splinters. But best of all, WVS ladies, ever cheerful in their green overalls, were smilingly handing out tea and a wad to each sailor. It didn't matter that there were no cups. Those lovely ladies had found a supply of empty jam jars to replace the blast-broken crockery. The thin glass was so hot that Sam had to pull down the sleeves of his jersey in order to hold the jar, but that didn't matter, he was drinking nectar! The stale station bun had to be better than ambrosia - although he didn't know what ambrosia was supposed to taste like, nor nectar, for that matter.

After a while, the crew, frugally fed and watered, were herded back on the train which then continued its journey to Hebburn on Tyne, near Jarrow from where the hunger march to London of two hundred unemployed men began in October 1936, some five years before. As it was getting light, the train wound slowly through the dockyard area.

Sam had not seen such evidence of poverty before. It gave the impression of a ghost town. Broken window panes were covered over with cardboard or had rags stuffed in the holes. Paint was peeling from the woodwork. Small gardens stood neglected and dotted with domestic debris. It was as if the people living there had lost their pride with their jobs. Through an open downstairs window a woman could be seen washing. She made no attempt to cover herself as the train crawled by not ten yards from her back door. There were no catcalls from the sailors. They were silent in unaccustomed sensitivity, just like the people in Sam's compartment when the Cornwall train passed through the blitzed streets of Plymouth. Sam realised that although his family was not prosperous, he was privileged to have been born in Coverack. Plenty of village families suffered during the Depression but they scraped along by cultivating their gardens and fishing to eke out the money received on the dole. He was glad that his ship had provided some work for the long-suffering Tynesiders.

The train stopped with a clanging of buffers. There, in that historic yard, regenerated by war, they saw their ship, the *Pathfinder*, shining grey in the misty morning light, the distinguishing pendant numbers G10 standing out in bold black on her sleek sides - she too was to have a place in British history.

The sleepy sailors had no time to sit and admire their new home. They disembarked hurriedly and were mustered on the quayside, shivering in the cold Geordie air. The Coxswain, British through and through but with an unpronounceable Polish surname, called out names and gave each one his Mess number. As they filed on board, each man was given his Station Card. Sam was in Number Three Mess in the fo'c'sle. His Gas Locker was No.39 and his Kit locker No.59. He was in the second part of the Port Watch and his Special Duty was to be Bosun's Mate. His Fighting Station was in the Lookout or loading ammunition in the magazine. The card was signed by C.W.Malins, Lieutenant R.N. He was the First Lieutenant or second in command and like all First Lieutenants was referred to as "Jimmy the One" by the sailors. After a much-needed wash and shave, Sam duly reported to the Killick of his mess. He was Leading Seaman "Lew" Wilton, a tall, dark, softly-spoken Cornishman from Bodmin. Sam was beginning to feel "at home" already. He was grateful that the majority of the crew came from Guz. He suddenly realised that the ship was full of "Janners". That might be rather confusing in due course. Meanwhile he set about having the first meal aboard *Pathfinder*. It went down "without touching the sides" as one of his shipmates put it.

It goes without saying that Sam thought the *Pathfinder* was the most beautiful ship he had ever seen. On first looking at her he found himself remembering some lines Miss Naytor had made him learn from *Henry V* - "I see you stand like greyhounds in the slips." Of course, the king was referring to his soldiers, not ships, but Sam thought the description was apt. She was a ship of 2,000 tons of the *Onslow* class. Her 40,000 horse power engines could drive her at 40 knots when called for. With her trawler bow, and a streamlined funnel abaft a slightly raked tripod mast, she fitted the description of a greyhound of the sea. She had four single four-inch High Angle guns, named from bow to stern, A, B, X and Y. Those guns, coupled with the faithful four-barrelled pom pom, plus four 20mm fast-firing Oerlikons, were to prove the ship's salvation in air attacks. The eight torpedo tubes, though impressive, were never to be fired in anger, but the sting in the tail, so to speak, of a hundred depth-charges which could be despatched in patterns of four, six, eight or ten on a lurking U-boat, were to bring fame to the ship's captain and her crew and terror to their enemies.

The first few days aboard the *Pathfinder* passed in a frenetic attempt by all the new crew members to shake-down. The men who had been standing by the ship for the past two or three months were key ratings and already knew the ship inside out. They were a great help to the new arrivals, although in some cases the old hands had a sort of proprietorial air and seemed reluctant to share their knowledge. Sam's Divisional Officer, Lieutenant Fowkes, R.N., seemed a decent chap, giving orders in a calm, quiet way. He was aware that about half of the seamen in his party were on their first ship and wisely did a few "dummy runs", practising the handling of steel hawsers and going through the anchoring drill. It was just as well he did because when it was time to move downstream a strong breeze was blowing and one of the river tugs found herself being pulled over as the wind began driving the *Pathfinder* towards the river bank. The foreshortened hawser was quickly cast off from the fo'c'sle and the little tug righted with a "whoosh" as the water cascaded off her sloping deck. When the ship was nudged into the mainstream the tugs cast off and the local pilot took her towards the river mouth under her own steam.

The *Pathfinder* continued working up for a week or so. The rookie seamen gradually got used to the routine of getting ready for sea, making fast to a buoy, exercising the seaboat's crew, manning the falls (ropes). Before long the whaler could be poised above the waves, "slipped" -

dropped - on to the crest of a wave when the crew would pull away smartly from the ship's side. On coming to a mooring buoy, the whaler was slipped and pulled up to the buoy by the duty watch on deck heaving on the falls. A couple of experienced seamen would jump on the bobbing buoy and thread the mooring wire through the ring to hold the ship while the anchor cable was being attached. It was dangerous work but satisfying. Everyone knew that other naval ships would be watching the manoeuvre so it was a matter of pride to execute it smartly. Sam enjoyed being a member of the seaboat's crew. It was preferable to being on deck manning the falls, despite the fact that he ususally got a drenching before returning on board. One consolation was that the crew were pulled up to the davits in the whaler - an exhilarating end to the operation. He did not find it quite so exciting later on when the ship was in mid-Atlantic and the seaboat's crew sometimes lost sight of her due to the long, heavy swell. He felt very much alone at such times when lowered to pick up survivors or inspect wreckage to search for clues leading to the identity of the ship it came from.

When on the open sea, Sam did duty as a lookout. He had a powerful pair of binoculars and being on the wing of the bridge, he was able to survey his "half" of the ocean and report all movements of ships or floating objects to the Officer of the Watch. It was every lookout's ambition to spot a U-boat's periscope. Sam was to see only one during his naval career. Being on the upper deck of the *Pathfinder* was all Sam had ever dreamed about. It surpassed anything he had read concerning life at sea. He was lucky that he never felt seasick, possibly because he had spent all his spare time in small boats in Coverack, coupled with the fact that he came from a long line of seafarers on his mother's side. When the ship returned to the Tyne from the grey sea and steamed slowly up river between the green banks, he experienced a feeling of peace and satisfaction he had never felt before. It was difficult to believe they were preparing for war.

The war preparations ceased one weekend. Sam fell in with the liberty men and went ashore with his mate Dick Davis. They went up-river about eight miles to Newcastle by train from South Shields. Predictably, they were soon eating as huge a meal as could posssibly be obtained in a wartime YMCA canteen. After that important exercise was completed they took a tram and viewed the city from the upper deck. Servicemen in uniform could travel anywhere for a few coppers. It was a lovely city. Due to lack of time they could only view the cathedral and the elegant nineteenth-century squares surrounding the city centre from their vantage point on the tram. They strolled through the shopping area for a while before finding their way back to the station. The people were very friendly, going out of their way to help a couple of young rookie sailors, but all too soon it was time to get back on board. Their Station Cards were marked U.A. That meant they were under 21 years of age. In turn, it meant they were not allowed out in the town after 2300. It seemed incongruous that they were combatants at sea in wartime yet considered not responsible enough to be let loose in port after 11 p.m. The U.A. stamped on their cards also indicated they were not entitled to the daily tot of rum so beloved of sailors. These restrictions did not particularly bother Sam and Dick. They were both just out of school and had not yet developed sophisticated tastes. They didn't even take advantage of duty-free tobacco as neither one had started smoking. Chatting together on the way back to the ship they both agreed to pay another visit to Newcastle as soon as possible. It was not to be.

A couple of days later, *Pathfinder* cast off and began making her way to Rosyth, prior to starting working up in earnest in Scapa Flow. After a short voyage of a hundred miles or so they entered the magnificent Firth of Forth. It was a curious feeling approaching the famous cantilever bridge on the water. One had the impression that the ship would never get under it. When the *Pathfinder* was directly below, it became apparent that two or three of her tripod masts could comfortably be placed one on top of another and there would still be plenty of room to pass beneath. At the dockyard in Rosyth the ship was formally handed over to the Royal Navy. The few remaining dockyard "maties" from Hawthorn-Leslies, who had remained on board for the sea trials carried out en route, left the ship and returned to Hebburn on Tyne.

The next day, *Pathfinder* set sail for the Orkneys. They steamed slowly along the coastline, passing Aberdeen, Fraserburgh and Banff - all names familiar to Sam due to the visits of Scottish fishing boats to the Western Approaches. They were not always welcome in Cornwall because the trawlers scooped up the fish from the traditional Cornish fishing grounds and the local men considered they had a right to the fish in their own area.

Scapa Flow was a wild, desolate place, totally dedicated to the Royal Navy. The "stripeys" - sailors with long-service good-conduct stripes - told Sam and other new recruits that after the scuttling of the German fleet there in 1919 the base had been allowed to run down - in the name of economy. Their Lordships had assumed the German High Seas Fleet was no longer a threat. A month after the outbreak of the Second World War, the U47 penetrated the waters of Scapa, using photos supplied by the Luftwaffe, and sank the battleship *Royal Oak* with the loss of over 800 men. The ensuing scandal explained why, by the time *Pathfinder* arrived at Scapa Flow, the place was bristling with boom defences, minefields, barrage balloons and radar stations, plus shore-based coastal defence and anti-aircraft batteries.

The day following her arrival *Pathfinder* began "working up", that is preparing to take her place in the Fleet as an efficient war machine. The ship was under way most of the time and Sam began to be familiar with the local place names. The Old Man of Hoy, a bluff, steep cliff, reminded him of the coast of Cornwall, as did Lyness Harbour, though he never found out if the Orcadians claimed that they too had a lost land beneath the waves as did the people of Land's End. He learned also to respect the name "skerry" which warned of a reef covered by sea at High Water or during a storm. During torpedo trials he spent long hours in the whaler, turning the handle to pump air to the diver searching for a lost torpedo. Practice torpedoes had brilliant-orange-coloured, harmless warheads and were easily spotted when they remained afloat after they had finished their trial run. Sometimes the torpedo inexplicably dived to the bottom and remained there. Each machine was worth several thousand pounds so it had to be recovered. While they were recovering a lost torpedo, *Pathfinder* went off to continue working up. She was a magnificent sight steaming at speed when chasing a contact and though the whaler's crew grumbled about being left in an exposed position while the ship went swanning off, they were secretly proud of her. At least, Sam was.

It was not all hard work. The crew was allowed ashore at regular intervals and as stated earlier, Sam and Dick Davies made the most of the opportunity to explore the islands. On one memorable occasion the liberty men were landed in Kirkwall. Sam tasted beer for the first time in his life. He was not over impressed and wondered why the Wesleyans in Coverack made such a fuss about remaining teetotal. However, he enjoyed the company in the bar and got to know the Killick of No. 3 Mess, Lew Wilton, a bit better, as he had persuaded Sam to accompany him. He was a young married man and had to take care of his money so he didn't want to go ashore and drink all his pay in one go as some of his messmates did. It was a cold, blustery day and after working in an open boat Sam didn't fancy wandering about Kirkwall. He took a look at a rather grim-looking Church of Scotland building out of curiosity and after a quick tour of the shops, where he bought some postcards, he retired to the warmth of the pub.

Torpedo trials over, the next item in the work-up programme was testing the asdic apparatus. Asdic is the acronym for Anti-Submarine Detection Investigation Committee, and the electronic apparatus used for hunting submarines was thus called the asdic. The sonar device was housed in a dome below the waterline near the bow of the ship. It sent ultrasonic waves out under water. They detected the presence of a submarine, or indeed any other underwater object, by sending back an echo to the operator who sat in a small cabin on the bridge, listening to the "ping" through headphones. The "pings" were relayed to the bridge by loudspeaker when a contact was made. The "pings" went on and on until the echo was heard, telling the asdic operator there was something beneath the waves. Then the sound pattern changed to "ping-ping, ping-ping". When the captain decided the sound represented a submarine he sounded Action Stations on the alarm and ordered the helmsman to steer towards the object. Meanwhile, the torpedo men on the stern prepared their depth-charges. As the ship approached its prey, the "ping-ping" became louder and faster. This added to the excitement of the chase. The torpedo men set the charges to go off at the depth indicated by the asdic apparatus. Each steel canister contained about three hundredweight of explosive. Six were launched from twin rails on the stern of *Pathfinder* and four others were fired, two on each quarter. From his Action Station in the lookout by the bridge, Sam could see the T-shaped depth-charge "cradle" shoot up into the air from the ship's sides and then fall into the ocean with the depth-charge. Theoretically the U-boat was in the centre of the ten exploding charges. As soon as the sweating torpedo men had fired the charges, they set about reloading, ready for the next attack. It was tough, dangerous work, especially in the dark on a wet deck with the ship rolling heavily. Of course, only dummies were used in practising with the duty sub. at Scapa. Small, harmless explosives were dropped to indicate to the submarine she was being attacked. The submarine captain would keep the "score", which was relayed to *Pathfinder* at the end of the exercise.

It was essential to perfect the technique of U-boat hunting before going on convoy duty, so the practice went on day after day until the new crew was declared to be proficient. It must be remembered that not only the asdic and torpedo men were involved. Each time the ship "closed up" for

Action Stations, the gunners rushed to prepare to fire at the submarine should she surface, the engine room staff had to provide full steam at a second's notice, magazines had to be manned to serve the guns, signals sent to the Commodore of the convoy, lookouts warned to watch for a periscope, and the ship's movements recorded on a chart for future reference, plus a hundred and one other duties to be performed such as preparing for casualties and being ready to deal with damage to the ship should she get hit. Sam found the frenzied but calm action enthralling and felt proud to be part of it. He had certainly not expected this! It so happened that within hours of leaving on her first convoy duty, *Pathfinder* hoisted the long black pendant known as the contact flag, to warn all ships in view what she was about, and went into action.

The hours and hours of patient drilling paid off. The depth-charges were dropped and after a short interval which seemed endless to Sam, the sea astern began to boil and huge spouts of water went high into the air. It was a magnificent, frightening sight. There was no result, apart from some dead fish floating on the surface. If a U-boat was lurking, preparing to attack the convoy of troopships, the attack served to drive her off as no further echoes were heard and after completing a search in company with the *Derwent*, she took up her station again on the flank of the convoy. Everyone was aware that if there had been a submarine observing the convoy, a signal would be sent to Germany giving details so that another attack could be mounted at a later date.

CHAPTER NINE

CONVOYS

The boiler clean was to take a week, so each watch - Port and Starboard - was given three days' leave, half remaining on board at a time. Sailors were allowed four free railway warrants a year so in view of the cost of travelling to Cornwall from Glasgow, Sam elected to take a free warrant. The buzz was that *Pathfinder* was going to the tropics. It was fairly obvious after Jack Dusty had been seen taking large packages of tropical kit on board. Sam reasoned that if they were sailing southwards it could be for a long time so it was worth using up a precious pass.

There was an "end of term" type of atmosphere on the quarter deck as the liberty men were inspected prior to going on leave. They had been praised by the captain for their enthusiasm in the working-up period and were now looking forward to seeing their families. Unfortunately there was no opportunity to see anything of Glasgow. In any case it was getting dark by the time they got there and the men had to catch the night train to Euston. Seats were at a premium in wartime trains. No one fancied spending a night in the corridor so all the southbound sailors were waiting well before the train was shunted to the departure platform. Civilians were not partial to travelling with a bunch of rowdy sailors so all the "Pathfinders" found seats together and spread out to deter anyone intruding on them. Third-class carriages were designed to seat four people on each side of the compartments but the brawny sailors sprawled to make it three. Room was only made for a fourth person if she happened to be "worth the best of three falls" as a Cornishman who followed wras'lin' put it.

On this occasion Sam was fortunate enough to secure a corner seat. He was well prepared for the night journey, having bought a couple of pork pies on the station. In his "ditty box", which contained all the luggage he needed for such a short leave, he had three bars of "nutty" bought from the NAAFI shop on *Pathfinder*. It had been a surprise to him to find a NAAFI manager on the ship. He was technically a civilian but wore a naval-type uniform and shared the hardships and dangers of life on a destroyer. His Action Station duty was a non-combatant one in the Sick Bay.

After a long, not very comfortable night on the train, Sam rushed across London from Euston to Paddington with three of his shipmates. The four of them splashed out on a taxi to make sure they caught the morning train to Penzance. It was Sam's first glimpse of London - just a blur of buildings and people. On Paddington Station he bought his mother a book by E.F. Benson, her favourite author, who was the son of the first Bishop of Truro. George Exelby was a pipe smoker so Sam had already bought a half-pound tin of duty-free tobacco for his father before going ashore.

The journey to Gwinear Road was long but uneventful. The weather was fine and outside London the countryside was green with the promise of spring. Sam spent the first hour or so looking out of the window and chatting with his mates. After passing through Reading he opened his newspaper and began to catch up on the latest developments. He hadn't read a paper for weeks. He had instinctively bought a *News Chronicle* before boarding the train as his family were true Cornish Liberals. There was news of the award of the George Cross to the island of Malta by King George V on the 16th April, 1942. The recent blitz on the city of Exeter by fifty German bombers was also referred to obliquely. Sam was surprised to read that the Japs had dared to attack Colombo in Ceylon, but pleased to see that the RAF subsequently claimed to have shot down twenty-five planes. Another small item caught his eye. The latest fashion was for women to go bare legged. It was claimed that ladies who went without stockings were patriotic. The government had praised the idea without giving reasons. Sam chuckled to himself. He knew that if the idea caught on there would be a saving of valuable cargo space and ships bringing imported goods would be able to carry more essential supplies instead of being cluttered up with silk stockings and the newfangled nylons from the USA. He read the article out loud to his mates and they were unanimous in their approval, adding a few salacious remarks of their own for good measure.

The train stopped quite a while at Temple Meads in Bristol. This time, Sam managed to get a cup of char and a wad before they moved off. After being in some rough weather, china cups were scarce on board *Pathfinder*, so before the men went on leave, the Killick of the mess had exhorted his mates to "liberate" a cup or two from the railway companies. It was the custom of passengers to place empty cups under the seats in carriages so that staff could collect them when cleaning out. Sam decided he would do his duty on the return journey. He wouldn't "half-hitch" a cup from the Great Western Railway but take one from the LMS instead. Sam slept after leaving Bristol, passing through Exeter and going along the coast through Dawlish and Teignmouth and waking just before arriving in Plymouth, where the exodus of a large number of servicemen gave him a chance to rush to the refreshment room and buy another cup of tea. He was nearly home now and began to savour the idea of spending some time in Coverack. He had plenty of time to think about it, because the train crawled maddeningly from station to station as it had done on his last leave. Indeed, it did every time he went home during the war, but he was always in such a buoyant mood by the time he had crossed the Tamar into Cornwall that he couldn't envisage it happening again, but it always did. He blamed it on "Sod's Law" in the end, as most sailors did, knowing that if there is a chance of anything going wrong, it would do so.

In due course, the train puffed slowly into Gwinear Road. After sampling a really fresh home made cup of "Cornish" tea in the cosy tea room behind the station, Sam boarded the branch line train for Helston. This time he was alone in the compartment so he took the opportunity to stand up and brush down his uniform, then he rubbed up his new shoes. In common with other young sailors he had invested in a pair of shoes with buckles on. They were more comfortable and smarter than regulation boots and he wanted to give a good impression when he arrived.

As he boarded the bus for Coverack a few village people greeted him with: "Home again, Sam?" Resisting an urge to say that he had been away since Christmas, he replied, "Ess, you," in the approved fashion and settled in his seat. Before boarding the bus he had learned from the clerk in the ticket office that he would have to leave home again the next day but one. He had suspected as much when he was given his leave pass. He didn't want to start his "furlough", as Granny still called it, by being unpleasant to anyone. He was determined nothing was going to spoil his long-awaited break from routine.

No one was waiting for him when he got off the bus, but he had an exciting welcome from Rover, his cousin James' dog. Rover was a good-natured mongrel, an obvious cross between an Alsatian and a Red Setter, but somewhere in his ancestry there must have been a Scotch Terrier. He had a Setter's body and tail, an Alsatian's ears, a head the size of an Alsatian's but with a distinct Terrier shape. He was indeed unique. Rover, true to his name, wandered about Coverack for most of the day. His master, James Rickard, was a "donkeyman" in the Merchant Navy. James' mother, Lisa, - Sam's mother's sister - was a lady of ample proportions and disliked the exercise involved in taking Rover for walks so she simply let him loose whenever he clamoured to go out. At first, Sam's progress through the village was erratic as Rover ran on ahead, barking joyously for about twenty yards or so, then he would come bounding back to jump up and greet Sam all over again. Sam knew what the dog wanted and in the end he gave in and allowed him to carry a woollen glove in his mouth. Rover then trotted quietly by his side, wagging his tail non-stop until they reached Sunny Cove.

An enticing aroma of hot pasties greeted Sam as he opened the door. His mother, flushed from cooking, flung her arms around him, covering his carefully brushed greatcoat with tiny specks of white flour. Mary took a pace backwards and declared, after studying Sam for a moment, "Sam, you've grown taller, but you're so thin! You need feeding up."

Sam laughed. He was getting used to this kind of greeting when he arrived home.

"And look at your face," Mary continued. "It's some red! Have you been in the sun?"

"No, Mum, that's the wind," said Sam.

"Now look at your hands, my 'an'some. They're in a bit of a mess, aren't they?"

"Don't worry, Mum," said Sam. "That's because I've been handling ropes and doing a lot of rowing. I'm not a schoolboy now remember."

At that point Mary decided not to probe any more for the time being and began taking the pasties out of the oven just as George came in from work. "Sorry I couldn't meet you, Sam," he said. "I've been plastering Mrs. Snell's wall and I promised it would be finished today."

"Don't worry, Dad,' said Sam. "Rover came to the bus shelter and escorted me home. You're looking well, anyway."

"Ess," said George. "You been out in the wind by the look of 'ee."

"Plenty of that in Scapa Flow," laughed Sam, and Mary joined in.

"I know, boy," said George. "'Tis like being out by the Manacles in East wind."

The two men went out to the "cow's house" to wash their hands while Mary set the table, and then they sat down to the meal she had lovingly prepared.

Sam had to relate everything that had happened since he had been away - well, nearly - but Mary wasn't quite satisfied that her boy had told all and said with a hint of anxiety in her voice that she hoped he hadn't been drinking with the lads. At that point, Sam diplomatically remembered the gifts he had brought and got up to get them from his attaché case, conveniently refraining from answering Mary's implied question. Luckily she did not repeat it. She could not resist delving into her new book. George filled his pipe with pusser's tobacco and father and son began to wash up after clearing the table, while Mary sat by the fire, still wearing her apron, avidly reading the first chapter of the latest adventure of Miss Mapp.

The next day went by in a flash. Sam didn't get up early, but declined Mary's offer of breakfast in bed. After a lazy morning chatting to his mother and getting the "feel" of home again by going from room to room, picking up familiar ornaments and putting them down, having a look at the papers and magazines piled up in the window box and reading the letters sent home from his soldier siblings, Emily and Alexander, he had a quick lunch, went off in search of Elsie and took her for a walk across the cliffs. She was disappointed he wasn't wearing his uniform. Somehow or other he knew that his old clothes were what he should wear in Coverack, despite the fact that he was growing out of them fast. Elsie was appeased when he promised to send her another photo of him in uniform, now that he was a "proper sailor", who'd been on Atlantic convoys, entitled to wear "H.M. DESTROYER" on his cap tally. He was very proud of that. Fortunately he was not aware of the fact that, statistically speaking, there were more casualties among destroyers than any other type of warship. You do not even think about it when you are eighteen and enjoying life to the full. Sam and Elsie enjoyed their time together but had to cut it short as Sam had to make some "duty" calls before going off the next morning. They both promised to write as often as possible but Elsie was working hard in school, hoping to get accepted at a teachers' training college, and Sam was eager to be off to sea, so it seemed rather a bleak prospect.

Sam enjoyed being spoiled by his grandmothers. They still thought of him as a little fair-haired boy. Granny Trengilly vied with Granny Exelby in making sure he was well fed. Cornish women have an inborn dread of their menfolk going hungry and are inclined to encourage them to eat more than is really good for them. This tradition is probably due to the lean times when near starvation forced Cornishmen to seek their fortune in the mines overseas. So in each house Sam was plied with buns and strong tea while each grandmother complained about "that old Navy" - "They ought to be ashamed of themselves, giving such a short leave." Sam knew he had to agree, but the second time round in Granny Exelby's house, he left as soon as he could, using the excuse that it was getting dark and that he wanted to get home before blackout. He arrived back in Sunny Cove, laden with enough food for half a dozen to eat on the train the following day.

After tea he went down to the Fishermen's Club for a while, then he went on to Henry Mundy's shoemaker's shop, gleaning the latest news and enjoying the company of his friends. Nothing had changed, yet Sam felt almost like a stranger. He realised he was living in a different world, so he said little about his recent activities. He just sat, eagerly drinking in the atmosphere, sensing that it might be quite a while before he would be able to enjoy his next evening in Coverack.

It was getting late when he arrived back home. His mother and father were sitting quietly by the fire. Sam knew they had been talking about him. They were in a sombre mood so in order to reduce the tension he volunteered to make a cup of cocoa for them, knowing his untypical offer would educe a light-hearted comment. While he was preparing the drinks he told his parents the latest village news he had gleaned from his visits, trying to be as casual as possible. George, equally casual, asked his son if he knew where he would be going on his next trip. Sam truthfully replied that he didn't know but hinted that he might be going to a warmer climate. Mary was clearly upset about his going back to sea, but Sam did not overdo his assurances that it would be all right in case she began to think he was worried too, and was making light of the prospect of a rough passage, just to stop her worrying. Instead, he asked her if she was coming to Helston with him in the morning. Mary was delighted. Suddenly she was all smiles and said she needed to get some more blackout material anyway. Sam privately hoped there wouldn't be tears at the station. He couldn't bear to see his mother cry, but he was glad her mood had lightened before she went to bed.

All went well the following morning. It so happened that Mary's friend Ann Reseigh was on the bus and she asked if she could come to the station with them. Her presence made the parting relatively easy because the two friends had decided to go shopping together. In future years Sam was to discover that to send his wife and daughter shopping was an unfailing remedy to most of life's little problems.

At Gwinear Road Alan Emmett's grinning face appeared as the train from Penzance drew in. He shouted, "Over 'ere, Sam. I've got a place for 'ee." He had saved a corner seat for Sam. The two mates travelled together all the way to Glasgow Central. The journey up to "Smoke" passed pleasantly enough in the Quartermaster's company. He had been in submarines before being drafted to *Pathfinder* and Sam was fascinated by his account of life in the "boats" as submariners termed their ships. They had time to spare when they reached London so they crossed by tube. Sam had not been on the Underground before and was glad to come up for air at Euston. He certainly did not envy the lot of Londoners who had to use the station platforms as shelters during bombing raids. The two mates met a number of "Pathfinders" on the departure platform before getting on the night train. Coming back from "leaf" as the Devonport men called it, they were all well stocked with food for the journey and some had obviously tanked up at the station bar as well but they caused no trouble before boarding and once settled in their seats were not long in nodding off.

As the train sped through the night and the chattering died down, Sam reverted to his game of making up words to match the rhythm of the wheels. Going up an incline the train slowed to a steady beat of three, thumpthumpthump, thumpthumpthump, thumpthumpthump - what message could it be? Thumpthumpthump. Ah, yes, grabamug, grabamug, grabamug. It wasn't difficult. They were all shipmates in the compartment so he felt under the seat, found a mug and put it in his attaché case in the space from where he had just removed a greaseproof paper bag containing one of his mother's pasties. It was not quite as tasty when cold but Sam ate it with relish and was lucky enough to get a cup of tea at the next stop to wash it down. With a good meal inside him, he settled down to sleep. The next thing he knew, Alan was shaking him by the shoulder, saying, "Come on, mate. Stop dreaming about Elsie - you're up Scotland now!" Sam reached for his case, put on his cap and left the train hurriedly.

Well before midday, when their leave ended officially, they were back on board and getting ready to take over from the Starboard Watch who were going on leave.

"'Tid'n worth it, boy," said Alan jokingly to "Ginger" John, his opposite number in the Starboard Watch. "You might as well go ashore here and enjoy yourself." John came from a mining village in South Wales and had well publicised the fact that he was an expectant father.

"Not a chance, boyo," he replied. "I rang last night and she's counting the hours till she sees the smoke from the Swansea train coming up the valley." Everybody laughed as John picked up his case and went up on deck. It seemed to Sam as if he had never been back to Coverack. This was his home now.

The mess decks were quite roomy, due to half of the crew being on leave, but the luxury of having plenty of space ended abruptly when the Starboard Watch returned. As soon as the last liberty man had reported on board, Sam was given the order to pipe "Special Sea Duty Men", which meant that those who had been assigned positions for leaving and entering harbour should "close up", that is, go to their place of duty. They were experienced men needed in key places such as the fo'c'sle, the bridge, the helm, the engine room telegraphs, the flag deck and so on. Orders were given to the men on the bow and stern by flag to avoid the misinterpretation which can arise when an order is shouted during a storm or when there is a lot of engine noise or when under attack. For example, when it is necessary to drop anchor quickly to take the way off a ship or to slip a tow as happened on the Tyne near South Shields. Sam's Uncle Sam Trengilly, after whom he had been named, gave his "call" or Bosun's pipe to his married sister when he left the navy. Mary passed it on to her son Sam and he used it for the first time when he called the Special Sea Duty Men. Mary would be pleased when he wrote to tell her.

The ship went straight away into Defence Stations, wartime sea-going routine. Four hours on watch, four hours off round the clock. *Pathfinder* joined the troopship convoy mentioned earlier as they left the Clyde. They were in good company. The "battle wagon", HMS *Rodney*, like the *Pathfinder*, was a Devonport-manned ship and her captain was in charge of the important convoy. The *Pathfinder* was one of three destroyers screening her. That is why when contact was made, the captain ordered a ten-charge pattern to be fired. The navy could not afford to lose another battleship, nor could the army sustain the loss of manpower caused by the sinking of a liner carrying troops to the Eastern Theatre via Freetown. Sam had learned from his soldier brother's letter that he had just landed in India on the way to Burma after sailing that very route.

It was not long before they encountered bad weather. Sam again blessed his parents for providing him with a good stomach. He didn't feel ill at all and at meal times volunteered to eat the meal belonging to anyone feeling queasy. He was ravenous! He got used to the ordered clutter of a messdeck at sea. At first he slung his hammock and slept like a log during his watch below but after a while, having to lash up and stow it in the netting provided in order to give the other watch space to "sling" became a chore he could well do without. He decided he would emulate his more experienced shipmates and only use his hammock when they were "cruising", doing four hours on and having eight off, or when in harbour. At other times he turned in "all standing", sleeping on a messdeck form in his duffel coat and with his lifebelt half inflated. It had been proved that men in the water lasted longer when wearing lots of clothes as they provided a form of insulation with the air trapped in between layers, so Sam felt safer like that. He went to sleep with his arm round a stanchion so that he wouldn't fall off the form. It worked very well, though he couldn't understand why he remained there when asleep. His Uncle Alexander Trengilly had told him that when he used to steer his boat all night on passage to Coverack from Plymouth, he simply kept the tiller in the crook of his arm and dozed off. The tug of the wind in the sails would exert pressure on the rudder in the water and that in turn moved the tiller which nudged his arm and he would then come to and steer on another tack. Sam concluded that in the same way the roll of the ship made him subconsciously hang on to the stanchion when he was in danger of falling and consequently it scarcely disturbed his sleep.

Being at sea in wartime was a strange existence. There were upwards of two hundred men on board *Pathfinder*. Each man went about his duties, conscious of being part of a well drilled team, yet because of the watch system it was possible to do a two- or three-week convoy and never see certain members of the crew from the beginning of the voyage to the end. Sam probably saw more of the crew than most because as Bosun's Mate he regularly visited nearly all parts of the ship. During one patch of bad weather it was forbidden to go along the iron deck in the waist of the ship, which connected the forepart to the Quarter Deck in the after part. That posed a problem when Sam had to call the First Lieutenant for his watch. All Watertight Doors were closed so it was not possible to reach the after part of the ship by a circuitous route below the iron deck. A steel wire was permanently rigged at a height of about a fathom and a half above the deck from the bridge ladder to the searchlight platform. Lengths of rope had been spliced round "thimbles" - metal rings with grooved edges to accommodate the rope - which were threaded on to the wire. These lifelines were there for sailors to grab in order to steady themselves as they moved along the slippery deck in rough weather. Sam was in a dilemma. It was not quite a Hobson's choice, it was nearer that of the Catch 22 situation which was to be described in Joseph Heller's novel of the sixties. If Sam crossed the iron deck he would be in the "rattle". If he didn't call Jimmy the One he would again be in trouble for not doing his duty. Sam decided he had to go. He knew he could make it if he waited by the bridge ladder until the ship lifted on to the crest of a wave. Then he could slide down the wire, holding on to a lifeline with both hands and lifting his feet off the deck. It was a similar situation to that of launching the lifeboat down the slip in Coverack in rough weather, the trick being to time the slide at the precise moment. He waited and as he felt the ship reach the crest of a wave he launched himself down the wire. It worked! He found himself bumping in to the searchlight platform much sooner than he expected. He duly called the First Lieutenant - ratings were not allowed to "shake" sleeping officers, they had to repeat their call until they got a verbal response - then he travelled back to the forepart in the same manner by waiting until the ship buried her nose in a deep trough. It was an exhilarating ride but frightening to see the rollers towering above the iron deck. He got very wet in the process but was pleased with himself, though as far as he knew no one witnessed his unorthodox movements. He lingered by the ladder, hoping to witness Jimmy's performance, but remembered he had to call the Port Watch so he missed it.

Everyone had to take his turn at being "Cook of the Mess". There were 18 men in number three mess. Vegetables had to be prepared, meat cut up and made ready for cooking and a dessert had to be concocted. More often than not the sweet turned out to be a plum duff. It was a sort of pudding, made with flour, margarine, sugar, eggs and milk. The "plums" were usually tinned; if they were not available, currants or sultanas were substituted, but it was still called "plum duff". The pudding was very filling and very welcome after a cold, wet watch on deck. Sometimes there was stewed fruit which was usually prunes, plus custard made from sweet condensed milk. Sam's favourite was rice pudding but that was rare as it could only be made when there was still fresh milk available. After a couple of days at sea it was back to condensed milk. Sam got so used to having it in his tea that for a couple of years after the war he took sugar with his tea to compensate, despite the fact that Cornish Wesleyans, by tradition, never took sugar in tea as Wesley had persuaded the eighteenth-century converts that it would be tantamount to condoning the slave trade.

The diet was balanced, but didn't vary a great deal. Meat was often in the form of tinned stew, or corned beef - known as corned dog - vegetables were tinned more often than not as fresh vegetables took up valuable space; similarly, fruit was tinned or dried. There was plenty of bread and jam and seemingly unlimited kye. The latter was solid cocoa, which had to be shaved off the block with a sharp knife before having hot water poured on it, then milk and sugar were added. It was really delicious.

Wonderful for keeping out the cold. Sailors would always cover for a shipmate who volunteered to go and make some during the night watches. Sam became quite adept at making kye because in his capacity as Bosun's Mate he was able to move about the ship legitimately and no one questioned the fact that he was carrying kye to his mates when he was on watch.

To return to the duties of the Cook of the Mess. When the meal was prepared it was carried to the galley in baking tins bearing the number of the mess. The Petty Officer Cook then dealt with the meal by adding the necessary touches which had been omitted by the duty mess man, then it was cooked. When the pipe "Cooks to the Galley" was called, the mess cooks went along to the galley and carried the meal to his mates. Woe betide anyone who dropped the cooked meal or slipped on a wet deck. No excuses were tolerated! Number three mess had "democratically" decided - at the insistence of the older hands - to have a plain breakfast each morning. It consisted of tea, bread and marg. plus jam or marmalade. Each man was allocated 1s 10d per day for meals which was credited to Mess Funds. The three-badge A.B.s liked to make a profit from the catering. This was shared out just before going on long leave. The young sailors didn't dare demur, they simply topped up their meagre meals with nutty and biscuits from the NAAFI.

One of the duties of the Quartermaster and Bosun's Mate was to light the oil-fuelled galley stoves for the ship's cooks early in the morning watch, usually at about 0430. Sam had noticed that some of the messes had egg and bacon for breakfast. It was a tempting sight. One morning when they were in harbour, the Quartermaster on duty with him asked if he would like a cooked breakfast. The answer was in no doubt. The Quartermaster "lifted" an egg from one mess, a slice of bacon from another, bread from another and in no time at all two eggs, bacon and bread were sizzling away. They then shared a cooked breakfast. Sam wondered how they were going to get away with it. "No sweat," said the QM. "I know which cooks of the mess put in an extra egg or a slice of bacon for themselves, so I've taken their perks. They won't dare complain!" The two "thieves" cleared up all the evidence of their deed and carried on with the watch. Clearly it wouldn't do to repeat their crime too often but Sam was to enjoy quite a few early breakfasts after that.

It was part of the job of being cook of the mess to clear up after meals and make sure everything was shipshape and ready for inspection. Cleanliness is paramount in a crowded man of war so standards were high and fairly easy to maintain in a new ship. Sam managed to do his duties without complaint from "above". Before the cleaning could be started it was necessary to check that all the kit and personal belongings were stowed away. For centuries life on a warship has revolved round the need to be ready for instant action against an enemy in wartime. Sailors have always been trained to expect the unexpected in order that the ship can remain as a fighting unit despite damage caused by enemy fire. That is why watertight doors are kept closed unless it is absolutely necessary for them to remain open to allow movement on the ship at sea or in harbour. Should the ship be holed, causing an ingress of water, there were damage-control parties ready to stop up the gaps temporarily if at all possible and there were pumps to get rid of water flooding compartments. Sailors therefore had to make sure their lockers were firmly shut so that in the event of an explosion or collision they would not fly open and spread kit all over the messdeck. That is why caps, towels, books and other personal belongings were not allowed to be left lying around or perched on the tops of lockers, trunking, wiring or mess tables etc. It went without saying that the cooks of the mess would tidy away any objects which would offend the eye of any inspecting officer. It was not a pernickety prohibition as some people thought, because should water flood a mess, necessitating the lowering of a suction hose into it, all the kit left lying around would be drawn to the end of the hose and block it. To obviate this, there was a wire mesh on the end of the hose but that too would be clogged by woollen jumpers and so on, wrapping themselves round to it when drawn by the suction.

While he was scrubbing a particularly dirty part of the messdeck one morning, Sam said to himself, "Mess is the right word for this!" The ship's writer was passing at the time and asked Sam what he had said. Sam repeated his "drip".

"I'm surprised at you, Sam," said the Writer. "You did Latin at school, didn't you?"

"Yes, worse luck," replied Sam.

"Well, think about it. Each mess has a table and a number."

Then it dawned on Sam. "Of course, it must come from 'mensa', a table. I was told Latin would come in useful when I grew up!"

The Writer laughed and went on his way while Sam continued his scrubbing.

It was during times when he had been "told off" to do chores in the mess that Sam was able to take stock of the situation. Work in the mess was usually done when the rest of the hands were on deck. That gave him a chance to take it all in. The lights were permanently on and in spite of the forced air blowing through the trunking the atmosphere always seemed rather fetid, which was actually quite welcome when coming down from the chill of the upper deck. There wasn't a spare square foot of room. Each man had a locker for his personal possessions. During the day, hammocks were stowed in the racks provided - still called netting, from the days of sail. Because of the lack of space, bedding had to be aired when decreed by the First Lieutenant. On a fine day, with no spray blowing on board, the bedding was taken to the upper deck and lashed to the guard rails to get the fresh air blowing through it. The operation was best done in harbour but *Pathfinder* was scarcely ever in harbour so the bedding was aired when the odour on the messdeck and the weather conditions dictated.

To return to the messdeck. There was a constant blowing noise there as the air circulated through the trunking. Like many people who lead open-air lives, sailors were not keen on too much fresh air indoors and had a habit of closing the nozzles which were designed to direct the forced air in any chosen direction. It's not difficult to imagine the result. On the other hand, if you went to sleep in your hammock with a stream of air directed on you, it was almost certain that you would catch cold and that would then be spread throughout the messdeck's inhabitants. Added to the noise of the forced draught was the creaking and grinding of the ship as she lifted on the waves and the thump as she went down in the troughs. It was a cacophony of sounds. Sam could not identify them all. Some were due to the newness of the ship and others were introduced when hunting a submarine or rounding up a straggler in a convoy, and *Pathfinder* had to go at a greater speed than would normally be advisable in adverse sea conditions. Added to all these, was the forces' radio when the ship was in range. It was impossible not to know the words of the current popular songs as they were repeated ad infinitum. At times the matelots would join in the chorus, adding to the din. Now and again a song would be the butt of caustic comments. Once, when called to Action Stations because of an air attack, Anne Shelton was singing, "For all we know, we may never meet again." One can imagine the shouts of derision which greeted that song whenever it was repeated after that, despite Miss Shelton's fine singing voice.

It was easy to become disorientated when below, especially at night when the deadlights were clamped over the portholes in response to the pipe "Darken ship." The deck vibrated gently in time with the throbbing engines. It was a very reassuring sound. The turbines were capable of producing 40,000 shaft horse power and could propel the ship at 40 knots if required. When the engines stopped at sea, usually to enable the asdic operator to get a better fix on a U-boat, there was an unearthly quiet, as if everyone on board was holding his breath. Those were the times when the seamen recalled the presence of the stokers and engineers down below. They were the most vulnerable of their shipmates and too often taken for granted, as is often the case with people who do their job well and are rarely found wanting.

All ships in the convoy had to conform to a prearranged zigzag pattern of movement so that an attacking U-boat could not easily calculate in advance the course they were steering. This added a fair percentage of extra mileage to the normal distances travelled between ports. *Pathfinder* and all the other escorts had to cover even greater distances in the performance of their duties such as racing up and down, rounding up stragglers, charging "strong" asdic contacts in positions where Admiralty signals had indicated the possibility of U-boat activity, and investigating suspect ships sailing on their own and purporting to be neutral. Because of this, the *Pathfinder* had to oil at sea.

Taking on fuel in mid ocean was a tricky operation. Special Sea Duty men went to their stations and the Engineer Officer, accompanied by an Engine Room Artificer and a couple of stokers, appeared on deck. *Pathfinder* closed with the Royal Fleet Auxiliary tanker *Brambleleaf* and the captain of the fo'c'sle fired a line aboard the *Brambleleaf* with a Schermuly pistol. The rope was then bent on a wire hawser which was pulled across the gap between the two ships to ensure they didn't yaw too far apart. The quarter deck party carried out a similar exercise on the stern. The oiling was done at a steady ten knots plus to avoid the ships becoming a sitting target for a U-boat. Next, the all-important oil pipeline was hoisted across the water and hauled on board by the stokers. It was then carefully attached to the fuel-inlet valve embedded in the deck. It was essential that no oil be spilled, leaving a tell-tale trail in the ocean. It was filthy, glutinous stuff which would take hours to clean from the ship's deck and sides should it gush out by accident. *Pathfinder*'s Coxswain was at the wheel and two Quartermasters on the Engineroom telegraphs. The manoeuvre had to be done precisely, and only the most skilled were allowed to be at the controls. The same applied to the engine room staff. While the oiling was being done, the eyes of the men at defence stations were everywhere, scanning the surface of the sea and the air. No one wanted to be caught in that dangerous situation - least of all the RFA men on the *Brambleleaf*, sitting on all that fuel. Sam marvelled at the slickness of the operation. Nevertheless it took a long time and the sea began to get very choppy, the water between the two ships turning white with foam, the pressure shooting miniature spouts up in the air, which sent a fine spray over the men on deck. At last, Lieutenant Mercer was satisfied, the pipeline stopped up and winched back on the tanker. The wires were cast off, *Pathfinder* gave a short whoop of thanks on her siren and went off at speed to resume her station on the flank of the now distant convoy, while the Sea Duty men went below for a well-earned cup of char.

In a subsequent oiling at sea, Sam was to witness a wire snap and come snaking back on the fo'c'sle, breaking both legs of a seaman. He had to be hoisted aboard the Nelson in a Neil Robertson stretcher for treatment and the battleship sent a replacement seaman aboard *Pathfinder* at the same time. Paradoxically it transpired that after a few days the AB became so ill because of her movement in rough weather that the Irish Surgeon Lieutenant decided, with some relish, that the man should be returned to the battlewagon as he was "cluttering up the Sick Bay". This was done amid shouts from *Pathfinder*'s crew telling Nelson's men to "Get some sea time in" and other comments quite unprintable. There she was, the proud battleship steaming steadily through the waves while *Pathfinder* was going up and down in the swell "like a yoyo" as one seaman put it. That is why, whenever they had an impromptu SODS' Opera, usually after a game of tombola in harbour, the crew ended the entertainment by singing the chorus, "Roll on the *Nelson*, the *Rodney*, *Renown*, this one-funnelled bastard is getting me down!" Most of them didn't mean it, of course, for they preferred the more easy-going discipline and camaraderie of a small ship. When civvies asked sailors what the word SODS meant, the reply, given with a straight face, was "Sailors' Operatic and Dramatic Society". The civilians would then often express surprise and pleasure that such a cultural activity was in progress aboard one of His Majesty's Ships in wartime.

The troopship convoy proceeded steadily southwards in its zigzag way. *Pathfinder* went to Action Stations for an hour or so at each dusk and dawn, the traditional times for attack by U-boat because of the poor light. Men were reckoned to be at their lowest ebb at these times. It was indeed a tiring schedule, especially for those who had been on the Middle Watch from midnight until 4 a.m. They were called at dawn and sometimes kept at Action Stations until about 6 a.m. They then had until 8 a.m. before going on watch again. There were other Action Stations as well, when an echo was picked up on the asdic and depth charges dropped to keep the suspected submarine well down until the convoy had passed out of harm's way.

One of Sam's Action Stations, depending on the state of the watch, was in the magazine. He and his mate had to load the "cruet" of four 4-inch shells, then it was carried by electric hoist to the deck above. The shells were then unloaded and rammed up a chute for a member of the gun crew to grab and load it in the gun. There was always a stack of shells in the Ready Use locker on deck so that firing could commence immediately the alarm bells went. It was an eerie feeling in the magazine, surrounded by racks of shells. The watertight hatch above was shut so that in the event of being holed, water could not rise to the messdeck above. In addition there were sprinkler valves in the deckhead which would be turned on from above should fire break out. It was not a happy situation to be in! Sam definitely did not fancy being in the magazine if that happened. He and his mate used to stand by the loaded hoist as the ship gathered speed prior to firing depthcharges. The noise and vibration added to the tenseness of the situation and when the explosions occurred, the noise rendered them temporarily deaf as the thin plates of the hull withstood the impact of the increased water pressure. Frequently it seemed as if the sides moved in and out again with each explosion. Fortunately there were no air attacks on the convoy to Freetown, though they did go to action stations when a Dornier appeared from time to time when they were in range. Being a reconnaissance aircraft, it didn't attack the convoy but radioed details of size and position etc. to its base. Occasionally it would loose off a few rounds of machine-gun fire in retaliation when a warship fired a couple of shells to warn it not to go too close to the troopships. At times there would be a German plane on one side of the convoy and a British Sunderland on the other but they appeared to ignore each other, no doubt because of orders from on high. In any case they did not have sufficient fuel to be able to engage in combat before returning to base. The German Condors could go as far as 20° West.

The voyage was not just work and sleep. As they entered the tropics the weather became really warm. Camp beds were made available for a limited number of men to sleep on deck. One afternoon Sam saw his first flying fish skimming the waves. It was like a slim mackerel with wings but not so dappled. The "wings", of course, were the fins. A few landed on the iron deck, so Sam picked one up and had a good look at it before tossing it back. There wasn't much flesh on it so it didn't end up on a plate in the mess. The crew were in tropical rig during the day, reverting to blues for the night watches until it got so hot that they stayed in whites all the time.

When at last the convoy turned to approach Freetown, small patches of flotsam from the land were in evidence plus the occasional tree trunk and once they saw a corpse of a West African. Fortunately it was considered too dangerous to stop and retrieve the body as they were still scores of miles from land, so the sea boat's crew was spared a grisly job. It was a known fact that some U-boat captains waited near ports of destination, hoping to make an easy "kill" when the ships' crews were less vigilant than usual as they were looking forward to going ashore.

When land did come into view, the dark green "fuzz" on the horizon was indeed a welcome change from the endless sea. As they got nearer they became aware of the smell of Africa. It was not unpleasant, it was a warm, sort of faint vegetable smell which contrasted sharply with the salt air of the ocean. Sam would not have believed it if he hadn't experienced it himself.

After enjoying a rest in Freetown it became clear to the crew that another convoy was about to begin. The buzz which had begun in the Clyde was deemed by the old hands to be correct. They were going to the Eastern end of the Mediterranean. They must have been waiting for the battleship *Nelson* because a few days after her arrival, *Pathfinder*'s crew were informed they were making for the Cape, just before they slipped from the buoy. There were the usual exchanges of friendly banter as she steamed past the troopships to take up her station:

"It's time you got your knees brown, mate."

"Don't get your feet wet, sailor!"

"Have you got room for another passenger?"

"Where are you hiding the nurses?"

Normally *Pathfinder*'s crew lined up on the fo'c'sle and quarter deck when leaving harbour and when she passed a warship a "pipe" from the Quartermaster would bring the crew to attention as a mark of respect for a senior officer. In turn, his QM would call the men working on deck to attention. The troopships were anchored a way off shore and *Pathfinder* had already passed the warships still at anchor, so the men on deck were no longer on parade, so to speak. The soldiers were cooped up like chickens on board the liners. Sam was glad he was a sailor.

Now that they were actually under way, the buzz-mongers spread another rumour that the ship's company would be given leave in Capetown. Everyone was pleased about that and began looking forward to some South African hospitality. There was a strong Cornish contingent of miners and shopkeepers in the Cape. Two of Sam's great uncles had been mining in South Africa and there were people he knew who had emigrated there from Coverack in the late thirties. *Pathfinder*'s crew had already benefited from the generosity of the people of the Cape. The South African Fire Appliance Company had generously given every member of the crew a sheepskin "liberty bodice" - a large toggled waistcoat which could be worn over a duffel coat if need be. Sam found his a godsend during cold night watches. He used it throughout the war and for many years after, before passing it on to his son.

The ship soon settled down to escorting yet another convoy. As they approached the equator the days became even warmer and the periods of uncertain light at dusk and dawn got shorter and shorter, which meant less time closed up at Action Stations. Sam tried sleeping on deck and found it a pleasant experience. One night he had a bit of a shock when he noticed that Leslie, a three-badge AB, appeared to be asleep on his folding camp bed with one eye open! Sam asked him later, when he was definitely awake, if he really had been asleep. Leslie assured him he had and told him it was due to a faulty eyelid. Apparently it got stuck when he was a baby and by the time his mother took him to a doctor it was too late to do anything about it.

On the day they were due to cross the line, Commander Gibbs gave permission for a canvas "bath" to be rigged on the iron deck. The stokers filled it with sea-water and King Neptune, alias the PO Gunlayer, who directed the ship's gunfire in action, appeared with his rosy-cheeked, topless, hairy-chested Queen, resplendent in a skirt made with "ginger string" which was normally used for lashings. "She" had been beautified with lipstick which no doubt came from one of the homosexuals on board who had been seen going ashore all "made up". The two "royals" climbed on to the pompom deck to their throne and nodded to their aides. They were two ABs wearing swimming trunks and fancy hats. The two men grabbed the nearest onlooker and hauled him to a chair behind which stood the "barber" who had a huge wooden cutthroat razor about two feet in length. His assistant had a bucket of flour and water to serve as shaving soap and a deck mop as a shaving brush. When the initiate was liberally covered with the sticky mess, the barber proceeded to shave him to the cheers of the onlookers. The operation finished, the brawny assistants tipped him into the bath where he was ducked a few times before being allowed to climb out. In turn Sam became a willing victim, although he had to struggle in accordance with tradition. It was not every day a sailor crossed the line for the first time. The water was lukewarm and Sam enjoyed the ducking as well as the ceremony. He was surprised to learn that some of the senior hands had not crossed the equator before. They were winkled out and duly ducked to the cheers of the "green" sailors. They were all grateful to the captain who was taking a bit of a risk in allowing the ceremony to take place. He too was ducked, although doubtless he had crossed the line quite a few times.

While the jollifications were proceeding the Duty Watch carried on with their work, conscious of the fact that if a U-boat's Kapitan were to observe the celebrations, he would deem it an ideal chance to fire a torpedo. It so happened that while the fun was going on, the noisy gathering on the iron deck became aware of the ship picking up speed and leaving the convoy. They fell silent. Then the alarm bells went. A strange looking lot of matelots turned up at their places of duty! *Pathfinder* had in fact been ordered to approach a large ship on the horizon which was travelling alone, at speed. She could be a German raider, bold enough to shadow the convoy in the hope of picking off a straggler, in spite of the presence of the *Nelson* which could dispose of her with one salvo from her nine sixteen-inch guns. *Pathfinder* went straight for the stranger and challenged. She gave the correct recognition signals as she was being approached. Commander Gibbs went close, just to make sure, and then he allowed the hands to return to King Neptune's bath. He had decided to introduce a little levity into the proceedings and passed close to the merchant ship so that they could see the shenanigans in progress. Her crew clapped and cheered while *Pathfinder*'s partygoers waved and shouted back. It was a day for both crews to remember with pleasure. Ships which could cruise at fifteen knots were not considered an easy target for U-boats and often travelled alone as this one was doing. It was not a comfortable situation for the Merchant Navy seamen to be in, as Sam was to find out when he did a voyage on the *Mahanada*, which was carrying torpedo warheads in her hold.

While *Pathfinder* was returning to the convoy the crew was stood down from Action Stations and King Neptune, with the help of his retinue dismantled the "court". A couple of days went by without incident. Early one morning a cruiser hove into sight and began signalling on her Aldis lamp. There was a flurry of activity on the bridge, with consultations among the officers. At Stand Easy it was announced on the ship's public address system that they would not be going to the Cape after all. The cruiser was taking over the convoy and *Pathfinder* would be returning to Freetown. What a disappointment. To quote one of Sam's messmates, "Everyone was going round with a 'drip' a mile long!" The Andrew had done it again. Their Lordships had a habit of springing unpleasant surprises just when all seemed to be running smoothly. This time it was not just the *Pathfinder*. The *Nelson* and the other destroyers in the Flotilla left the convoy as well.

After another boiler clean in Freetown when once more the ship was invaded by hungry-looking local "dockies", *Pathfinder* started working up again, going to sea and doing target practice like mad, in company with the other destroyers. Something was about to happen, but what? At one point the buzz went round that they were going after the *Richelieu* which was under the control of the Vichy French and had holed up in Dakar, some six-hundred-odd miles to the north of Freetown. She was reputedly one of the most powerful ships afloat. An attempt to winkle her out on behalf of the Free French had failed in September, 1940. The buzz was given more credence when *Pathfinder* did some torpedo runs but the rumour turned out to be false.

The messdeck buzz pedlars were not privy to secret orders received by the captain. The force did indeed leave Freetown and sail northwards after the fortnight of frenzied battle practice but they went on past Dakar, much to everyone's relief. No one wanted to take part in another strategic failure. It soon became evident that they were UK bound. That compensated for the loss of some shore leave. Nevertheless, everyone knew that the work-up was not thought up just to keep the hands busy. There had to be an ulterior motive.

The ship settled down once more into the familiar routine of going to the various degrees of readiness according to the area through which they were passing. Well out to sea and not within range of enemy aircraft it was the "T" state, when the torpedo men were ready with their depth-charges and B gun was manned so as to be able to deal quickly with a raider or a U-boat on the surface. Action Stations at dawn and dusk began to last a little longer and each day was a little chillier than the previous one. The destroyers had no merchant ships to jolly along but they were conscious of the all-seeing presence of the *Nelson* and the *Rodney*. One calm evening, just an hour or so before midnight, when the ship was off the Azores, the Lieutenant RNVR who was Officer of the Watch spotted a U-boat quietly proceeding on the surface, only yards away. The OOW sounded Action Stations and made for the submarine, fully intending to ram her. Sam was asleep when the bells went. He dashed up to the lookout by the bridge just as the change to continuous ringing of the bells told everyone who could to lie down as they were about to ram. Meanwhile, the submarine had seen *Pathfinder* steaming straight at her and she too made a violent alteration of course and began to dive. She slid beneath the waves, her klaxon horn still blaring out as *Pathfinder* steamed over the very spot where the submarine had been a few seconds before. The Gunner (T) who had also been on watch with the Lieutenant was ready by this time with the depthcharges and fired the starboard throwers which landed right in the swirl left by the crash-diving U-boat. The Action Log recorded that it was under a minute from the time Action Stations was sounded to the moment when the depthcharges were fired. *Pathfinder* then did a pattern search of the area but the asdic did not pick up a single echo. There was no evidence to prove that the submarine had been sunk but the crew had the satisfaction of knowing that at least the sub. had been driven off in time to allow the two prize battlewagons to pass out of range of the enemy. *Pathfinder* could only claim another "probable". Everyone was amazed that neither the radar nor the asdic operators had picked up the submarine's presence on their instruments, nor had the lookouts seen her. It seemed likely that the sub. had just surfaced when she was spotted. She too was obviously unaware of the presence of the flotilla. None of the other warships had any indication of the enemy. The whole episode underlined the importance of perhaps the finest instrument of all - what the sailors term the Mark 1 Eyeball. But for the Lieutenant's keen eyesight and instant reaction to the situation, that night could have been a disastrous one.

A few days later the Mark 1 Eyeball was once more to prove its worth. During the afternoon watch lookout Ordinary Seaman Ritchie spotted a ship's boat just as she was dipping into the trough of a wave. He reported the bearing to the OOW. At first the officer thought Ritchie had been mistaken but keeping his eyes fixed on the bearing he spotted the boat again on the crest of a wave. Just in case the boat was a decoy to lure a ship to heave to and present a stationary target to a waiting U-boat, the *Pathfinder* went to Action Stations and approached the lifeboat with caution. The asdic gave no indication of a sub. in the vicinity so scrambling nets were lowered as the ship formed a lee for the pitching ship's boat.

As was the case when *Pathfinder* rescued some airmen who had been shot down and were in their rubber dinghy, the men in the lifeboat were reluctant to come on board. It was not surprising. The seamen on deck were wearing an assortment of apparel, including some rather garish football jerseys. The White Ensign was tattered and very dirty due to the fumes from the oil-burning engines. It could have been any old flag. However, when a matelot enquired, "Don't you want to be b----y well rescued?" they had no longer any doubt about the nationality of their rescuers. They were too unsteady to clamber up the short distance to the iron deck, but as mentioned earlier a man in his sixties made it. It was subsequently discovered that the 7,000-ton cargo ship *Cortona* had been torpedoed eleven days earlier in position 32° 30' North, 24° 47' West. Thirty of her crew were lost and two of her six DEMS gunners. The ship's boat had been trying to make for the Cape Verde Islands, but unknown to the survivors, they had gone past them and were on course for the barren coast of Mauretania. The seamen were given spare items of clothing by some members of *Pathfinder*'s crew and they were supplemented by some pusser's items from Jack Dusty's store. After a few days' rest and gentle feeding up, the merchant seamen began making themselves useful on deck as a practical way of expressing their thanks for being rescued. It was a sobering experience for the destroyer's men who did their best to make the survivors feel "at home" until they were put ashore. Sam was struck by the fact that many of the men had swollen feet and naturally preferred to go about the ship without shoes until the swelling went down.

The convoy proceeded ever northwards. There were the usual alarms and hunts for contacts but nothing definite was found. *Pathfinder* put in to Londonderry for fuel and to land the *Cortona*'s survivors. Sam learned later from an officer who came to live in Coverack that while the ship was there her pay and stores ledgers were put straight by the base Paymasters. The ship had moved about so rapidly that there had been no time to have the books checked.

While moored quite close to the old wall protecting Londonderry a local boat came alongside and Sam made her fast. One of the crew asked him if he could do with some butter. Thinking of Mary, who was still running her café in Coverack, Sam did a deal with the man and got a few pounds of butter in exchange for a couple of tins of tickler. Shortly after, the *Pathfinder* set sail again. Having made her way to via the Minches once more, *Pathfinder* did not moor up with the rest of the escorts. She was directed to go alongside a US destroyer. The American sailors were a friendly, confident bunch of chaps. It was their first visit to the UK in wartime. Each man was sporting a medal ribbon and it transpired, according to one of the sailors, that a campaign medal was automatically awarded for crossing the Atlantic. The *Pathfinder*'s men were bemused by this, as they were by the pipe, "Hands muster abaft the after smoke stack for ice cream and candy." The Americans were equally puzzled by the *Pathfinder*'s pipe, "Up spirits", followed by the usual unofficial chorus of "Stand by the Holy Ghost!'" intoned by those deputed to draw the daily tot of rum for their mess. The Americans seemed to have plenty of everything on board. They were a generous lot and plied *Pathfinder*'s crew with Lucky Strike cigarettes and candy bars. They even had a washing machine churning away on the Quarter Deck, much to the envy of the British sailors, most of whom had never seen one before.

The Americans were intrigued by the West Country brogue of the British crew. One or two even asked if they were "Canadian British". While moored alongside the American destroyer, Sam managed to get his butter sent home by Maritime Mail. The crew was kept busy taking on stores and ammunition but they did have some time off. Sam and Dick had another afternoon ashore, cycling round the farms and enjoying a glass of fresh milk when offered one. They were to remember that tranquil afternoon all their lives. It was the calm before the storm.

CHAPTER TEN

MALTA

On the 31st July 1942, *Pathfinder* cast off and left Scapa Flow at the beginning of the First Dog Watch. In order to introduce variety into watch keeping at sea, the watch from 4 p.m. until 8 p.m. is divided into two. The First Dog Watch is from four until six and the Second Dog Watch is from six to eight. This is to ensure that those who do the Middle Watch from midnight until 4 a.m. do not always do the same watch in every twenty-four hours. If they did they would quickly become exhausted and of course it would be very unfair. Instead, everyone takes it in turn to do the Middle Watch, because of the Dog Watches. The name is probably a corruption of "docked", meaning reduced or shortened, but no one knows for certain.

Once more, *Pathfinder*, known by her pennant numbers as G10 to the other ships in the convoy, was escorting the battleships *Nelson* and *Rodney*, in company with the Tribal Class destroyers *Ashanti, Eskimo, Tartar* and *Somali* together with the *Quentin*. They made a truly brave sight as they wended their way south to join a convoy of merchant ships. It was still deemed necessary to have some battle practice en route and the inevitable buzz went round that they were indeed going to the Mediterranean, to Alexandria; not via the Cape this time, but straight through the Med. via Malta. That meant there would be a running battle all the way. The island had been awarded the George Cross but the fight was not yet over. In fact, the islanders were close to defeat and in desperate need. The "Malta" buzz gained credence when they had joined the fast-moving merchant ships and began carrying out complicated manoeuvres with them as they steamed towards Gibraltar. The weather was not very kind in the Bay of Biscay. It hardly ever is. Added to that, they made contact with three or four U-boats which meant long hours at Action Stations. Sam was seasick for the first time since joining *Pathfinder*, as mentioned earlier. Although most members of the crew were not privy to the ciphers received from the Admiralty, it had become clear on previous convoys that *Pathfinder* was being given details of the probable position of enemy submarines. Sam did not know at the time about the work of the code breakers at Bletchley, who were able to supply vital information re movements of German warships, nor did he realise that the Wrens who were stationed in Coverack were monitoring German broadcasts to their ships in the Atlantic. Like other members of the crew, Sam was fully occupied with his shipboard duties and scarcely gave a thought to the work of naval intelligence which influenced the strategy of convoy protection. At lower deck level, the fact that they had taken on six airmen who were on passage to Gibraltar lent further credence to the buzz about Malta.

The convoy itself was obviously something special because of the heavy escort. It was relatively fast and consisted of fourteen fine modern merchant ships, including one modern American-built oil tanker which was flying the Red Duster. One of the old hands told Sam that such a collection of ships was almost certainly Malta-bound as only fast ones stood a chance of getting through. Sam had heard that Captain Samuel Champion from Coverack had lost his ship, the *Bhutan*, a month or so before, when leading a convoy eastwards through the Med. from Alexandria to Malta. It was beginning to look as if the fourteen were in for a lively time.

When they arrived in Gib., the airmen were put ashore and mail was sent and collected. Sam was pleased to get another letter from Elsie and a postcard from his brother Alexander who was stationed temporarily at Fort St. George, Madras. The card had been posted on the 21st June. It began to look as if the *Pathfinder* were part of a master plan, or perhaps a pawn in the game? Fancy the Fleet Mail boys knowing that she would be in Gib. on the 8th August 1942! What would the buzz-mongers make of that? Mail was a great morale booster. Many of the crew were going about with happy faces after reading letters from home, so Sam decided he wouldn't spoil the atmosphere by informing his mates that someone in the Indian Fleet Mail Office obviously knew where the *Pathfinder* would be on that particular date. Besides, he had something else to think about. Alexander had informed him that he was about to become a father and that meant he would become "Uncle Sam". He would probably see the new arrival before his brother returned from the Far East as that posting was usually for three years. What bad luck. Poor old Alexander. He should have gone in the Andrew! Sam didn't have much time to dwell on family matters. There was no shore leave. As soon as some supplies had been loaded, the ship left harbour. One of the crew managed, however, to slip ashore and his absence was not discovered until they were well out to sea. No one seemed to know whether he had missed the ship by accident or design but it was not a popular move, due to the fact that his mates would have to carry out the deserter's duties until he could be replaced.

Sam was disappointed that he had not been able to visit Gib. His seafaring uncles had sent him picture postcards of "The Rock" many times and he had been looking forward to sending them one each to prove he'd been there too. He was also disenchanted with the weather. There he was at the gateway to the Med., yet the previous night he had found it necessary to wear a duffel coat on watch; he wouldn't mind betting the weather was warmer in Coverack - after all it was on the Cornish Riviera and it was the month of August! His uncles must have been swinging the lamp when they boasted about the idyllic Mediterranean climate. Sam himself was also to be found guilty of telling tall stories about his travels in foreign lands. Sailors are prone to this weakness when they have the attention of a gullible listener.

When they got into the open sea Sam soon forgot his disappointment as he watched the dolphins leaping out of the water like gigantic, graceful black-and-white porpoises. He had never before realised they could swim so fast, as they dived playfully beneath the bows while *Pathfinder* was steaming at twenty knots. Like the peaceful afternoon Sam and Dick had spent on Scapa, the dolphin interlude was to become a treasured memory in contrast with the events of the following week.

On the second day out of Gib, when they were south of the Balearic Islands - perhaps better known in modern times as Ibiza, Mallorca and Menorca - the *Pathfinder* took oil from a fleet tanker which had another destroyer fuelling on the other side. The three ships were steaming at ten knots and presented a fine target but the manoeuvre passed off without any problems and after an hour or so, *Pathfinder* cast off and steamed away at speed to take up station on the port side of the convoy.

There were eighteen destroyers forming an arrow-head-shaped screen protecting the front and sides of the convoy and three more destroyers brought up the rear. HMS *Nelson* was in the van, flanked by the cruisers *Nigeria, Cairo, Manchester* and *Kenya* - the last had a delicate shade of pink camouflage. Astern of the *Nelson* were the aircraft carriers *Victorious* and *Indomitable*; Sam was to join the latter in Singapore when the war was over. Three more cruisers, the *Sirius, Charybdis* and *Phoebe* formed a solid wall at the back of the convoy. This formidable array of firepower was there to protect the fourteen merchant ships, seven of which were on the starboard side of the carriers and seven on the port. So far so good. The weather had improved and the afternoon watch on board *Pathfinder* was settling down to a warm spell of convoy duty when a lookout reported smoke and water spouts coming from the *Eagle* which was on the far starboard side of the convoy. She had been torpedoed. At that distance it was impossible to see clearly what was happening. In the course of their duties, lookouts study the ships in view quite closely through powerful binoculars; *Pathfinder*'s starboard lookout just happened to be carrying out a sweep past the *Eagle* when he saw the smoke erupt as the torpedo struck the ship. The noise of the explosion did not reach *Pathfinder* for a few seconds due to the slower speed of sound. It was then that the people on the bridge realised what had happened. In seemingly no time at all the carrier developed a list and aircraft could be seen sliding off the flight deck into the sea; then she became enveloped in thick black smoke. In about five minutes the *Eagle* had sunk beneath the waves. All that could be seen was a pall of thick black smoke hanging in the air. Sam had witnessed his first sinking, yet could not believe he had done so. Nor could anyone else. Of course, rescue ships were ordered to the spot to pick up survivors. Destroyers began firing depth-charges. *Pathfinder* carried on protecting the port side of the convoy, every man saddened and doubly alert in the performance of his duties. The name *Eagle* has proved to be an unlucky one for the Royal Navy. Much later, when he had time to think about the disaster he had witnessed, Sam remembered from his reading of the history of his beloved Cornwall that a ship called the *Eagle* had sunk off the Isles of Scilly in the year 1707. She had struck the Cribinicks a few miles SSE of the famed Bishop Rock when following the pigheaded Admiral Sir Cloudesly Shovell who had ignored advice from a Scillonian seaman on board and piled his fleet on the rocks, causing the deaths of some two thousand men in the process.

To return to the action. After a disastrous beginning worse was to come. As dusk came creeping across the dark sea, a crowd of twin-engined JU88 planes bombed the convoy. The noise was horrendous. *Pathfinder* was ready for the attack as were all the ships. The barrage put up prevented the planes from scoring any serious damage but *Pathfinder* had quite a few small holes to show afterwards. Down below in the magazine, Sam and his mate were working hard sending up shells to the mess deck from where they were passed up to B gun. The noise and the demand for ammunition told the two sailors what was going on overhead. The four-inch-high angle guns fired lines of shells into the path of the approaching bombers, with the intention of forcing them to remain up high. The bangs went on and on, as if some gigantic drum were beating on the upper deck; then, as the planes got closer, the four-barrelled 40 mm. pom pom began firing steadily. Sam found the pom-pom-pom-pom explosions a comforting sound. At first he was confident no plane would penetrate that wall of shell bursts; but many did and when the planes got really close the magazine men could hear the 20 mm. Oerlikons begin firing rapidly. That was just before the bombs hit the sea close to the *Pathfinder*, the underwater explosions sending shock waves against the thin plates of the destroyer's hull. Although they could not see it, Sam and his mate Harry were told later that one JU88 came too low and was hit by a shell from the pom pom. She went off, leaving a trail of smoke, losing height rapidly and crashed into the sea. Not a bad beginning for *Pathfinder*'s

HMS *Pathfinder*'s pom-pom gunners
The ship relied on their expertise when attacked by Stukas and JU88s.
(Photo J.C.Buchan)

gunners. The attack died away and the convoy carried on into the approaching night. At that point, everyone knew what to expect in the future.

The Italians and Germans did not disappoint the waiting convoy the following day, which, as "Jock" Campbell remarked to Sam, was the first day of the grouse-shooting season. It was the twelfth of August. There was plenty to shoot at. The planes came over in droves from early morning and on until nightfall. The convoy ploughed steadily on, the merchant ships following the manoeuvres they had practised on the way down to Gibraltar.

First of all came the bombers which released their cargoes from high up, due to the heavy barrage. Then came the dive bombers. For the first time Sam heard the howling scream of the JU 87s, better known as Stukas. It was believed that the noise was caused by some kind of attachment to the wing. It was certainly blood curdling. It was just a noise but ever after when Sam heard it he cringed. Those pilots just kept coming, whatever was thrown at them, and released their bombs at the last moment before pulling out of the dive, firing their machine guns all the time. That first day, thank goodness, *Pathfinder*'s pom pom didn't jam and the steady thump-thump-thump-thump as the four barrels fired in turn was a lovely protective sound to those being attacked. After the dive bombers came the low level Heinkel 111 torpedo bombers, weaving through the shell bursts a hundred feet or so above the water. It seemed impossible that planes could get through the air which was dotted with puffs of black smoke from the exploding shells, but they did. *Pathfinder*'s crew was not accustomed to the high-speed evasions necessary but in retrospect it was declared an exhilarating day, thanks to the gunners and the engineers who kept the ship moving at speed, unscathed apart from a few more bullet holes in the fo'c'sle. It did not do to dwell on the loss of life suffered in the other ships: the grieving for them would come later.

That day, the "glorious twelfth", Sam's first Action Station was in the lookout and he had a grandstand view of the approach of attacking planes. He was glad of his tin hat and the white flash gear he was wearing. B gun was only a few feet in front and below the lookout station and every time it fired a hot blast of air came Sam's way. The cotton "balaclava" covering his face, neck and shoulders certainly prevented flash burns, as did the gloves for he had to keep his hands on the large handles guiding the binoculars. In a later action he didn't have time to don his flash gear before getting to the lookout and the right side of his face was singed.

The ship's Surgeon Lieutenant plastered it in Gentian Violet and he went about looking like something from a horror film for a few days. One consolation was that it was not considered necessary to have gas masks at the ready. They would have been a real nuisance to carry on the chest because of the semi-inflated lifebelts each man wore without having to be told.

Of course, while the air attacks were going on, the asdic team and lookouts could not entirely forget the possibility of an encounter with a submarine. The Italians were known to have over one hundred in the Mediterranean. There was a fleet of German U-boats as well. Towards the end of the forenoon an echo was located ahead of the convoy and *Pathfinder* went after the enemy submarine and dropped a ten-charge pattern to keep her down out of harm's way until the convoy had passed. Another destroyer, the *Zetland*, came up and joined in the hunt, dropping more depthcharges but with no positive result. Meanwhile the convoy was steaming on, still under attack from the bombers and possibly in danger of being torpedoed by another submarine through the space left unguarded by *Pathfinder*, so Commander Gibbs left the hunt to *Zetland* and went after the convoy at thirty knots. It was a wise decision for shortly after she got on station again another echo came loud and clear: ping-ping, ping-ping, ping-ping, ping-ping. Once again Commander Gibbs ordered the long black contact flag to be hoisted to indicate to the convoy what was happening and to warn them of the possibility of a torpedo attack, then increasing his speed to twenty knots he went to the spot where the sub. was calculated to be and dropped two five-charge patterns, hoping the attack would force the submarine to dive deeper and consequently be unable to position herself to fire her torpedoes. Commander Gibbs continued to hunt. It was not easy to concentrate when an air attack was mounting as well. In the end he had to hand over to another destroyer, the *Ithuriel*, which was protecting the rear of the convoy, and dash back to help drive off the latest wave of bombers. Much later, Commander Gibbs discovered that his attack had indeed forced the Italian sub. to dive. The pressure became so unbearable that the submarine had to come up and she was spotted by *Ithuriel* as she surfaced. Once more the submarine dived and was again depthcharged by *Ithuriel*. It was too much. She had to come to the surface again and was rammed by *Ithuriel* before she could man the gun to defend herself. Naturally the destroyer stopped to pick up survivors, among whom was the *Cobalto*'s captain. When *Pathfinder*'s crew learned what had happened they decided they could legitimately add "half a sub." to their list of successes.

Pathfinder arrived back on station just in time to deal with the next air attack. All hell was let loose overhead and through it all came a damaged Hurricane which pancaked into the sea close enough to allow Commander Gibbs to bring *Pathfinder* right alongside the pilot, who was held up in the water by his Mae West life jacket. The pilot had hardly boarded *Pathfinder* before a lookout reported another pilot parachuting into the sea. Away went the seaboat's crew to pick him up. Sam and his mates in the whaler did not appreciate being machinegunned while they were doing it, especially as the rescued pilot turned out to be an Italian. He didn't enjoy being machinegunned by his compatriots either. Leading Seaman "Elsie" was in charge of the seaboat and as soon as the pilot had been pulled inboard, shouted to the rowers to pull hard for the *Pathfinder*. They didn't need a second bidding for no one fancied being left in a wooden boat while the destroyer moved off to avoid being a sitting duck for the next lot of bombers. It must have been one of the fastest ever hoists of the seaboat when they got back alongside. The *Pathfinder* was already under way. The many practices they had carried out under less hazardous conditions had paid off. Sam never actually discovered Elsie's real name. He had acquired the nickname as he always added a veiled threat when he gave an order, as in the above incident, when he shouted, "Give way together!" adding, as was his custom, "Or else". Sam had never associated the Leading Seaman in his mind with the delectable Elsie Barker from Coverack, although they shared the same name! One day, "Elsie" stopped by Sam's locker to admire Elsie's photograph and asked Sam her name. He did not dare repeat it so he said "May", which was Elsie's mother's name. From that day on he had to remember Elsie's "nom de guerre" when girlfriends became the topic of conversation on the messdeck.

After a lull, just as it was getting dark on the "glorious twelfth", the Stukas turned up again, diving and screaming like demented seagulls swooping on a fishing fleet gutting the catch as it returned to port. This time, the aircraft carrier *Indomitable* was hit and set on fire. Her planes could neither land nor take off so a decision was taken to retire her from the convoy and the other capital ships went with her, leaving the destroyers and cruisers to plough on through the night with the precious merchant ships.

It was a dark, moonless night but the planes still kept coming despite the withering barrage lighting up the sky with shell bursts and tracer bullets. The convoy was due to pass south of Sardinia, within easy flying distance from the airfields and also not far from the Italian surface fleet. These narrow waters were mined. *Pathfinder*'s crew had been warned on the ship's public address system that it could be "quite a night". As far as Sam was concerned, that was a typical naval understatement.

By now, everyone on board was tired. Elated, in that so far they had survived both air and submarine attacks, but tired. During one of the air attacks in the afternoon, Sam was in his lookout position and happened to look down on B gun. The gunners were behind a shield but it was not a turret as in larger ships, the thin armour was designed to protect the controls of the gun rather than the men firing it and afforded little protection from stray bullets or even the weather. A gun on the fo'c'sle was only manned at full Action Stations for this very reason because the gunners could get very wet and cold if stationed there for any length of time. On this occasion, Sam noticed Gunlayer Able Seaman Jim McLoughlan sitting calmly on the round stool, rapidly turning the handles to bring the gun to bear on an approaching aircraft with his bellbottoms rolled up to the knees and his bare feet in a bucket of water! Even at that rather tense moment, Sam could not repress a laugh. Much later, he asked Jim why he had his feet in the bucket. Jim replied, "When you get to my age, Sam, you'll have corns. Salt water is the finest remedy out, so I took the opportunity to soak my feet while I was sitting down." That image of Jim remained in Sam's mind ever after and when he got into a frightening situation he willed himself to think of good old dependable Jim, who had been in the navy twenty years and never sought promotion because he was happy as he was and saw no reason to change. The memory always made Sam laugh and drove his fear away, temporarily at any rate. Jim was one of those rare types whose philosophy was to take life as it comes, never worry in advance and never do anything until it becomes absolutely necessary. Jim was the navigator's steward and did his dhobiing. One day he came rushing up to Sam and asked him if he had a pair of clean white socks. "Why, yes, Jim," replied Sam. "Do you want them?" "Yes please, mate," said Jim. "Navvy is going ashore and wants a clean pair. His weren't very dirty so I've been wearing them to save using my own. If you lend me yours, I'll give them back when Navvy's finished with them."

Sam could barely repress his mirth, but hurriedly handed Jim the much needed socks. What a character! Sam had learned another lesson of life. He didn't want anything in return and Jim knew that but nevertheless he told Sam he would get "sippers" at the end of the week.

"No, mate," said Sam, "I want 'gulpers'!" It was the custom in the navy to reward a mate for a favour by allowing him to have a sip of rum ration. A big favour demanded a gulp of rum. Jim agreed laughingly for he knew Sam was teetotal and Under Age to boot. It was good for Sam and the other young sailors to have men like Jim around.

The dusk air attack had died away and the convoy was once more shepherded into a tightly guarded formation when disaster struck. The cruiser *Cairo* was hit in the stern by a torpedo. Almost immediately there was another flash and an explosion and the cruiser *Nigeria* got hit. While Sam was staring dumfounded at the two ships, out of the corner of his eye he saw flames leap into the air. It was the tanker *Ohio* which was on fire from another torpedo. She was the only tanker in the convoy. It was unbelievable. All Sam could do was report what he was seeing. The reports seemed superfluous but he did what he had to do. The OOW replied non-commitally each time, "Very good". There were no histrionics. Naval custom and discipline have their uses, despite some misguided detractors. *Pathfinder* altered course to go to the *Ohio*. The two captains spoke for a brief while; then *Ohio* bravely continued on her way, the fire now under control, and *Pathfinder* remained close by. Some time later she was ordered to go to the *Cairo* and sink her. She was another vital ship as she was an anti-aircraft cruiser which gave orders to carrier-borne aircraft when the convoy was being attacked. Now she was a danger to navigation and the Admiral in charge of the convoy decided she should be sunk. Four torpedoes were fired at her. The first three missed. The fourth struck the target but she remained afloat so Commander Gibbs decided to try depth-charges. She still stayed above water. At that point it was with some relief that *Pathfinder* was ordered to rejoin the convoy and the *Derwent* sank the cruiser by gunfire. The *Derwent* always seemed to be around when the *Pathfinder* needed support. It was discovered later that the torpedoes had faulty steering components. No one knew that at the time so the torpedo men spent some anxious hours wondering how on earth they could have missed a sitting target, especially after all the practice shoots carried out at Scapa and Freetown. They were also wondering how they would fare when ordered to attack the Italian surface vessels which would probably try to intercept the convoy in the morning. That thought was at the back of everyone's mind as the night wore on but subsequent events soon drove away those dark forebodings.

While rounding up the scattered merchant ships once more, *Pathfinder* came across another stricken ship and went alongside to see if she needed any help. It was the *Brisbane Star*. She had been torpedoed but was able to proceed slowly. The two captains spoke and incredibly, the captain of the *Brisbane Star* said he was going to go on to Malta independently. That decision took courage of the highest order. No one would have looked askance if he had said he was going to go back to Gibraltar. In later years when successive governments allowed the British Merchant Fleet to run down in favour of flags of convenience, Sam would think of the *Ohio* and the *Brisbane Star* and wonder how on earth British politicians and businessmen could be so blind and so ungrateful. Probably not one man aboard *Pathfinder* believed those two ships would ever make Valetta Harbour but they did.

Sam was to learn much later that in his letter to the owners of the *Brisbane Star* - the Blue Star Line - Captain F.N. Riley reported that as he crept along the coast he was boarded off Souse and ordered by an armed Tunisian Naval Officer to bring his ship into port and was promised he would not be handed over to the Germans nor the Italians. Captain Riley refused and pleaded with him, as a fellow seaman, to let him go. The Tunisian hesitated but eventually shook him by the hand, wished him luck and let him go - fortified, according to an eyewitness, with a liberal drink of whisky, though the gallant Captain did not mention that in his report. Worse was to come. Deputations from his own crew came to ask him to consider scuttling the ship, quoting that they were in a far worse position than the *Graf Spee* had been when she was scuttled. The bluff Irishman would have none of it. He consulted the Chief Officer and the two persuaded the dissenting voices that they had to go on, knowing that a direct hit would blow them all sky high. What a man! He wrote, "I am pleased to say that their opinions were short lived and they were with me in next to no time." He had no Naval Discipline Act to back him up. The men were paid a paltry sum for the risks they were taking and they had their families to consider with no prospect of a government pension for them should they be killed. Nevertheless, they agreed to follow their Captain to what must have seemed certain death, probably preferring that to being found wanting. The crew were men of courage and they were going to help out an island of courage which was depending on them.

There was no time to ponder over the fate of the two merchant ships that night. *Pathfinder* had to obey orders and lead the second half of the convoy past Cape Bon as swiftly as possible. The enemy aircraft had not long retired to their base on Sardinia before another battle commenced.

This time Italian E boats - fast motor torpedo boats - from the island of Pantellaria were attacking the convoy. Sam had never heard of Pantellaria but that night the name was engraved indelibly on his mind. They "played" a deadly cat-and-mouse game with the E boats. As *Pathfinder* approached the scene of the battle she was ordered to go to the aid of the cruiser *Manchester* which had been torpedoed and was listing badly. *Pathfinder* went alongside and took off nearly two hundred men. The cruiser was indeed sinking but her captain decided to remain and try to salve her, so non-essential personnel were transferred to *Pathfinder* to avoid subsequent loss of life should the remaining crew be unable to keep her afloat. The men who stayed on board were in fact taken prisoner by the Vichy French as they had to abandon ship and make for the nearby North African coast.

Pathfinder cast off and was immediately attacked by E boats which dashed out of their smoke screen and began firing. The searchlight crew came into their own at this point and lit up the white-painted boats long enough for all the guns that could bear to commence firing. It was very frightening. The E boats disappeared for a short while then reappeared, firing wildly, and went back into the smokescreen like fleeting ghosts. Each time a few more holes appeared in *Pathfinder*'s superstructure - a few of them just above Sam's head, as he discovered at daybreak - but no serious damage was done and no one was hit, despite the extra two hundred men on board. The *Manchester*'s men must have wondered if they had jumped from the frying pan into the fire! Each time they came at *Pathfinder*, the E boats were fired at, but she could not pursue them as she had to protect the merchant ships. The minesweeping destroyers had gone ahead of the convoy to clear a narrow passage for the merchant ships to follow but *Pathfinder* went well beyond the confines of the swept channel when driving off the E boats. They had a much shallower draught and were no doubt trying to lure *Pathfinder* into the minefield where her deeper draught would detonate a moored mine. That would enable them to pick off the merchant ships at leisure. Fortunately that didn't happen. Neither did the Italians know that *Ohio* was limping along behind, following the destroyer *Ledbury*. It was a long night, punctuated by periods of tense expectation followed by short moments of intense activity. There was to be no respite. When the sky began to lighten, announcing the dawn, everyone knew the Stukas would be back.

The ship was pretty crowded but during the night the *Manchester* survivors had turned to, organising themselves into parties to back up

Pathfinder's crew. There were essential chores to be done, bombers or no bombers. Proper meals were out of the question but drinks and corned dog sandwiches were brought round and the regular crew men relieved so that they could go below to answer the call of nature and have a quick freshen up. At one point when everything seemed pretty hopeless and they were awaiting the arrival of the Italian surface fleet to finish them off, the NAAFI manager turned up, to Sam's delight, with some free nutty. What bliss! Sam was a non-smoker and didn't have cigarettes to calm his nerves but the chocolate quietened the rumbles in his tummy. Fortunately the Italian navy was ordered to return to port so *Pathfinder* never found out if her remaining torpedoes had dud steering mechanisms, but of course, no one knew about the withdrawal of the Italian cruisers.

Some time after the eventful day, the NAAFI manager was gently teased about how he was going to account for his depleted stocks, now that they were safely through the minefield and there was no longer a possibility of being sunk close to the coast and being taken prisoner as befell the men who remained on board *Manchester*. It was all good-humoured fun, in which the manager joined, saying he would charge double for nutty in future to make up the money he had lost.

True to form, not long after daylight down came the dive bombers and the torpedo bombers again. All *Pathfinder* could do was to keep firing. It never ceased to amaze Sam that they survived at all in view of the ferocity of the attacks. It also seemed that no plane could get through the hail of shells and bullets but many did, only to miss their targets. It was all very confusing, especially to someone not long out of the sixth form at Helston.

During a lull Sam had to go below to answer the call of nature; on the way back to his Action Station another attack started. Sam was close to an unmanned Oerlikon so he quickly got into the harness, pressed his shoulders into the padded U-shaped butt rests and began firing, using the 300-knot outer ring sight. He had the satisfaction of seeing some of the bullets strike the fuselage as the plane went screaming past and on towards a merchant ship. It was pleasing to be able to fire back for a change, even if they were tyro shots as the grouse-shooting fraternity would call them. After a few minutes the regular gunner turned up and Sam left him to go back to his Action Station by the bridge.

The lull being over, another wave of SM79 torpedo bombers was sighted. They were heading straight for the *Ohio*, which was obviously their No.1 target. She was steaming along at a good speed some way astern of the *Pathfinder*, despite the damage sustained the previous night. The P class destroyer *Penn* was escorting her, assisted by the smaller destroyer *Ledbury*. Commander Gibbs decided at this point in the action that enough was enough. This time, instead of waiting for the bombers to come to him, he turned towards them, increasing speed and ordering all guns that could bear to open fire when he gave the word. Perhaps he was disobeying orders to leave his defensive position in the convoy but his crew did not think about that: it seemed the right thing to do, to "engage the enemy more closely" in the tradition of Nelson at Trafalgar. The torpedo bombers came in low over the sea. The pilots were no doubt not a little surprised to see the little destroyer pointing straight at them, her guns firing as fast as they could. One of the leading planes got hit and started to veer off course, losing height rapidly and leaving a trail of thick black smoke drifting across the path of the following aircraft. That discouraged the rest of the flight because they hurriedly dropped their torpedoes and turned away. Commander Gibbs had done what he intended. *Pathfinder* had damaged the enemy planes and none of their torpedoes scored a hit. He swept round in a tight circle and made for the convoy again at speed, the whole ship's company feeling satisfied with their achievement. No doubt the observers on the merchant ships shared a little of their jubilation for the night before had taken its toll. *Pathfinder* now had only three ships to protect, the *Melbourne Star, Port Chalmers* and the *Rochester Castle* - names which were to go down in the history books. *Penn* and *Ledbury* were now some way behind with the crippled *Ohio* and heaven only knew what was happening to the brave *Brisbane Star* making painfully slow progress scores of miles astern and virtually defenceless.

The next lot of planes to be reported by *Pathfinder*'s lookouts were Spitfires. What a beautiful sight they were! Sam was elated when he saw them hare off in the direction of the retreating torpedo bombers. It was high time the enemy tasted some of their own medicine. It was now a gloriously hot day - the Mediterranean climate was living up to its reputation. If action there had to be, Sam decided it was much better under a warm sun than in the cold waters of the North Atlantic. As the day wore on the island of Malta became visible; some naval patrol vessels came out to take the convoy in. *Pathfinder* passed a Royal Navy submarine on the surface. Her crew on deck waved cheerily. It was a relatively peaceful scene - in a strange sort of way. Sam's thoughts turned to speculation. Were they going to continue their voyage to Alexandria or have a night in Malta before proceeding? It was in the lap of the gods - or rather, Their Lordships. True to form, signals began arriving in the wireless telegraphy room; when they had been decoded the crew learned they were going to go back the way they had come. For once even the buzz-mongers were speechless. Before there was an opportunity to comment orders came to clear up and get ready for another action. As some wag said, "After all there's a war on!" That relieved the tension among the seamen and they began making ready with a will for another lively passage through the "narrows".

In common with most of his mates, Sam was probably too tired to think about whether the convoy had been worthwhile in the eyes of the beleaguered Maltese. They had been enduring air attacks such as they had just undergone for months and months, spending much of their time in chilly, uncomfortable underground passages which served as air raid shelters. It was common knowledge that when ships were loaded for the Malta run each one carried a variety of stores such as food, clothes, ammunition, fuel in cans and barrels and a hundred and one other small necessities of life. In this way, even if most of the ships were unable to get through, those that did would be able to relieve the current shortages in most things for a little while longer. The *Melbourne Star, Port Chalmers* and the *Rochester Castle* were almost literally meat and drink in the eyes of the islanders when they arrived in Valetta and their crews were given a rousing welcome.

Likewise the lone *Brisbane Star*. She arrived on the 14th August. Although in sight of the island, a Ju 88 flew low over her and dropped bombs which fortunately landed a few feet off in the water, showering the deck with shrapnel but only injuring one crew member. The DEMS gunners, firing at almost point blank range, set the plane on fire and bits of it landed on the upper deck. As if that were not enough, the next thing they knew, they were being attacked by an Italian torpedo bomber. A Beaufighter from Malta went to the aid of the *Brisbane Star* and shot down the Italian. Concluding his letter, Captain Riley wrote briefly, "Discharging commenced on arrival and it is hoped to have it completed in ten days. Repairs are to be of a temporary nature and it is expected to have them completed in a few weeks time." When Sam read that he realised once more how fortunate he had been to have taken part, though a very small part, in the convoy which owed its success to men such as Captain Riley of the *Brisbane Star* and Captain Mason of the *Ohio*.

Ohio arrived much later at a snail's pace, helped by the destroyers *Penn, Ledbury* and *Braham* together with M.L.s from Malta and with the wreckage of a German Junkers 87, which had crashed on the tanker, still strewn about the bridge and deck. The E boats had made one last unsuccessful attempt to torpedo her and she had also narrowly missed drifting into a minefield. Her engines had finally packed up but she had arrived, albeit slowly sinking, with the bulk of her fuel intact, and settled on the bottom of the harbour just after her fuel had been pumped out. This meant that the planes and ships defending Malta could carry on the fight for a good while longer. Sam and his fellow crew members knew nothing of this incredible achievement of the *Ohio* at the time. They were on their way back to Gibraltar when the celebrations started in Grand Harbour, Valetta.

There were no merchant ships to escort on the return journey to Gibraltar. The pink-painted cruiser *Kenya* had a large chunk of bow missing but the hole had been shored up and she was steaming along quite happily with the cruiser *Charybdis*, astern of the Tribal class destroyer *Ashanti* and followed by *Pathfinder* and three other destroyers. This time everyone knew what to expect as the little flotilla approached Pantellaria in the narrows between Sicily and Tunisia.

True to form, the E boats attacked off Cape Bon. *Pathfinder* was ready and illuminated them with searchlight and star shell, opening fire simultaneously. Once more all hell was let loose. Although he was expecting it, Sam was quite startled when the *Kenya* joined in with her more powerful guns but he had the satisfaction of reporting the retreat of the torpedo boats which went off at speed, tossing smoke-screen canisters into the churning wakes caused by their powerful engines. To crown it all, Sam heard later that while *Pathfinder* went after the E boats a submarine on the surface fired a torpedo at *Kenya*; she avoided it, and crippled as she was, tried to ram the U-boat which was forced to do a crash dive. It was an eerie sensation, hunting the E boats. As before, the white, ghost-like ships appeared suddenly, fired, and disappeared just as rapidly, almost before their presence could be reported. *Pathfinder*'s gunners had to open fire on sight, all the time being conscious of the fact that they could just as easily open fire on one of the other escort destroyers engaged in the hunt. It was very confusing, exciting and frightening. The dark magnified the fear but at the time everyone on deck was concentrating so hard on sighting the enemy and firing back that the feeling of fear was only identified as such in retrospect. When Sam was asked about those nights off Pantellaria, all he could remember was the tension mounting as they waited for the enemy to appear, the quick call of the sighting to the bridge, followed by the loud bangs and the sudden rushes of the E boats. There was no time to think about getting hit: he had not long celebrated his nineteenth birthday and still had a teenager's supreme confidence in his own invulnerability, which had been bolstered by the presence of near misses evident all about the ship. Sam interpreted the bullet holes as signs that he would come through unscathed. Indeed, somehow, all the other ships got through the narrows in the night without sustaining serious damage, so perhaps there was some justification in his youthful confidence.

As dawn broke the flotilla was in the open sea and everyone knew what to expect. Their presence was not a secret! The destroyers went ahead of the cruisers, which in the absence of heavily laden merchant ships were now the "plums" for the JU 88s. They came in waves, seemingly every fifteen minutes, right through the forenoon. Sam did a stint in the magazine with Harry and once more got deafened by the noise despite wearing regulation rubber ear plugs. He was so busy passing the shells up to the messdeck that he could not envisage what was happening overhead. What was patently obvious was the fact that there was not enough ammunition left in the racks to go on firing at the rate they were doing. Paradoxically, the enemy planes and the deteriorating weather were responsible for solving the problem of ammunition shortage. A lookout reported three aircraft dropping parachute mines ahead of the convoy. This caused the ships to make yet another diversion. It turned out to be a blessing in disguise. Almost simultaneously a sea mist began to close in. The ships continued on their new course and the next wave of bombers could be heard searching for the convoy, presumably on their original track. After a while the noise of engines decreased and then could no longer be heard.

The grateful sailors realised the planes had decided to return to their base in Sardinia. Once more everyone turned to, clearing up after the depredations of the day. They worked with a will. Gib was becoming a goal worth working for! Just as it was getting dark, contact was made with reinforcements from the Rock. Once more the skies were in the control of the Fleet Air Arm. What a blessed relief!

Not surprisingly the men on *Pathfinder* were looking forward to a rest and a run ashore. Sods' law came into operation once more. The ship went alongside a jetty to take on fuel and supplies of food and ammunition. There was an unexplained absence of "dockies" so shoreleave was out of the question and everyone turned to. Sam spent a couple of hours on the winch loading ammo. He had not operated it before but soon got the hang of it after "Elsie" the Killick showed him how. After that Sam went off in the ship's motor boat. There was a scare on about the possible presence of Italian divers riding "human torpedoes". These daredevil commandos had already wrought havoc in Alexandria and succeeded in putting the battleship *Queen Elizabeth* out of action. No one had devised a method of detection other than by asdic so the drill was to go round the harbour tossing hand grenades in the water at random to persuade any lurking Italian to abandon his intentions and go back to his parent craft. No one knew for certain if the Italians had penetrated the harbour defences so the destroyers had the job of discouraging them if they had. At the end of their "tour" of the harbour *Pathfinder*'s motor boat was hoisted on deck once more and Sam went below, hungry as a hunter.

One consolation for not having any shore leave was that "Postie", the ship's postman, had been commissioned to bring back bags of "curlies" after he had been to the Fleet Mail Office. The fried scampi was delicious, a wonderful treat after shipboard fare. The appetising smell lingered on the messdeck for some time, making those who were not in No. 3 Mess envious. Sam ate his portion while reading a "newsy" letter from Elsie. He wondered what she would say if he told her about his last convoy. On reflection he decided it would be politic to say nothing, for two reasons; firstly because it might constitute a breach of security and not pass the censor, secondly because he didn't want to tempt fate by bragging about it. He hadn't had time to write since leaving Gibraltar so he could change his mind later if he so wished. That night Sam slept the sleep of exhaustion. All too soon it was time to go on watch again. He could hear the wire hawsers being dragged along the fo'c'sle telling him that the ship was already preparing to cast off. When he got on the upper deck someone told him they were bound for Freetown. That meant they were going to Alexandria via Capetown. He would see Table Mountain at last! The buzz-mongers were crowing, perhaps justifiably, about the accuracy of their predictions.

CHAPTER ELEVEN

CARIBBEAN DIGRESSION

Sam had little time to admire the scenery. The fo'c'sle party had already shortened in the springs and head rope and they were ready for the order to slip. Alan, the Quartermaster, told Sam to pipe "Special Sea Duty Men" as he was wanted on the Engine Room Telegraphs. Sam was told he had to join Alan in the wheelhouse when the Sea Duty men were stood down. It was a beautiful day, the stiff breeze raising white horses which contrasted sharply with the dark blue sea. The events of the previous weeks seemed far away. In the distance could be seen the brilliant white buildings of Tangier, fringed with dark green vegetation. "Perhaps," mused Sam, "the pre-war recruiting slogan was right - 'Join the Navy and see the world' - but now it should be amended to read - 'Join the Navy and see the world, but not visit it'!" He dismissed the idle thought. He had nearly seen the next world on the Malta run and should be grateful that he was still in one piece. He climbed swiftly to the wheelhouse, to find that the Coxswain had relinquished the wheel to Alan, and Sam was ordered to take over the Engine Room Telegraph from the Sea Duty man. *Pathfinder* was doing a steady twenty knots, escorting the new cruiser *Sirius* and the not-so-new *Phoebe*, in company with their old friend the *Quentin* and the *Vansittart*. There were not many orders from the bridge for the telegraph, just adjustments to the number of revolutions in order to keep station with the cruisers. After a while Alan told Sam to take the wheel.

Sam reported to the Officer of the Watch that he had taken over. It was his first spell on the wheel and he enjoyed it immensely. His experience as a helmsman was limited. The lifeboat at Coverack was the only craft in the harbour with a wheel. All the rest had tillers. Sam had been allowed to steer the motor lifeboat when she was out on practice runs and could keep her on a compass course. *Pathfinder* had a magnetic compass but the gyro was used most of the time and that was easier than watching the compass card. It was not possible to look astern from the enclosed wheelhouse to check that the wake was a straight line of white bubbles marking the dark blue sea but Alan had warned Sam that the OOW would be doing just that when checking to see that each ship was keeping station. After two hours the two men were relieved by the Quartermaster and Bosun's Mate from the Port Watch. Sam felt it had been a forenoon well spent and was looking forward to his dinner. Foremost in Alan's thoughts was the prospect of savouring his rum ration, so he too was in a good mood and remarked as they were climbing down the ladders, "There you are, boy, you're doing ob'n now, aren't 'ee?" Sam laughed. He loved being addressed in the Cornish dialect but answered in his posh voice, "Well, naturally, old chap, thanks to your good advice!" They were both laughing as they entered the messdeck which was filled with the enticing aroma of bangers and beans. For once, Sam was feeling quite confident about his ability as a seaman and told Alan he was looking forward to his next "trick". The two sailors sat next to a very crestfallen looking man. He was the one who had literally missed the boat in Gibraltar when they were on the way to Malta for Operation Pedestal. Brian had been before the Captain and sentenced to ninety days in "chokey" - to be served in Freetown - a punishment which was quite appropriate. Alan and Sam were non-committal when Brian told them of his fate: neither Cornishman could bring himself to sympathise, nor enquire as to why the man had been so foolish. They ate their meal hurriedly and left the unhappy fellow sitting alone on the backless form staring into space. Being shunned by his shipmates was probably a greater punishment than having to endure the harsh régime of a naval detention centre.

The voyage to Freetown from Gibraltar passed almost without incident. Two cruisers and three Fleet Destroyers steaming in company at twenty knots in a southerly direction past the neutral islands of the Canaries and Madeira attracted no attention from U-boats, which were no doubt literally lying low, waiting for troopship convoys. In a curious way Sam found the lack of action quite tiring as continued vigilance was essential in spite of the relatively remote possibility of being "rewarded" with a call to Action Stations. As the weather got warmer it was all too easy on a dark night to lose concentration when on lookout. Indeed, one of the Petty Officers doing the rounds suspected a lookout was sitting at the binoculars with his eyes shut, so the PO leant over and put his cap over the lenses. The lookout didn't respond so the PO charged him with being asleep on duty. Bernie was a scouse and vehemently denied the accusation in his strong Liverpudlian accent, saying he thought the PO was having a game with him so he went along with it for fun. In fact, the scouser was known to be a bit of a skiver, but shirker or not, "asleep on duty at sea in wartime" was a serious charge, so after much swearing and arguing, the PO gave Bernie the benefit of the doubt, adding an unequivocal warning that he would be watched very closely from that day on.

One evening during the First Dog Watch the *Sirius* called up *Pathfinder* on the Aldis lamp. Sam could hear the bunting tosser reading the message aloud for his mate to write down. The *Pathfinder* was to prepare a dinner for four people by 2000 and pass it to the cruiser. Sam could scarcely believe his ears. Surely it was a joke? It was nothing of the sort. Orders were sent to the galley and some hands sent down to the Quarter Deck with a Petty Officer to prepare a paravane for "streaming". At 2000 when Sam came back on watch after a couple of hours free time in the Second Dog Watch, sure enough the cooks appeared on the Quarter Deck with four large safari-type jars; these were lashed securely to the paravane which was streamed astern and hauled inboard by some seamen on the *Sirius*. As an exercise in seamanship the complicated procedure was faultless but Sam and his fellow witnesses could not help wondering what would have been said if the cruiser had been torpedoed while steaming slowly astern of the *Pathfinder* to receive the evening meal - and what would have happened if the paravane had been damaged and rendered useless, preventing minesweeping operations from being carried out. The whole episode was an anachronistic reminder of the kind of "capers" the Royal Navy got up to during peacetime manoeuvres and was quite unnecessary. Commander Gibbs, imperturbable as ever, gave no sign that he had been irritated by the orders he had to carry out but it was virtually certain he agreed with the rather undiplomatic comments being made sotto voce by the men who had to effect the exercise.

Sam began to look forward to his "tricks" at the helm. In due time he got the feel of the ship, under Alan's guidance, and was able to judge how to "meet" her when there was a following sea. This demanded rather delicate adjustments of the wheel in order to stay on course when, due to the stern lifting as the bow plunged into the wave, the rudder did not have sufficient depth of water round it to ensure a simultaneous response from the wheel being turned in the wheelhouse high above.

When they were approaching the area of the Cape Verde Islands, a lookout spotted an "unidentified object" on the horizon. Thinking it might be a trap set by a U-boat or even a lifeboat with survivors from a U-boat sinking, *Pathfinder* left the little flotilla, went to Action Stations, to be on the safe side and approached the "object" with caution. It was a stormy afternoon with a long low swell which made movement along the wet, slippery iron deck particularly hazardous. When they got closer it became evident that the lookout's "object" was a small fishing vessel. She was riding out the storm and as *Pathfinder* circled her to ascertain that all was well the hardy fishermen on deck waved cheerily and were probably wondering what all the fuss was about. It is doubtful if anyone on board *Pathfinder* would have willingly changed places with the fisher folk in that weather. They really were superb seamen and seemingly quite unaware that they had caused concern. The unexpected diversion reminded Sam of the incident when they picked up the survivors of the *Cortona* and he wondered if any of the rescued men had gone back to sea - and if they had been given paid survivors' leave as you were in the Royal Navy if your ship was sunk. He suspected they were not entitled to that, being part of the hard-headed commercial world. It was well known that Merchant Seamen didn't receive paid leave under normal circumstances. Sam was pleased when, a year later, in 1943, he learned that it had been decided to grant paid leave to Merchant Seamen - two days for every month at sea. Dick Davies came up to him while he was deep in thought, to ask if he would like to go with him on another run ashore when they reached Freetown. After some discussion it was decided they would forgo a swim in favour of a sight seeing tour of the town and possibly a local meal in preference to an imported one of dubious quality in the NAAFI canteen.

By now the tropical routine had become familiar to the recently recruited sailors on board *Pathfinder*. They welcomed the daily drink of "goffers" - lime juice made from "real" limes which could be seen floating in the wooden barrel situated by the screen leading to the iron deck. Some matelots swore bromide or some such substance had been added to the goffers in order to keep the libido of the sailors under control during the periods at sea when they were necessarily deprived of feminine company. Because of this "interference" in their personal liberty, these chaps declined to drink the goffers provided. In reality it must be said that due to refrigeration and frequent top-ups of fresh food at ports of call there was little chance of scurvy breaking out on board; nevertheless Sam and his contemporaries enjoyed the refreshing drink and made good use of the surplus left in the barrel by their more suspicious older shipmates. No one looked forward to the compulsory daily dose of quinine but it was accepted as a necessary evil to ward off the malaria, which was still rampant in "the white man's grave" of West Africa.

On his regular trips to the Engine Room to record the sea temperature, Sam would emerge wringing wet but his clothes soon dried when he got back on the upper deck. In spite of the obvious drawbacks of being a seaman in foul weather, Sam decided he definitely preferred the open air to the noisy, hot, smelly, claustrophobic Engine Room, and even worse, the Boiler Rooms, even though the stokers didn't have to stoke the furnaces with coal as in days gone by. No one was allowed to enter these parts of the ship, even in the tropics, unless wearing a boiler suit or the rig of the day because of the consequences of being scalded by escaping steam or being flung up against a hot metal casing during a storm or when being attacked, with the ship taking evasive action. It was a great temptation to Sam to avoid spoiling the appearance of his tropical whites by going down stripped to the waist as his opposite number in the Starboard Watch was in the habit of doing, but he wisely decided it was not worth the risk of a reprimand or, worse still, suffering the painful consequences of an accident. In any case, as a regular visitor he had the unofficial privilege of being able to dry his dhobi there in double quick time and he was much in demand by his messmates when they had to wash and dry an article of clothing in a hurry.

Not long after the pointless paravane streaming exercise the duty operator reported a strong echo. Action Stations was sounded and *Pathfinder* increased speed to reach the spot indicated by the asdic and fire a ten-charge pattern while *Quentin* and *Vansittart* tried to box in the suspected U-boat by dropping their depthcharges in a prearranged pattern. *Pathfinder*'s asdic team had a justly deserved reputation in the fleet and it was demonstrated on this occasion to the watchers on the cruisers who saw the long black contact flag being run up on *Pathfinder* well before the other escorts followed suit. After the upheaval caused by the exploding depthcharges, there was no evidence of damage to the U-boat, if indeed there was one. The truth would probably come out after the war when naval historians would have the opportunity to examine the log books of the protagonists - if the researchers ever connected the three British destroyers with the movements of the German submarine. Sam and his mates were not particularly troubled by their lack of success in the action. They were enjoying the relatively peaceful passage and looking forward to stretching their legs in Freetown.

The little flotilla reached its destination after five days at sea, and the following day Sam and Dick got on a liberty boat and went ashore to do some sightseeing. To be truthful there was very little of outstanding interest to see. Down by the landing stage they had some fun throwing pennies to the boy divers. It seemed doubtful if any coins ever reached the bottom before being scooped up. Each one thrown into the water attracted three or four lads who were not averse to giving their rivals a crafty kick while swimming down to retrieve the shiny, swerving coin as it sank towards the bottom. The boys were superb swimmers. Having been brought up in Coverack, Sam was no mean swimmer himself but he knew the African boys were far better than he could ever hope to be. He was rather saddened by the obvious fact that these boys were really fighting for their very existence. They did it in a good-humoured way. Experience had taught them that by clowning and larking about they were more likely to attract contributions from the visiting matelots, who were regarded by the boys as wealthy white men.

When they left the building the two pals realised they would only have enough time for a quick walk round the churchyard before going back to the ship. There was plenty of evidence that this was the "white man's grave" but Sam found no headstone marking the final resting place of anyone from Coverack. Contrary to their expectations, the lads agreed they had done nothing spectacular, but as they chugged along in the liberty boat on their way back to the ship they concluded their little jaunt had been worthwhile, and they resolved they would plan their next "run" ashore so as to get the maximum benefit from it in the time available. Of course there was the usual chatter going on about the colossal amounts of beer consumed on shore and the comments about the local lassies, referred to pejoratively as "black ham". No one was interested hearing about what Sam and Dick had been doing. That was probably not strictly true but at least no one appeared to take an interest because it would spoil the image being cultivated by devotees of the machismo to which the majority of sailors aspired, or claimed to do so, at any rate! This was borne out by the fact that on their next run ashore two or three interested shipmates asked Sam and Dick if they could go with them, so it was a comforting thought that not all their account of the sightseeing trip fell on deaf ears.

After a couple more days in Freetown the cruisers *Sirius* and *Phoebe* left harbour unaccompanied. *Pathfinder* slipped her moorings a day later in company with the *Quentin* and a "newcomer" called *Vimy*. Speculation was rife. The crew did not have long to wait, for the crippled battleship *Queen Elizabeth* came out to join them and the four ships proceeded to sea in a north-westerly direction. When they were well out to sea it was announced to *Pathfinder*'s crew that that the *Queen Elizabeth*, or *QE* as she was known on board, was bound for the States to be repaired. Those who claimed to be "in the know" immediately assumed they were all going to Boston. The rest wanted desperately to believe the buzz about

Boston and began dreaming of going ashore in a land of plenty where there were no blackouts, no bombs and hordes of lovely ladies waiting to make the acquaintance of the brave British sailors!

Be that as it may, work had to be done. The ship settled down to a leisurely convoy routine but all members of the crew were once again warned that they had to be doubly vigilant as the slow-moving battlewagon was a prestigious target for all the U-boats in the Atlantic. Her destruction would a blow to the morale of the Royal Navy and one up for the Germans over their Italian allies, so everyone on board was keen to ensure that *Pathfinder* would not be responsible for any laxity leading to the sinking of the *QE*.

As they ploughed their way westwards and reached a convenient meridian, one of Sam's jobs was to go round the ship and put the clocks back half an hour. That meant half an hour longer on watch. No one had a "drip" about this because when they came back from West to East the clocks would be advanced and the watches reduced by half an hour. While doing this chore, Sam began thinking about the early navigators and marvelled at their skill in determining longitude with their comparatively primitive methods. Early navigators always had trouble finding their position due to the fact that although they could calculate local time from their observations of the height of the sun and other "heavenly bodies", they could not accurately calculate the time prevailing in their own country in order to work out how far east or west of that meridian they were positioned. It took them about three or four hours to find the time now standardised and known as Greenwich Mean Time, by using observations of the moon, but this long, laborious task was made more difficult by the incidence of poor weather and the fact that for almost a week in every month the moon could not be seen. Mr. Archer, Sam's Geography teacher at Helston, had told the class about this problem. Mr. Archer was keen on the subject and when he joined the Royal Navy he became a navigating officer on a cruiser. Thanks mainly to the eighteenth-century clockmaker John Harrison who designed a ship's chronometer which was amazingly accurate, *Pathfinder*'s navigator was able to pinpoint their position with relative ease and all Sam had to do was make sure all the clocks were synchronised. The *Manual of Seamanship* was not a great deal of use in understanding longitude: only one paragraph was devoted to longitude and that just gave a simple definition. As explained in the chapter "Growing up", Sam had studied spherical trigonometry in the Sixth Form and he also did some elementary celestial navigation exercises when in the Air Training Corps, so he had some idea about the problems of determining the ship's longitude. Of course, as mentioned earlier, there was the well-known fiasco of the disaster in 1707 in the waters round the Isles of Scilly. The fleet, led by Admiral Sir Cloudesly Shovell's ship *Association*, was returning to the UK after fighting the French in the Mediterranean and the Spanish over the occupation of Gibraltar. Nearing the Isles of Scilly in dirty weather, a seaman, reputedly a Scillonian, who had been working out the ship's longitude each day during the homeward voyage, warned the Admiral that they were standing into danger. Incensed by the temerity of a lower-deck man who dared to question his calculations, Shovell had him hanged from the yard arm for insubordination. Shortly afterwards the *Association* struck the Gilstone Rock off the Western Rocks. She was followed by the *Eagle* and the *Romney,* which impaled themselves on the Crebinnick and the Crim Rocks to the South South East and North of the well-known Bishop Rock respectively. Knowing how seamen are superstitious, Sam was surprised that another ship was given the name *Eagle*. Perhaps the aircraft carrier which had been sunk during Operation Pedestal would be the last Royal Navy ship to bear the name. The navigational error resulted in the deaths of some two thousand men, including the heartless, arrogant Admiral. Many years later Sam was to use this episode to illustrate to junior teachers the fact that one should never underestimate the ability of a person, especially a child, because of an apparent lack of academic prowess. He spent many years working with so-called backward pupils and never ceased to wonder at their persistence in acquiring the necessary skills to enable them to pursue an interest which motivated them strongly. He was to find many inexperienced teachers were unmindful that there was more than one kind of intelligence and needed to be told that they could learn much by treating pupils firmly but with respect.

But for the need of unceasing vigilance demanded for the protection of the *QE*, the voyage towards the States began to resemble the peacetime passages across oceans that Sam knew about from his reading and conversations with his seagoing uncles. The Atlantic was warm and calm, so it was possible to sleep on the upper deck, using the steel-framed canvas camp beds provided, and there was always the opportunity of slaking one's thirst with the readily available lime juice. In addition, of course, there was the pleasant prospect of going ashore in Boston. America had been a tempting El Dorado to all adventurous, job-seeking Cornishmen since the failure of the tin mines in the eighteenth and nineteenth centuries. Now Sam would see for himself. He had relations in San Francisco and his great uncle Trengilly had written home glowing accounts of the abundance of food in Arcadia, California, even during the winter months. The slow, steady progress through the tropics lulled everyone on board into a state bordering on euphoria in contrast with the turbulent time in the Mediterranean.

The good old Royal Navy was not long in shattering the illusion. One calm afternoon, the officers on the bridge went into a huddle, talking in low tones which made the buzz-mongers prick their ears up. There followed a lot of coming and going between the WT office. the bridge and the chart room and the Captain's sea cabin. Soon there were the inevitable rumours circulating. No one wanted to contemplate the possibility of a change of plan, but when *Pathfinder* went alongside the *Queen Elizabeth* and took on board some fresh supplies and, ominously, a bundle of chart tubes, it became abundantly clear that there was going to be a "mid-ocean substitution of intention" as one garrulous buzz-monger expressed it.

The new Watch was just settling down to the forenoon stint when three U.S. Navy destroyers hove in sight and closed on the little flotilla. There was much signalling on Aldis lamps as the allies took up station on the *Queen Elizabeth*, then with no more ceremony than a whoop of farewell on her siren, *Pathfinder* went off at speed in a south westerly direction with the *Quentin* and *Vimy* following. That nailed the buzz about returning to Freetown, so what was happening? Were they going to attack a pack of U-boats loose in the South Atlantic? Rumours were rife. Sam, who was beginning to consider himself a seasoned sailor now that he had the letters TM (Trained Man) marked on his service sheet, decided to follow the example of the three wise monkeys. As he moved about the ship, performing his duties as Bosun's Mate, he heard the word Trinidad mentioned a few times. That would certainly account for the course and the speed, which created a frothing bow wave and drove off the flying fish in all directions.

The officers remained tight lipped about future plans and, of course, the "sparkers" never ever revealed what they knew. The seamen knew better than to probe. Out there, in mid ocean there were no friendly dockyard maties who could tell them where they were bound!! However, in the fullness of time it became clear that they were indeed making for Trinidad. Sam began to suspect that the Captain knew all the time that they were not going to the States. Commander Gibbs, being the quintessential destroyer captain, usually detailed one of his officers to prepare a short talk on the next port of call. The talks ended invariably with the exhortation to remember that the ship's company were all ambassadors from Britain and had to uphold the traditions of the Royal Navy and the honour of *Pathfinder* in particular. The Officers' Stewards had not been able to report on any appropriate books being left lying around nor of any Ward Room conversations about life in the States in general or Boston in particular. It became apparent as time went on that the officers were privy to the plan of escorting the *QE* part way across the Atlantic before being sent on another mission. It also became clear that even the Captain was taken by surprise when the next assignment was revealed because of the appropriate charts having to be handed over to *Pathfinder* in mid ocean and then being lent to the *Vimy* and *Quentin* while proceeding southwards so that they could do tracings for their own use. Fortunately for the buzz-mongers it was some time later that it was discovered the *Queen Elizabeth* was destined for Norfolk, Virginia and not Boston so they were spared the disgrace of being likened to a lot of old women with their dangerous gossip. It was, in fact, Josiah Fox of Falmouth who founded the naval base at Norfolk, so it was pleasing to Sam that there was a Cornish connection for the *QE*. In later years Sam was to wonder if the sea-going Wrens assumed the mantle of buzz-mongers when they were integrated in the ships' companies!

The ship settled down again surprisingly quickly and the matelots were soon almost their normal cheery selves, being accustomed to making the best of a bad job. At least there were no sudden "For exercise only" trial attacks on submarines, so that gave the lie to the buzz that they had been detailed to seek out and destroy a pack of enemy subs.

During the long quiet watches, Sam was able to take stock of the situation and reflect on their progress. He remembered from his lessons with Mr. Manx that in the eighteenth and early nineteenth centuries, ships sailed what became known as the "Slave Triangle", carrying a mixed cargo to West Africa, selling or bartering cheap cotton cloth and other manufactured goods prized by the Africans and the Arab slave traders and obtaining slaves for transportation to the West Indian sugar plantations and the cotton fields of the southern states. Having crossed the Atlantic they would then bring back cargoes of raw cotton, sugar, tobacco and other crops to Britain. He wondered idly if *Pathfinder* would complete the triangle after visiting Trinidad by bringing a convoy of oil tankers back to the UK.

One late afternoon during the First Dog Watch, when Sam was about to leave the bridge to do his duty rounds of the ship, the hitherto peaceful existence of the passage was shattered by the strident ringing of the alarm bells calling the crew to Action Stations. Jimmy the One had heard the ping ping of the asdic and pressed the button before receiving the report from the operator giving details of the echo. There was another very good reason for this because as the ship was altering course to attack, a torpedo could be clearly seen driving its way close to the surface towards the patch of disturbed water astern caused by the sudden thrusting forward of *Pathfinder*'s propellers as she changed speed and direction. By now the captain was already in his "high chair" on the bridge, having raced there from his sea cabin, and he was reportedly heard to utter, "Christopher Columbus, I do believe that's a torpedo!" How everyone envied his coolness under fire, including the officers. Anyone who swore while on the bridge was always commanded immediately, "Leave the bridge, that man." The ensuing embarrassment suffered ensured that the offending individual never again swore in earshot of Commander Gibbs.

After such a relatively long period of inactivity everyone on board was keen to make the most of this contact. Each man had a vested interest in despatching this U-boat which had very nearly sunk their ship. This desire for revenge was made even greater when those not on deck learned that the torpedo, having missed *Pathfinder,* started to turn towards *Quentin* and indeed narrowly missed her. Meanwhile *Pathfinder* picked up speed and fired a ten-charge pattern, set to explode at 150- and 300-foot depths. Despite the fact that she was only 600 yards from the given position of the submarine when she turned to attack, there was no evidence of immediate success. The three destroyers began a painstaking search pattern to locate this daring commander of the U-boat. During the process, *Quentin* dropped a six-charge pattern and *Vimy* fired fourteen when she obtained a seemingly accurate echo. By now it was dark. The ship had been at Action Stations for three hours with no result so the captain ordered the crew to resume normal watchkeeping duties. That meant that Sam stayed on duty. He didn't mind particularly, nor did anyone else in the Port Watch, because while *Vimy* was left to continue the search, working a pattern towards the North West in the direction of Tobago, *Pathfinder* and *Quentin* began back-tracking eastwards at about thirty knots in the hope of finding the U-boat on the surface, making good her escape. Everyone began to look forward to a bit of excitement to liven up the watch. The sailors were not disappointed. Before long, gunfire was heard astern of the two destroyers. Sam saw star shells lighting up the night sky. It looked very much as if *Vimy*, which had been fitted with superior submarine detection apparatus, had found the German on the surface and was engaging in a gun battle with her. *Pathfinder* and *Quentin* turned at speed on to a reciprocal course and went to the aid of *Vimy*.

By the time the two destroyers came dashing in for the kill their role was reduced to picking up survivors in the dark. Sam went down to the iron deck to help the prisoners over the side. Many were clad only in light blue bathing trunks. They were not physically distressed due to the warm sea but some appeared to be suffering from shell shock. The sea itself is an implacable enemy but to be depth-charged repeatedly, trapped below the surface in a damaged submarine, then just as salvation seemed at hand to be rammed by a British destroyer, must have been a terrifying experience. It was an eerie situation for the destroyer's crew too. They were well aware that there was a possibility of another U-boat lurking nearby and getting ready to fire another torpedo into their stationary ship, regardless of the fact that the British were following the code of the Geneva convention and saving their enemies from a watery grave. Sam didn't have time to think about it. They all wanted to pick up the Germans, switch off the deck lights and get under way again in order to present a more difficult target, so in common with his mates he got on with the job in hand. One German sailor raised his hand in a Nazi salute as he was being helped over the guard rail. Quick as a flash "Jock" Mackenzie, mistakenly thinking the Jerry was about to toss a grenade on to the torpedo tubes, knocked the unfortunate man back into the hoggin with an uppercut to the jaw. It was discovered afterwards that the man was saluting the ship, as all sailors should do when they come aboard, but everyone agreed that "Jock" was right to thump first and ask questions afterwards.

When the deck lights and the searchlight were turned off and the whaler and scrambling nets hoisted inboard, the crew were stood down from Action Stations. Sam accompanied the Germans, who had been lined up on deck under armed guard, down below to the stokers' mess which was beneath the seamen's mess deck. He then climbed wearily back and prepared to get his head down for two precious hours before he was to go on watch again. Of course, there was some chat before he actually went to sleep. It's not every day that you have a skirmish with a U-boat and actually meet your enemies face to face as it were. Now the battle was over, the crew felt some sympathy for their prisoners. Not one man on board would have changed places with them.

It transpired that *Vimy*, which was a First World War destroyer, had been specially adapted to act as an escort vessel to serve in what was later called "The Battle of the Atlantic", and her superior radar had detected the U162 on the surface. In due course the commander of the sub. told his captors that *Pathfinder*'s first attack was a near miss and caused a great deal of damage, rendering it impossible to remain submerged. When *Vimy* attacked and rammed, the U-boat's crew was actually in the act of abandoning ship, hence the red flares as both a signal of distress and a wish to surrender, but in war, when fighting an enemy known to be ruthless, expediency demands that one should shoot first and ask questions later. The Germans had indeed been surprised when *Vimy* opened fire and rammed. In the heat of the moment, *Vimy*'s captain could not possibly have known what was going on aboard U162. As far as claims were concerned, it was decided subsequently that *Pathfinder* would have to share the honours with *Vimy* and *Quentin*.

When Sam turned to for the next watch he was told to go down to the tiller flat and relieve the sentry who was guarding the U-boat Captain. At last he was going to meet his first German. Sam was given a revolver and webbing with a pouch of ammunition and off he went. The sentry told him the German was quiet and had given no trouble so Sam stood looking at the German, wondering what he ought to say. He didn't have to wait long because the Captain strolled to the door of the officers' bathroom which was serving as a temporary cell and began speaking in a low voice which was difficult to hear above the noise of the machinery. Sam's imagination began to work overtime and he thought the German was trying to get him to come close enough to be overpowered, so looking as fierce as a nineteen-year-old is capable of doing, he ordered the Captain to sit on the stool by the end of the bath and Sam leaned on the bottom half of the divided door, glaring at him and fingering his revolver. Hoping to give the impression that he was aware of the Captain's intentions, Sam remarked that there was no point in trying to escape as he would never be able to get back to Germany from the West Indies. The German laughed, rather condescendingly, Sam thought, and said, "But that is exactly what I intend to do, young man." Sam couldn't help laughing in turn. At that very moment an officer appeared and told Sam not to talk to his prisoner. Sam explained what had been said and the officer relented and laughed as well, giving the German a rather pitying look as if to say, "You must be mad!" After a couple of hours Sam was relieved and went to return his revolver, ammunition and webbing. He then realised that he had omitted to load the revolver, so it would not have been much use to his prisoner after all! Little did Sam realise that some fifty years later he was to learn that Commandant Jürgen Wattenberg very nearly succeeded in returning to the Fatherland.

The trio of destroyers approached Port of Spain through the entrance known, rather ominously, as "Dragon's Mouth". From the way in which the Navigating Officer and his colleagues paid close attention to the copy of the borrowed chart it seemed likely that not one of them had any personal knowledge of the port. It was a spanking day and to mark the conclusion of a successful voyage, they were escorted in by three MTBs. Sam noted that the leader was No. 333, the name given to a type of State Express cigarette which was a popular choice on board *Pathfinder* at the time. In actual fact, the torpedo boats were there for a more practical purpose. When *Pathfinder* came to the mooring buoy MTB 333 came alongside and collected her prisoners. The Germans seemed quietly resigned to their fate. At least the nightmare of being depthcharged was over for them. After saluting the Quarter Deck, Commander Wattenberg, with the suspicion of a condescending smile on his lips, nodded to Sam as he stepped lithely over the side.

Tired as he was, Sam had no intention of missing a run ashore in Port of Spain. He had just completed the second "leg" of the Slave Triangle. In addition, this was one of the ports of call of the fast sloops known the world over as "Falmouth Packets", which did not sail in convoy, relying on their superior speed and the seamanship of their crews to escape from marauders determined to plunder the mail and luxury goods they carried. Sam had always been impressed by the granite obelisk on the Moor in the centre of Falmouth, erected by public subscription to the memory of "the gallant Officers and Men of HM Packet Service, sailing from Falmouth 1688-1852". He recalled the bitter comments of his history master who pointed out that those lovely ships were taken away from the port of Falmouth and replaced by Admiralty brigs which were dubbed "coffin ships" by the seamen who sailed in them. Mr. Manx had asked his young pupils to consider why the government had decided to take the successful Packets out of circulation and replace them by the inefficient brigs. At the time, Sam was not particularly interested in the rhetorical question but at that stage in his seagoing career he could see the point of the long-forgotten lesson.

The thought of seeing a new country and getting away from the petty restrictions of shipboard life served to banish any thoughts about slaves and Packets from Sam's mind and after a welcome shower and changing into shore-going tropical rig, he found himself standing in the row of liberty men beside Dick Davies, Ordinary Seaman Jim Ritchie, the lookout who had spotted the *Cortona* survivors, Jack Dusty, a Coder, whose name Sam could never remember - he always thought of him as the "Quiet Coder" - and a couple of seamen who had asked if they could accompany them when they were talking about their last run in Freetown. This time, however, it had been decided that it wouldn't be a "cultural" visit but more in the way of a celebratory tour of the town.

Trinidad had been hurriedly leased as a military base to the United States by Churchill in August 1940 in part exchange for 50 mothballed First World War US destroyers at a time when Britain was desperately in need of escort ships. In addition there was the threat of invasion with the Home Guard recently formed to repel the Germans and a thousand bombers being sent regularly to attack London and the surrounding airfields, so there was no time to stop and consider the implications of the deal. Now that the affluent Americans were in control, Sam and his mates couldn't help having the impression that the people they encountered in the dock area had begun to look on the British servicemen as the poor relations. They wondered if the Trinidadians were pleased to have shrugged off the British yoke, partially at least. Nevertheless, the sailors were not going to let that spoil their enjoyment. Jack Dusty, the knowledgeable Supply Assistant, couldn't resist telling the "tourists" that Trinidad was the source of the cocoa beans used in the production of kye so beloved by everyone present when on the Middle Watch. However, in that steamy heat they were more interested in a cold drink so Jack didn't get the approving comments he had expected.

One bonus, as it were, of the American presence, was that for the first time they were able to sample the much-vaunted Rum and Coca Cola. Sam was still practically a teetotaller and found the fiery concoction quite breathtaking. Unfortunately while they were sipping their drinks a fight broke out between some locals who had been arguing at the other end of the bar. Knives were drawn and, not stopping to finish their drinks, the sailors beat a hasty retreat through the side door before any blood was shed. They continued their walk through the town somewhat apprehensively, but there was no further trouble. They found the locals away from the waterfront friendly and helpful. They were tempted to sample another American import when they found that Jeanette MacDonald was the star in "Smilin' Through", a film "photographed in technicolor" in which she was singing old favourites such as "It's a long, long trail" and "Drink to me only". After consulting their watches - and their pockets - they all decided it would be more prudent to wander back to the jetty and catch an early liberty boat back to the ship which was moored a long way out. On the way back to the port they bought a few souvenirs purporting to be made of local silver and some fresh fruit to eat when they got on board again. Apart from the change of scenery it was a disappointing afternoon. They knew they would be off again soon and were not likely to have another chance to sample the delights of Port of Spain. In one way it was like many small, isolated "boom" towns which owed their recently improved affluence to the presence of oil - rather brash and for want of a better word, soulless. However, the ship took on a consignment of goat carcasses the next day, which provided the crew with fresh meat for the coming voyage, and for that welcome change of diet they were all grateful.

When Commander Gibbs went ashore he visited both the British and the U.S. Flag Officers. The American Admiral was loud in his praise of the sinking of U162. He revealed that his own ships had been hunting the U-boat, known to them as "The Trinidad Spy", for months as she was sending information to Berlin regarding the formation of convoys crossing the Atlantic from the Caribbean so that packs could intercept them at a position where they could do the maximum of damage with the minimum of risk of retaliation.

Many years later, Sam was able to read a German version of the action in an account entitled *Erfolge der Achsenmächte* (Successes of the Axis Powers) by Lieutenant J. Rohwer. It read as follows: "After an abortive attack on the destroyer *Pathfinder* the boat had to surface south of the Barbados, after a six hour pursuit, taking in water and with engine damage. It was surrounded by the destroyers *Pathfinder, Vimy* and *Quentin*. Incapable of diving and in a hopeless position, the boat was scuppered so as not to fall into enemy hands. Position where sunk: 12°21' North, 59°29' West. Two dead, forty-eight saved." That was not the end of the story. Some forty years later, Bert Dean, a torpedoman on *Pathfinder,* sent his friend Sam a copy of the *Arizona Republic*, dated 23rd December 1984. It described how at a POW camp in Papago Park near Phoenix, twenty-five German Navy Officers and men escaped through a 178-foot secret tunnel on the 23rd December 1944. The officer who masterminded this escape was none other than Commandant Wattenberg of the U162! He had provided the escapees with names of people in Mexico who would be able to help them return to the fatherland to carry on with the war. It was, as Sam had naïvely predicted, impossible. Everyone was recaptured, the last one being the former submarine commander. Sam also learned that Commandant Wattenberg had been the navigating officer on the *Graf Spee* when she was scuppered following the Battle of the River Plate in December of the first year of the war. The daring Commandant made his way back to Germany and volunteered for service in submarines. He was responsible for sinking 85,662 tons of Allied shipping. His spectacular success ended on that fateful 3rd September in 1942, the third anniversary of the outbreak of war. Perhaps it was just as well that Sam had no idea of the true identity of the man he had guarded with an empty revolver! Thomas Carlyle was probably right when he claimed that "History is the essence of innumerable biographies". Commander Gibbs himself said, in his usual laconic fashion, that he wished he had sunk the U162 two days later as the 5th September 1942 was the anniversary of the sinking of the ship's namesake, the three-funnelled light cruiser *Pathfinder*, by the German submarine U21 in the North Sea in 1914. History seems to be littered with these near coincidences. But for the restrictions of old age, the story would have indeed come full circle, for the brave Commandant was invited, in 1995, to return to Phoenix with ten of his former comrades to "renew in friendship an association begun in anguish". Alas, at the age of 84 he was unable to make the journey. However, Alfred Hiller, another survivor from U162, managed to track down Sam's former shipmate, Bert Dean the torpedoman, and invited him to his home in Germany. Bert returned the compliment and the two former enemies became friends. Alfred lived in East Germany and told Bert that on his return there after the war, the four years' back pay he received was just about enough to buy a winter outfit. Such was the gratitude of a government to a man whose ship had been sunk by the enemy, forcing him to spend four long years as a POW in an alien country. However he was really thankful to have survived the war and in retirement decided to devote his last years to a one-man "Friendship with Britain" campaign. At the time it made Sam feel very uneasy as he had not put into practice what his conscience kept telling him to do as a result of his experiences and the passing of time. It did bring home to him the meaning of the hymn he sang on Remembrance Sunday in Falmouth in 1985:

"Not names in marble make
The best memorials of the dead,
But burdens shouldered for their sake
And tasks completed in their stead."

At the time of writing, Sam was still debating what he could do in a practical way, during retirement, to shoulder the burden of reconciliation. He consoled himself, on reflection, by remembering how he'd always insisted on describing the horrors and futility of war to his young charges when a schoolmaster, mocking the unrealistic way in which the film moguls portrayed personal involvement in conflicts as if they were glamorous, exciting, enjoyable adventures. He never omitted, however, the fact that there were moments of intense satisfaction to be obtained by destroying an enemy who is intent on doing likewise. He always hoped that his words might be remembered in due course and have some influence on the pupils when the time came for them to form their own adult opinions. After all, he had seen the point of a long-forgotten lesson about the Packet Ships when he visited Trinidad.

Sam could not but feel a sneaking admiration for Commandant Wattenberg. His bravery and patriotism were unquestionable. If he had been British his final failure after a brilliant second career as a submarine commander would have attracted the attention of war correspondents hungry for a scoop portraying a man's struggle against overwhelming odds and his humane refusal to sacrifice his comrades in a final act of pointless defiance. It was an illustration of the peculiarly British Dunkirk syndrome which translates honourable failure into national success. Sam considered the renowned Winston Churchill would have approved of Jürgen Wattenberg's conduct by showing a distinguished adversary magnanimity in defeat.

CHAPTER TWELVE

WHITE CLIFFS

In 1942 Vera Lynn began singing a song written by two Americans named Nat Burton and Walter Kent. It was called "The White Cliffs of Dover" and was broadcast daily, or so it seemed to *Pathfinder*'s crew, while the ship was in range of the BBC or Forces Radio. When the seamen were cleaning ship someone would start singing "There'll be bluebirds over ..." in falsetto and others would either join in or utter loud groans of mock disapproval, depending on the mood of the moment or the proximity of the PO in charge of the working party. Sam always enjoyed taking part in these sudden outbursts as they typified the attitude of his shipmates when they were given a boring or unpleasant task to perform. They grumbled, of course, but someone usually managed to lift their spirits with a well chosen ditty just to show "them" that the seamen were not downhearted, however sullen some of them might appear to be! When, after a few days' respite in Trinidad, *Pathfinder* slipped her moorings not long after dawn and once more made for the open sea in company with the *Quentin* and the corvette *Snowdrop*, it was prophetic that "White Cliffs" was being "performed" as the ship began lifting to the swell, for she was indeed homeward bound, though no one, not even the captain, was aware of the fact at the time.

The three naval ships had been assigned to take a convoy of eight oil tankers to Freetown. *Vimy* was unable to come due to damage sustained in the action against U162. HMS *Snowdrop* was specially designed for convoy escort duty and was a comforting sight to the merchant and naval crews alike as she had several successes to her credit in the business of dealing with attacks by U-boats. The First World War RFA oiler *Orangeleaf* flew the white flag with a blue St. George's cross, signifying that the convoy Commodore was on board. His deputy was aboard the tanker *Lucellum* which had a special team of asdic operators and communications ratings on board who were well versed in anti U-boat tactics. They were in touch with the operations centre, known as "The Dungeon", in Derby House, Liverpool. The operators there used the top secret German Enigma code which the cryptographers in Bletchley Park had broken, unknown to the German High Command. Thus they were able to instruct convoy Commodores to take routes to avoid the waiting U-boat packs.

Sam and his mates knew nothing of this but they were well aware that oil was needed in Freetown for the troopships and supply ships which called there on the way to the Far East and North Africa via the Cape. Whether or not they had any say in the "scheme of things" was irrelevant. They were indeed too busy to keep the reason for being where they were at the forefront of their minds. Despite the claims of the popular press, these *Pathfinder* "fighting men" were too concerned with the present to look ahead and visualise a "fit country for heroes to live in". They were gratified to be where they were, doing a job they considered worthwhile, even if they did need to have what amounted to a therapeutic "drip" every now and again.

Everyone was aware of the intelligence work which had been done by U162 and therefore very conscious of the possibility of another German sub. reporting the departure of the vital convoy for Freetown, which in turn would mean a U-boat pack gathering for the kill at a convenient longitude.

The *Pathfinder* soon shook down to the now familiar tropical routine at sea. Sam went about his business changing the clocks when ordered to do so. This time his work met with more approval as clocks were being advanced and watches consequently shortened. He was still grateful for his daily drinks of free lime juice and equally pleased the navy no longer insisted on sailors eating salted sauerkraut as prescribed by Captain James Cook in order to avoid scurvy caused by lack of Vitamin C. It was a slow convoy, making an average speed of eight knots. The three escorts, however, were destined to travel almost double the distance and Commander Gibbs decided they should all top up with fuel after steaming for twenty-four hours just in case the RFA *Orangeleaf* was torpedoed. She was the only ship which could refuel the escorts at sea. That night the *Lucellum* broke down and after a brief exchange of views with Commander Gibbs, who brought *Pathfinder* alongside, it was decided the tanker would have to be left to her own devices as the rest of the convoy would prove to be easy pickings for any waiting U-boat if there were only two escorts. Fortunately the engineers on *Lucellum* managed to get her engines going again and she rejoined the convoy a day later. Meanwhile the Vice Commodore's communications team had not been idle while *Lucellum*'s engines were being repaired and the escorts were informed that a U-boat had been reported trailing the convoy. The German sub.'s task was being made easier by the fact that *Pathfinder* was still leaking oil from her bilges due to the depthcharges she had dropped when attacking a U-boat on the voyage from Gibraltar to Freetown when accompanying the *Sirius* and *Phoebe*. This disturbing information necessitated *Pathfinder*'s having to leave the convoy every evening after the dusk stand-to and steaming off in a northerly direction so that the pursuing U-boat would follow a false trail and thus allow the convoy to put a greater distance between the tankers and their stalker.

After a while it became known that the shadowing had stopped but that a pack of submarines was forming ahead of the convoy to intercept and attack the tankers. Everyone on board *Pathfinder* was told about this and there was no need to be told how important it was that they should all be ready for instant action. What they did not know, of course, was that the vital information was due to the brilliant work being done in Bletchley by people like Professor Alan Turing and his teams of cipher breakers working on the German "Enigma" code. The Commodore decided to change direction and ordered his fleet to take evasive action by steaming due south for twelve hours, then they headed for Freetown on a new course. It was hoped that the manoeuvre would enable the convoy to slip past the waiting U-boat pack. The tankers stood a good chance because being oil-burning ships they did not make smoke which could give away their position.

Meanwhile, life continued steadily on aboard the escort ships with everyone taking that little bit of extra care that the officers were demanding in view of the potential danger and the dependence of the oil depot in Freetown on the success of the operation. Each tanker was bringing about twelve thousand tons, except the *Orangeleaf* which had five thousand tons before she refuelled the escorts, so all in all there was nearly a hundred thousand tons of ships' bunker fuel, diesel and aviation spirit. A prize the Germans would not lightly let slip by them.

As they were steaming slowly south towards the Equator on the diversion, Sam and Dick worked out how far off course they would have travelled after twelve hours. The convoy was travelling at a speed of eight knots. They were not doing a zigzag so it appeared they would only go a distance of about a hundred miles. It didn't seem very much of a diversion but they decided the Commodore must know what he was about. They were both candidates for officer training and felt it was incumbent on them to have a ready answer should anyone ask if they knew what was happening. Sam told Dick about the hapless seaman from the Isles of Scilly who dared question Admiral Shovell's calculations regarding longitude and they both felt relieved that it was no longer a capital offence in the navy for a rating to comment on the management of navigation on shipboard and that although flogging was still a legitimate punishment, it seemed to have fallen into abeyance! Concerning longitude, there was one hour's difference in time every 15 degrees of longitude they travelled as they were close to the equator. That meant they had to go a thousand miles east to gain one hour in time. Of course, at the poles where all the degrees of longitude converged there was no distance at all. While they were discussing this both Sam and Dick remembered their teachers cutting horizontal slices of an orange, which represented the earth, to show how the distances between degrees of longitude were much greater at the centre of the orange than they were near the top of the orange. Now that they were actually experiencing it, the simplified classroom explanation took on a new significance whereas at the time they were both more interested in the way the juice spattered their teachers' suits as they cut into the orange!

It was only natural that while they were reminiscing about their not-so-distant school days, their thoughts should turn to home. They were supposedly on their way to the eastern Mediterranean and were speculating on the chances of their Lordships changing their minds again when Action Stations sounded and they had to dash to their posts. The asdic operators had picked up very strong echoes. It was not long before there was an announcement from the bridge to the effect that if they looked straight ahead they would see a school of whales crossing their bows. The great lumbering creatures were casually moving in a southerly direction, occasionally showing their backs and tail fins and blowing spurts of water in the air. It was a fascinating sight and well worth turning to in order to witness it. After five minutes or so they were stood down and the crew carried on with the normal shipboard routine.

The convoy steamed steadily eastwards. Sam began to get accustomed to the pleasant tropical routine, punctuated only by the calls to Action Stations at dawn and dusk. As they were gaining time, so to speak, due to the advancing of the clocks, the free time taken out of their watch below for the "turn to" was not referred to as often as it had been on the voyage to the Caribbean. Sam felt he could get used to this kind of life and wondered whether he might become a professional sailor when the war was over. During the crossing they saw a few neutral ships steaming along in a blaze of light, declaring their uninvolved status to any watching U-boat. That added a sense of normality to the situation and gave a taste of what peacetime sea-going could be like. The crew was treated to a dinner of goat's meat at the weekend and though the taste was unfamiliar, it was very pleasant, rather like a cross between pork and beef, and it served to add to a sense of wellbeing. Sam began to feel almost guilty that he was enjoying life and didn't feel in the least bit like a "fighting man"!

After about two weeks of convoy escort a Sunderland was spotted approaching the little fleet of tankers. That brought Sam and his mates back to reality: they were in contact with the war once more. This was reinforced by having to go through a pile of floating wreckage, obviously caused by a recent sinking. It made everyone even more determined to be ready to defend the merchant ships from the "promised" U-boat attacks.

In spite of the evidence of recent U-boat activity in the vicinity there were no echoes reported by the asdic team and the convoy sailed serenely on. It appeared that the diversion to the south had paid dividends and they had avoided a confrontation. As they approached land the seabirds became more numerous and so did the patrolling aircraft. They were a welcome sight as they were becoming more accurate in their detection of submarines and the U-boats gave them a wide berth. Before long the now familiar waterlogged tree trunks from the coast of West Africa came floating by, usually surrounded by a collection of other land-based flotsam - foliage, dead birds, discarded household items and sodden clothing. It did not do to look too closely in case there was a corpse as well. Sailors are not keen on recovering bodies, especially in tepid tropical seas where the heat of the sun on a corpse combined with prolonged immersion produce a particularly obnoxious smell. However, with the proximity of land, the matelots began to walk with a more jaunty spring in their steps and it looked as if they would soon be sampling the rather questionable delights of Freetown within the next twenty-four hours, when it became apparent that one of the tankers had stopped. So near, yet so far. Nevertheless, Commander Gibbs ascertained that she would soon be under way again and the convoy slowed to a crawl so that all the tankers could enter harbour together. They passed through the boom just as the tropical night descended with its sudden darkness.

That night Sam slept soundly. It had been a long haul and he felt quite satisfied with the work he had been doing, as did the majority of the crew. There was the prospect of mail from home coming aboard in the morning and perhaps a lovely lazy swim off Lumley Beach in the afternoon. The mail did come and the usual pleasant silence descended on the messdeck as letters were being read, then quiet conversations began as men relayed news from home to their mates. There was a sudden, unexpected pipe and a mild pandemonium broke out. The duty Bosun's Mate summoned "Special Sea Duty Men" and almost before letters could be stowed away for another read later on, the seamen were on deck preparing to cast off. They had taken on oil the night before and now they were heading for the open sea once more at the maximum rate allowed in harbour. Good-bye Freetown!

Quentin was with them and speed was increased to about twenty knots as they went off in a westerly direction. The buzz-mongers had been caught napping. No one was prepared for this turn of events. However, "Ours not to reason why" misquoted Dick to Sam as they grumbled quietly about the latest turn of events, so once more tropical sea-going routine was established and the buzz was that the two destroyers were to escort another convoy going north and then on to Malta again. It almost goes without saying that the buzz was not quite true. They did indeed rendezvous with a convoy off Cape Verde Islands, reinforcing the merchant ships' escorts as they passed through the U-boat-infested waters - fortunately without a major incident - then when it was considered there was no further danger, *Pathfinder* and *Quentin* continued on their passage at twenty knots. *Pathfinder* continued to leave a fine trail of oil astern as she had done crossing the Atlantic.

One morning as they were approaching Gibraltar, Sam and Dick were warned that they would soon be given a seamanship test and were advised to brush up their manuals. "Can you give us any tips, Buffer?" asked Sam. "Well," replied the Petty Officer, "I've put you both down as TM (Trained Men) so they will expect you to know it all!" "Thanks, Chief," replied Sam rather unconvincingly. He thought it worth a try and called the Buffer "Chief", promoting him to get him in a good mood, but he was too old a hand to be impressed by that. Besides, he had more important things to think about, being responsible for the seamanship side of *Pathfinder*'s organisation.

It did not seem long before *Pathfinder* and *Quentin* were approaching "The Rock" once more. This time the crews were relatively fresh and looked forward to a proper run ashore in Gib. *Pathfinder* moored alongside *Quentin* and almost immediately she took on a dozen or so extra ratings. The *Quentin*'s crew were not ecstatic at the prospect of a voyage with a crowded messdeck. In casual conversation with one of the "passengers" aboard *Quentin* Sam learned they were bound for the UK. Sam kept quiet about this piece of information as it seemed almost certain that Sods' Law would come into operation and *Pathfinder* be sent elsewhere. The starboard watch had a run ashore and Sam and his mates in the Port Watch got on with some ironing and polishing in readiness for their turn the following day. They need not have bothered. Just when the Port Watch was waiting for the pipe announcing Liberty Men, they heard Special Sea Duty Men being called and the *Pathfinder* began to get ready to slip through the "gate" and leave Gibraltar in company with the *Quentin*. "Ah well," mused Sam, "it must all be part of the process of growing up." After all, he was only 19 and the schoolboy sailor had much to learn. He swallowed his disappointment and when he came down below off watch, having had the thrill of watching the battleship *Malaya*, accompanied by a strong escort, steaming at speed towards "The Rock", he decided to do some revision in readiness for the seamanship test. He couldn't settle down as he knew someone from Coverack was aboard HMS *Malaya*; he couldn't remember who it was, yet he knew he would want to tell the man's relatives of the sighting when - and if - he spent a leave at home. His train of thought turned to his native village, to his parents and to Elsie and before long he was nodding over his *Manual of Seamanship*, having pleasant dreams. They didn't last long. He awoke to find Alan shaking his shoulder, telling him to turn in properly as they had the Middle Watch. Sam stowed away his *Manual* and having made sure his lifebelt was still half inflated, lay on the messdeck form with his arm round the stanchion. Before long he was back in the land of nod - but all too soon he was called for the Middle before he had a chance to fall off the form. *Pathfinder* was steaming at speed, pitching in the waves of the Bay of Biscay but scarcely rolling. It was Sam's turn at the wheel and he found it difficult to concentrate on keeping on course in the darkened wheelhouse illuminated only by the green lights of the instruments. However he slowly came awake and started wondering how long it would be before a delicious cup of steaming kye would be smuggled in to him. Gone were the philosophical musings of the previous day: he was once more the schoolboy, thinking of his tummy.

The Watch crept slowly to its conclusion and Sam was more than ready to hand over to his relief at five minutes to four in the morning. He had seemingly just got into a comfortable position on the messdeck form which was still warm from the sailor who had gone on watch, when Action Stations sounded. It was only the dawn stand-to, no U-boats in the vicinity, so after an uncomfortable hour in the Crow's Nest, Sam went thankfully below to resume his sleep. No such luck. The cooks of the mess decided to start getting breakfast early and wanted him off the form. Sam gave up in disgust and went for a wash and shave as he was on Watch again at eight. He was just getting ready to face the elements once more, having stoked up on bacon and "red lead" - tinned tomatoes - when the Buffer appeared and told him it was his lucky day. He needn't go on Watch as the First Lieutenant was going to examine him at 1000. The Buffer graciously told him he could do some reading until then! Sam found a relatively quiet corner on the upper deck and sat down to study, trying to ignore the curious glances of his mates who were wondering why he wasn't being chivvied by "Elsie" the Killick in charge. It was a lovely day. Occasionally a sea would roll in on the iron deck but the sensation of steaming at speed with no ships to escort gave Sam such a sense of wellbeing that he found last-minute revision less compelling than the enjoyment of being in the open air, racing towards the White Cliffs that Vera Lynn was in the act of singing about at that very moment, the broadcast being relayed on the ship's public address system. "Right, lad, come with me," ordered the Buffer who had approached unseen by Sam. The "candidate" closed his *Manual* with a start and followed the Buffer to the Quarter Deck.

"Jimmy the One", or the First Lieutenant as he was officially designated, began by looking closely at Sam as if he had never seen him before, though Sam had often called him from his cabin to go on watch. Perhaps he had never really taken a look at his Bosun's Mate because Sam always had trouble in waking him. As explained earlier, tradition decreed that a sailor would not enter a cabin to "shake" an officer in order to wake him as a sailor bearing a grudge would be able to stick a knife in his sleeping superior, so Sam, in common with other ratings assigned to call an officer, had to stand by the door and call softly until the sleeping "Jimmy" deigned to answer. Then Sam would place a wet sponge in Jimmy's outstretched hand so that he could quickly freshen his bearded face before going on duty. Sailors have always found beards a convenient way of avoiding the tedium of shaving before going on Watch at an unearthly hour.

Lieutenant Malins produced a rope's end and asked Sam to put a back splice in it. Sam did the crown and was completing the first tuck when Jimmy stopped him, saying encouragingly, "Well done lad, now put a bowline on the other end." Sam obliged, thinking the Lieutenant should be called "Jammy", not Jimmy, as the test was comparatively easy. Then he was asked how he would cope if he was adrift in the ship's whaler close to a lee shore in a heavy sea with no oars, no rockets or flares, and the anchor rope had parted. There was nothing on that situation in the *Manual* that Sam could recall but he knew what his Uncle Alexander Trengilly would expect him to do so he described how he would make a sea anchor by lashing together moveable thwarts, bottom boards and any other bits and pieces in the boat, then he would make the line fast and stream the makeshift drogue so that the whaler's head would come into the wind and the drift to shore would be slowed down considerably. Jimmy decided that was enough for Sam in that department and went on to question him about the Rule of the Road and Pilotage. Sam managed to satisfy him on that score, though he did get confused about the lights carried by a minesweeper with both sweeps out. Perhaps it was because all the minesweepers Sam had seen didn't show any lights, but Sam refrained from commenting on that! The questions continued thick and fast and Sam had to read a simple message in semaphore sent by a bunting tosser who had been summoned to the Quarter Deck. Fortunately "Bunts" was acquainted with Sam and didn't send at his usual high speed so the "candidate" managed after a fashion. Next Jimmy asked for details about parts of the ship. He then produced flash cards of enemy aircraft. They were meat and drink to Sam as he had been familiar with most of the silhouettes since he was a cadet in the Air Training Corps and the Malta Convoy had rounded off his education in recognition. While Jimmy was recording marks he had awarded, out of the corner of his eye Sam saw Dick coming along the iron deck, preceded by Lieutenant Fowke, their Divisional Officer. "Trust Dick to have an easy time," thought Sam as he grinned at Dick. At that point, Jimmy declared the "trial" was over. To their amazement, the two friends were then invited to the Ward Room to meet Commander Gibbs. The other three candidates were already there, trying to balance coffee cups on saucers as the ship dipped into the swell. Commander Gibbs smiled a welcome and shook hands with Sam and Dick, telling them that their officers were pleased with their performance and that, combined with the reports by the Petty Officers, meant they would be recommended to go for Officer Training. Sam could scarcely believe his ears. Now that he had been selected he wondered how he was going to cope. He hadn't given that much thought as he didn't think he would make the required standard. To start with he didn't have the right accent, he had no money and he was "working class". There was no time to think about that. A brief exchange of small talk followed. The five young seamen were ushered out of the Ward Room and told they could resume their duties.

Sam went forward to the mess Deck in a daze. What was he going to tell his mates? They often referred to the officers as "pigs" when things were not going right. Sam didn't want to be a pig! Alan asked him straight away how he had fared. "All right, I s'pose," replied Sam. "They are going to recommend me," he mumbled. "Tha's obn boy," said Alan. "You go for un." It was like a breath of fresh air to hear Alan's rich Cornish dialect after the refined Ward Room talk. The subject was never mentioned again and Sam was grateful for that. A few other sailors gave him quizzical glances but they too decided not to probe. In retrospect Sam decided he must have proved his worth to them and after all, he had been to the Grammar School and that was regarded as the open sesame by all who had never been lucky enough to have a secondary education. They were in general a good bunch of lads, who overlooked Sam's youth and were always ready to help. In later years Sam was to fight tooth and nail to promote the cause of the comprehensive type of education where everyone had the same opportunity to advance and no one was permanently rejected because of a poor exam result at the tender age of ten or eleven.

In five days the *Quentin* and the *Pathfinder* were passing the Mull of Kintyre and preparing to berth in the Clyde as she sailed between the fresh-green-clad river banks in the chill October air. Of course, everyone on *Pathfinder* was expecting to have some leave. The oil leak had to be repaired and clearly they all needed a rest. There were no buzzes. No one was prepared to raise hopes that could be cruelly dashed. Meanwhile, Sam and his mates passed their time slung on staging over the ship's side, replacing the paint which had been worn almost to the bare steel by the pounding seas. The only consolation they were offered was that as it was a dirty job they could smoke while they worked. Sam decided he ought to take up smoking in earnest. To date he had only had a few fags and had not been impressed, despite the fact that the best brands of Duty Free cigarettes cost only sixpence for twenty and Woodbines could be had for fourpence. All that was to change, as was his lifestyle.

The next day *Pathfinder* moved to an Admiralty buoy, which meant they didn't have to paint ship as the sea was choppy and it was too dangerous to be slung over the side. Sam was grateful for that because it was all-too-easy to drop a paintbrush in the hoggin' when you were trying to hang on to the rope holding the staging without getting covered in wet paint. If you were foolish enough to lose a brush you were put on a charge and the cost deducted from your pay. When in receipt of only two shillings a day for his labours, Sam could not afford to subsidise the Andrew! Anyway, the ship was literally "shipshape" as a result of the time spent alongside so a "Make and Mend" was piped that afternoon and the sailors gratefully began catching up on all their neglected personal chores in the hope that there would be enough time to "crash" and have an hour's sleep before turning to for the dog watch. Sam was just returning from doing his dhobiing in a bucket on the iron deck when a cutter came alongside. The Coxswain Killick shouted to the duty Quartermaster that he had come to collect the CW candidates. Sam was a Commission and Warrant candidate so he rushed to the messdeck to tell Dick and they began gathering their gear together prior to packing their kitbags. It was fortunate that Sam had heard what was happening for in a few minutes "Elsie" arrived with a broad grin on his face and told them they had five minutes to lash up their hammocks for travelling and pack their kit as they were going to "Pompey". Just why they were being sent to Portsmouth instead of "Guz", as they were both Devonport ratings, was not clear but they refrained from asking and continued getting ready at high speed. Sam rolled his wet washing up in a towel and stuffed it on the top of his kitbag and in no time at all he was saying good-bye to his mates and going down the rope ladder to the cutter which was tugging at the painter as she rode the swell. Sam was pleased he had packed his greatcoat and was wearing his oilskin because as the cutter turned for the shore a sea came over the bow, drenching everyone on board. Those not in oilskins were to pass an uncomfortable night in damp greatcoats as they sped southwards. Everything had happened at such speed that it took a while to realise that they would not be going back on board *Pathfinder* again. Sam was genuinely sorry he had not been able to speak to Alan and a number of others who had become good mates. Some he was to meet again in the Far East, a few more at a reunion many years after the war and regrettably others just faded from his memory in the course of time.

When they arrived in Glasgow the RTO told the little band of seamen they would have to wait until 2300 for a train to Euston so they put their gear in the left-luggage office and went for a cup of char and a wad in the station refreshment room. It was wonderful to be back in the UK and they just sat and enjoyed being among their own people, even if some did have strong Scottish accents! The lads were gently ribbing "Mac" McPherson about not being able to understand the locals when Duncan said in his quiet way that as a matter of fact he lived a short taxi ride away from the station and asked us if we would like to go to his home for a couple of hours to pass away the time. Of course, the lads did not have to be asked twice so the five bundled into a taxi and went home with Mac. By this time it was dark and when they arrived it was clear no one was at home as the blackouts had not been drawn. Nothing daunted, Mac produced a key and in they trooped. The curtains were drawn in the lounge and they sat in unaccustomed luxury. Mac's father was a solicitor. Sam had never been in such a lovely room and once more he began to wonder how he would cope living with people like Mac. He need not have worried, for Mac was a really friendly type and had never ever given the impression that he was "superior" in any way. Mac went into the kitchen but was unable to find the precious tea ration so he offered everyone a noggin from his father's drinks cabinet. Sam was just taking his first ever sip of real Scotch whisky when Mac's mother and father arrived. They were taken aback but delighted to see their son and brushed aside the apologies of Mac's mates when they said how sorry they were for the intrusion. They were genuinely welcoming Scottish people and Sam warmed to them immediately, losing his initial feeling of insecurity. Mac and his parents went into the kitchen for a chat and all too soon for the reunited family it was time to go to the station. The sailors thanked the McPhersons for their hospitality and bundled into the taxi which their generous host had ordered.

The journey south was uneventful. They managed to get into the same carriage and after a while conversation ceased and they slept until dawn when they took it in turns to go and have a wash and shave before arriving at Euston. A quick dash to Victoria and they were on their way to Pompey. Of course they were not expected and there was no room for them in the barracks so although Sam and Dick were under age, they were allowed to go to the local YMCA for the night. The next morning they reported to the Regulating Office and joy of joys, they were told they were going home on leave and they would receive orders about going to HMS *King Alfred* at Brighton in about ten days' time. Why they could not have gone home straight from Glasgow was a mystery but no one was interested in finding out once the requisite leave passes, Railway Warrants and ration cards were handed over, so off they went, Mac back to Glasgow, Dick and Sam to the West Country and the keen-eyed Jim Ritchie to Liverpool with Bert Reynolds, the "father" of the little group. He was at least thirty years old!

Sam couldn't help smiling to himself as they hurtled towards Victoria in the Southern Railway train. He had nursed a secret desire to emulate the words of the song and view the white cliffs of Dover from the deck of the *Pathfinder*. What did it matter? He was going home. Soon he would be wearing his old clothes and wandering about the harbour, catching up on local gossip, so he settled down to a gentle snooze to pass the time on the way up to "Smoke".

In order to be in time to catch the Penzance train from Paddington, Dick and Sam found they were obliged to take a taxi across London. Still in a jovial mood, Dick handed the driver a tanner tip when they had unloaded their gear.

The taxi man looked at the sixpence in disgust and sneered, "Sure you can afford it mate?"

Dick was nonplussed for a moment; then he snatched the coin back and said, "No, I bloody well can't, so bugger off before I fill you in."

Sam burst out laughing as the taxi departed hastily with a crashing of gears.

"Well," growled Dick, "that tanner is 25% of a day's pay. If he doesn't want it, I do."

"Would you have given him a thump if he'd started arguing?" asked Sam.

"I was hoping you would do that for me," replied Dick. "You're the touchy Cornishman!"

The two friends were still laughing as they hastily boarded the Penzance train to be greeted by an old chap in the corner seat with, "Look out, the Navy's here!"

"Only just," replied Sam as the train started with a jolt. At long last they were well and truly on their way down the line.

CHAPTER THIRTEEN

JACK ASHORE

When the two sailors had stowed their ditty boxes and kit bags in the rack above their seats - the hammocks were propped up at the end of the carriage - the old chap asked where they had come from. Mindful of security they both replied, "Portsmouth".

"Nice place," he commented.

"Not bad," said Dick. "Where are you going?"

"Reading," replied the old fellow.

"In that case," said Dick, "I'll bag your seat when you get off."

"OK," he agreed. "Perhaps you would be good enough to reach down my case for me when we get to Reading. The porter put it up there and it's a bit too heavy for me to lift down."

"Right, Chief," agreed Dick.

"Funny you should call me Chief," said their fellow passenger. "I was a Chief PO once, and by the way, I don't think you boys got that tan in Pompey!"

"You're dead right," said Sam.

The ex-Chief asked if the Portsmouth Town Hall was still standing, but the lads couldn't tell him as they had not been in the town. "I expect it is," he said. "You probably know that if a virgin ever passes the Town Hall it will fall down, and there's little chance of that happening now, with all these Yanks around."

Sam and Dick laughingly agreed but reminded him that Hitler probably didn't know about the legend and it might get bombed.

"Oh, I doubt that," said the old salt. "It'll remain standing until doomsday, or a virgin passes by."

He said it with such conviction that Sam and Dick had the impression he believed what he was saying, so they changed the subject by asking him about the ships he had served on and before long they were talking as if they had known one another for ages. The community spirit which prevailed in the Andrew was working in its inimitable fashion. In seemingly no time at all they were in Reading and Dick helped the old Chief off the train and got a friendly porter to carry the case for "this fine gentleman", as Dick described him.

Now that Dick and Sam were sitting beside one another they began talking about the cadet training establishment, HMS *King Alfred*. Neither one knew much about it so most of their conversation was speculation. Sam was heartened to discover that Dick was just as apprehensive as he was but they agreed there was no point in discussing something about which they knew very little so they decided to get their heads down for a while. They woke up just as they were steaming into Temple Meads station in Bristol where Dick had to change for a branch line to his home which wasn't far from Bath. They wished one another a "good leaf" in true Guz fashion and arranged to look out for one another on Victoria station on their way down to Lancing. Dick went off along the platform cutting a swathe through the waiting passengers as they tried to avoid being clobbered by the unwieldy hammock he had slung over his shoulder and the kit-bag, which was so heavy he was dragging it along the ground beside him. Sam grinned as he watched his friend go out of sight. "That's not a very seamanlike manoeuvre, Dick," said Sam to no one in particular as he resumed his seat. The train pulled out of Temple Meads. Sam was reminded of the meeting with Emily there when he was on his way to join the *Pathfinder*. That little episode seemed to have taken place years and years ago. He wondered if his sister ate his sandwiches or gave them away to some hungry soldier on the gun site at Pilning when she got back. The thought of food made him feel peckish so he fished out the packet of spam sandwiches he had bought on Paddington Station and sat munching away contentedly as they steamed ever closer to his beloved county. His compartment was full now so when he had finished his meal Sam decided he would get his head down once more, or at least give the appearance that he was settling down to a snooze, so that he could have time to reflect on his future in the Royal Navy.

Although he was on his way to Coverack, in one sense it seemed further away than ever. He had had very little time in which to yearn for his home, life being so full and demanding. When it came to talking about Cornwall with his shipmates, Sam was very much a member of the Silent Service. He was used to all the jibes about being a Janner and always tried to give the impression of being unaffected. His connection with Cornwall was very Celtic in that it was spiritual. He was inwardly fiercely patriotic and always felt hurt by any nationalistic insult offered to his beloved Kernow, although he knew the criticisms were usually because of the crass ignorance of the person speaking and not deliberate. The longing for his land could at times bring tears to his eyes - a state for which he usually castigated one of his mates, blaming him for blowing smoke in his eyes. At times he could not hold his tongue and would deliver his retaliation with a passion that surprised his shipmates who had accepted him for what he appeared to be, an ordinary run-of-the-mill, devil-may-care young matelot. They then came to the conclusion that Cornishmen, though from the west country, were not quite like other "Janners" aboard the ship!

Now he was in for a spell ashore. No more Action Stations with all Watertight doors closed, which meant you stayed where you were in the magazine, passing up shells to your mates on the gun platform until the action was over, or, unthinkably, until the ship went down with you trapped inside, wondering what is brave about going down with your ship, not abandoning your post, when you couldn't do so even if you wanted to. Now, he was "Jack Ashore", free to do what he wanted to do - or was he? Here he was, on his way home, sporting a truly Mediterranean-blue sailor's collar, his white-topped cap flat aback, with a tiddly bow over his right eye, tying the cap tally announcing he was serving his country aboard "His Majesty's Destroyer". In the interests of security, ships' names were not allowed to be worn on cap tallies, but H.M. Destroyer was a proud emblem. Fortunately Sam didn't know at the time that the casualty rate in destroyers was higher than in any other type of ship. He had even unconsciously developed a slight sailor's roll when he walked, for he found it strange to be striding along on a "deck" that wasn't rolling and pitching beneath his feet. That combination should bring the girls flocking. But would it? Elsie was just about the only girl available to a lad of his age in Coverack and he had to admit that she had not been very much in his thoughts of late. And, what about becoming an officer? He hadn't given the possibility of a commission serious thought either.

In fact, mused Sam, as the train rattled on, he had developed some decidedly un-officer-like qualities during the last year or so, not that he had ever had any, but at least, he had been brought up to know how to behave in polite "society" and since joining the Andrew he had acquired a whole new vocabulary, not just naval terminology, but what his local preacher grandfather Exelby termed "swearing and cursing" - words which none of Henry's employees would ever utter in his hearing on the building sites. Messdeck humour would probably not go down very well in the Ward Room either. It was not considered an insult to call a shipmate "you old bastard" if you were mildly annoyed with him. The stock reply to that was, "You leave my Mum and Dad out of this": that was considered to be an apology and the incident would be closed, always assuming that the tone of voice was such that no affront was implied. A good loud belch after a "windy" meal was quite acceptable, as it is in the Middle East. Sam had been mildly shocked when he first heard it but after a while it became part of life on the messdeck and Sam would comment, "The wind's getting up." Frequently the response to that by the belcher would be, "Is it, Sam? I hadn't noticed." It was disappointing to Sam that no one appeared to appreciate his attempt at sly humour. Either they thought it "schoolboyish" or they were unaware of the practices of polite society. There were double standards regarding theft on board ship. As mentioned earlier, stealing from one's mates occurred in barracks but on board ship it was considered a heinous crime. It was, of course, a matter of honour to pinch cups from the railway companies when returning from leave. That was termed euphemistically "half hitching" and it showed what a thoughtful person you were to try to make good the loss of crockery sustained during the last storm before *Pathfinder* returned to port.

Sam wondered what sort of animal the naval officer really was. To a rating there was always the division between "them" and "us". Officers were "pigs". The Royal Marines were deemed necessary for a long time during the development of the Royal Navy to protect the officers from mutinous crews. Of course, much depended on the individual officer. *Pathfinder*'s captain was highly respected for his superb seamanship, his coolness under fire and unfailing courtesy even when very annoyed with a rating or a junior officer. Some other officers on board felt they had to be strict and even acerbic in order to get ratings to do what the captain had ordered them to achieve. Others tried to be too friendly and were branded as "crawlers", and one or two, like some of Sam's own shipmates, were declared by the lower deck to have "sloping shoulders" and would cheerfully slide their responsibilities on to their subordinates and subsequently blame them if things went wrong. Sam wondered what he would be like. He realised after some thought that there was little point in speculating because Sod's Law decreed that the least-expected disaster was bound to happen on occasions and that could not be circumvented. In his heart of hearts he knew that the answer was to face whatever came his way fairly and squarely and hope one's best was going to be good enough.

In fact, Sam, in his youthful, naïve way, had wondered how he would react in a truly desperate situation. He knew he wasn't brave and yet was sufficiently mature to dismiss what Wilfred Owen declared to be "The

Old Lie" - "Dulce et decorum est pro patria mori." He knew from his relatively brief experience of war that there was nothing pleasant and glorious about dying for one's country. He had never been able to understand why "Our Glorious Dead" was carved on War Memorials. His Granny Katy Exelby, on occasions when he had done her a good turn, used to tell him, "You'll have a crown in glory, my son." He had taken it to mean he had notched up another point towards his admission to paradise but he had dismissed it as Wesleyan family propaganda in the same way that "Dulce et decorum est" was cited by politicians to urge on the front-line defenders of the realm they were anxious to preserve, so that they, the politicians, could continue to exercise their power over the common people. Sam was not ready to be counted among the "Glorious Dead"! That being said, Sam had actually joined the Royal Navy firstly because he had always nurtured a desire to go to sea and secondly because he was fearful of what might happen if the Nazis occupied his beloved Cornwall. The Cornish do not take kindly to interference in their way of life, not even from the English! He genuinely wanted to do his bit in defending the British style of democracy from the fate which had befallen the occupied countries of Europe, but being eighteen years old he was confident that he, himself, would never be called on to make the supreme sacrifice. Now that he might become an officer, the goalposts would be moved, so to speak. Now, he would have to remain cool, calm and collected, showing a "stiff upper lip" and "all that jazz" as his American allies would say. He didn't know if he could cope with that, nor even if he wanted to try, so having come to an impasse in his adolescent philosophising, he wisely decided to take a nap and seek the oblivion which would bring him painlessly nearer home where he could forget all about the future for a while and revel in the pleasure of spending a few days in Coverack with his precious family.

Sam awoke just as they were pulling in to Exeter. While he had been asleep a gorgeous Wren had seated herself opposite him. She smiled when he looked at her and asked him if he felt better after his nap. "Yes thanks," stuttered Sam. "I hope I didn't snore." Sam found it difficult not to look at her legs. He had always considered Wrens, in their black nylons, looked more feminine than the ATS and WAAFs in their khaki or blue. "Oh, you behaved very well," said the Wren. "I'm getting off here, so perhaps you'll have the chance to stretch out if no one takes my seat." "Just my luck," groaned Sam inwardly, but he did pluck up courage and ask her if he could take her case down from the rack. She smilingly agreed and warned him it was heavy. Sam would have lifted it down if had weighed a ton, so he assured her he could manage and for good measure took it to the carriage door at the end of the corridor. He found he couldn't take his eyes off her shapely bottom as she struggled towards the St. David's Station exit with her heavy green pusser's case. He was so fascinated that he didn't even have a pang of conscience about Elsie. He was Jack Ashore! He was going to enjoy every moment of his "leaf", just like all the other sailors! Thoughts and doubts about becoming an officer had obligingly disappeared from his mind. He was going to Coverack - nothing else mattered.

The train thundered on and was soon skirting the coast line at Dawlish and Teignmouth. Sam wondered idly why the Germans hadn't bombed the line there as it would cause chaos, being a vital ink with the port of Plymouth. The friendly Wren had left a *Daily Mirror* on the seat she had occupied so Sam picked it up and looked for his favourite cartoon. As usual Jane was caught in an embarrassing situation clad in her undies. It was good to get back to normality! Now, he couldn't wait to get home. He could feel that indefinable yearning to cross the Tamar once more and breathe air, the like of which was not to be found anywhere else.

As usual the train disgorged a crowd of matelots at Plymouth North Road and Sam took the opportunity to dash along the platform to get a mug of tea from the refreshment room. There were only four people in the compartment now. Each one had a corner seat. Sam sat contentedly sipping the tepid tea as the train rumbled on over the Brunel Bridge into Cornwall. No one was tempted to crack the well-worn joke about passports; the four occupants just stared contentedly at the ships lying at anchor.

The soldier opposite Sam smiled at him and asked if he was looking forward to a spot of leave.

"Ess you," replied Sam. "I'm getting off at Gwinear Road with you!"

"My gar!" said Private Jack Bosence from St. Martin. "I didn't recognise 'ee, Sam. I thought you was still in the 'Secatary School'."

"No," said Sam. "I've been in the Navy since last year." Jack and Sam had been in the same woodwork class at St Keverne which was the Parish centre for teaching handicrafts to Council School pupils. "You bin away long?" enquired Sam, lapsing naturally into their local dialect.

"Bin up Iceland six months," said Jack. "Got browned off. There's nothin' do up there so I volunteered fer the Reconnaissance Corpse." Jack understandably pronounced the word just like it is written. "My Dad told me to never volunteer for nothin' but I had to get away. I speck he'll be mazed with me."

"I shouldn't think so," said Sam. "He'll be pleased to have some help on the farm."

"Ess, s'pose,"replied Jack unconvincingly, "but I've only got week, then I got start training up Scotland."

"Oh 'ang," sympathised Sam. "You'll 'ave to tell'n you've got a bad back."

"He wen't believe that," said Jack. "He do know I'm as strong as a 'orse." Sam laughed, the other two passengers joining in. It so happened they were all Cornish and they began to enjoy having a good chat without having to "translate" for the benefit of any "foreigners" listening to them.

Time passed pleasantly and swiftly. After leaving Truro, Jack and Sam got their luggage together and stood in the corridor, eagerly awaiting their arrival at Gwinear Road. Due to all the talk, they were "chackin" as Jack put it, and looking forward to slaking their thirst with good strong cup of "Cornish" tea made by the good lady who ran the station tearoom. They got off the train, waved good-bye to the two lads who were going all the way to Penzance, and having deposited their gear in a compartment of the waiting Helston train, strolled across the line to the tearoom where they drank their tea with relish and had a home-made yeast bun with it. They began to feel they were really home at last. There was no longer any need to keep an eye on their luggage, they were munching Cornish cake and they were talking "fitty".

When the next train arrived at Gwinear from up the line, the Helston driver gave a toot on the whistle and the customers in the refreshment room strolled back across the track and boarded the train. Jack and Sam were silent now, each one going over in his mind what he would say when they got home. There would be hundreds of questions and prompt answers would be expected! Sam didn't know where he would begin. So much had happened, yet he couldn't imagine how he could possibly relate what he had seen and done since he left Coverack. He wisely decided to follow Mr. Asquith's dictum and "Wait and see." Mr. Manx, his old History master, would have been pleased with Sam for remembering that! When they got to Helston, the two lads wished each other luck and boarded their respective buses for the final stage of their journeys. Predictably, as Sam heaved his kit aboard, someone piped up, "Home again, Sam?" "Ess," replied Sam. "Home again." He couldn't be bothered to point out he'd been away for the best part of a year!

Rover was at the bus stop by the beach in Coverack. It was uncanny to see the dog wagging his tail furiously and jumping up and down with excitement. How on earth did the animal know he was coming? There was no opportunity to think about that so he gave Rover a woollen glove to carry and set out for Sunny Cove. There was an "asterly" wind blowing but the tide was still flooding so the seas were not yet coming up over the cliff on to the road but Sam could feel the fine spray on his face and as he passed the low-lying thatched cottages by the beach he noticed that the shutters were in place on the downstairs windows, so he knew they were in for a good "blaw" that night. He could tell that from the seagulls' cries: they always sounded sad and forlorn when the wind was in the east. The fishermen used to declare they were the cries of lost souls who had perished in the wild seas off Coverack.

As he started climbing the hill to Sunny Cove Sam spotted his grandfather pushing an empty wheelbarrow up the slope in front of him. "Go on, boy," he said to Rover. "Find him!" Rover needed no second bidding: he opened his mouth, dropping Sam's glove on the wet road, and raced off towards Henry Exelby, barking loudly.

Henry turned round and saw his grandson struggling up the hill with his kit-bag and hammock, so he waited for him. "Father didn't tell me you were coming, Sam," said Henry.

"Well, I only sent the telegram this morning," said Sam.

"That doesn't matter," replied Henry. "You're here now, that's the main thing. How are 'ee un, boy?"

"All right now," said Sam as he put his kit on the wheelbarrow and started wheeling it up the hill. It was almost dark but Sam had no difficulty in trundling his load along the narrow path to his home, although there was a fifteen foot drop on one side. There were no street lights in Coverack before the war; everyone was accustomed to going about the village in the dark so the blackout held no terrors for them.

When they arrived outside the house, Sam unloaded the barrow and his grandfather went inside, saying, "Here, Mary, I've got something for you."

"What 'ave 'ee got this time?" asked Mary.

"Come outside and have a look," said Henry.

She followed Henry outside and there was Sam, grinning all over his face. "Hello, Mum, how 'ee gettin on?" said Sam.

Mary uttered a cry and flung her arms around him, saying, "Why didn't you let us know you were coming, Sam?"

"I sent a telegram," said Sam.

"Here 'tis," said a quiet voice behind them. It was Alexander Reseigh from the Post Office. "Sorry, Mrs. Exelby," said Alexander. "It's only now come through."

"That don't matter," said Mary. "I've got my boy back, that's the main thing." She smiled at Sam. He knew what was coming. "You're some thin, Sam. They haven't been feeding you properly. We'll soon put that right." Everybody laughed as Mary continued, "Come on in, Alexander, and chat to Sam while I put the kettle on. You'll stay for a bit, too, wen't 'ee, Granddad?"

"Ess, if you mind to," said Henry.

At that moment Sam's father came in and the hubbub started all over again. Sam sat back and grinned as he gazed round the kitchen. It was just the same as when he left. The sailor was home from the sea. He was Jack Ashore!

Mary Exelby had been given some mackerel that afternoon. It was the custom of the fishermen in Coverack to take fish to neighbours who had done them favours, so Mary often had an unexpected gift. It was doubly welcome, not only because Sam had come home but fish were scarce that week due to the east wind forcing the men to pull up their boats. Mary knew Sam loved all kinds of fish so it wasn't long before the delicious smell of mackerel frying, accompanied by a gentle sizzling, pervaded the kitchen. While waiting for the meal to be got ready, Sam began unpacking his kit-bag, throwing his dirty washing into the flasket which was always kept by the back door, ready to be carried out to the "cows' house" where his mother did the washing by hand after she had heated the water obtained from the rainwater tank in the backyard.

Mary scanned the growing pile. Sam had added his jersey for good measure as he wouldn't need it for a few days and he had discovered seamen's jerseys were never easy to dry completely on board ship as the heat in the boiler room was too fierce and tended to shrink woollen garments. Mary appeared to divine what he was thinking, as mothers often do. "I hope you always air your clothes before you put them on."

"Of course I do, mother. I believe I told you last time that I take the dhobi down to the boiler room and fold everything carefully so that the clothes will look as if they have been ironed after being dried in that terrific heat."

"Right," said Mary. "But you just make sure you don't put on damp underwear."

"OK, Chief," quipped Sam. "I shall obey your orders." He couldn't help smiling to himself at his mother's natural concern. In rough weather when he was on watch he was obliged to put a towel round his neck under his oilskin collar in order to keep the water out when *Pathfinder* dipped into a big sea, and furthermore invariably when the towel became sopping wet it let the cold water through and it would trickle down his back, slowly chilling him to the bone. If Mary knew that she would probably write a letter to the captain and complain about the treatment her baby son was getting!

After tea, Sam and his father cleared the table and washed up while Mary sorted out the washing to be done in the morning.

"They'll dry all right with the wind in the east," she said. "At least there won't be any rain."

"Don't be so sure," warned George Exelby. "I reckon the wind might go round to the north eventually, and we'll have mist and fog before that I expect."

"Oh well," sighed Mary, "I'm going to wash anyway and if 'tis damp, the clothes can dry off before the fire after they've had a good blow."

At that point George remembered the letter which he had propped up on the mantelpiece. "Here, Sam," he said, "I'll finish off these if you can nip down to the Post Office with that letter over there. I want it to go first thing in the morning. When you get back we can have a good yarn."

"Aye aye, Sir," laughed Sam as he picked up the letter and left the house, carefully adjusting the blackout curtain as he closed the front door.

The waves were pounding on the cliff now that the tide had come in and it sounded as if they were in for a rough night. Just as George had predicted, there was some misty rain on the wind and Sam was glad he had decided to wear his oilskin. However, he was bareheaded and could feel the damp penetrating to his scalp through the regulation "short back and sides" haircut. He hastened his step, walking confidently down the middle of the road which led to the harbour and the Post Office beyond. It was pitch dark, so to check his bearings he looked up, expecting to see the dark outline of the ridge of the roof of the cottage where his grandmother, Anne Trengilly, used to live when he was a little boy. All he could see was the open sky. The roof wasn't there. At that moment, inexplicably, he bumped into some Canadian fencing which was where the wall of his Granny's cottage ought to be. He stretched out his left hand to steady himself and found himself grasping a strand of barbed wire, which caused him to cry out. He stopped and tried to figure out where he was.

Five of the houses lining the cliff road to the quay were missing! He proceeded cautiously in the dark to where the cliff railing had always stood and was greatly relieved to feel the cold, wet metal in his grasp. Looking down he could see the white tops of the waves as they raced ashore and the outline of the Post Office building, so he kept close to the railing and went down the steps to post the letter. There wasn't a soul about, so Sam just stood stock still and peered into the space where five small cottages used to be. "My God," said Sam out loud. "They've bombed Coverack. I just can't believe it." He slowly made his way past the bombed site and went up the hill to his home, hastening his step after passing the gaping hole, and burst into the kitchen. His parents were sitting companionably at the long white table. George was doing his accounts and Mary busily knitting a pair of khaki socks, destined, no doubt, for Sam's brother Alex.

"Why didn't you tell me about the bombing?" asked Sam. "I'd have fallen down the crater if it hadn't been for the fence. Some nitwit has put barbed wire on the top and now my hand is bleeding."

"Oh, my goodness," said Mary. "We forgot to warn you. That happened months ago, in the summer, and we didn't like to worry you about it. Show me your hand, dear." She examined his hand, declared it was not serious, went to get the First Aid kit which she kept in the crockery cupboard, and poured some warm water into a bowl from the kettle which was always steaming away on the kitchen "slab". "Just to be on the safe side, I'll put some iodine in the water."

"OK Mum, I know the drill," said Sam, smiling, "and I promise I won't cry if it stings."

Mary laughed and the tension in the room was relieved, so George launched into a description of the bombing. "One afternoon in August, four Focke-Wulf 190s came in low over the village. Their black Swastikas could be seen plainly. They dropped their bombs and machine-gunned the beach where the village children were happily enjoying a beautiful summer's day in the water."

"The bastards," shouted Sam.

"Now, son," said George quietly, "I'll have none of that in this house."

"Sorry, Dad," said Sam, "but it's hard to believe they would fire at children. Carry on, Dad."

"I was on the phone," said George, "taking down a message about the Red Warning." George was the local Senior Air Raid Warden. Gradually, his parents told him about the events of that awful afternoon. Sam learned that Mrs. Hannah, the village lady warden, was killed outright while receiving the call about the warning on the telephone. Among the dead were a little evacuee boy who had come to Coverack from London to escape the bombing and another baby boy, the nephew of Alexander Reseigh, who had brought Sam's telegram to the house that afternoon. It took quite a while for Sam to take in all that had happened. He was seething inside but it appeared that with the passing of time his parents had come to terms with the tragedy. He decided he would play down the scenes he had witnessed from *Pathfinder*'s bridge, likewise the tomblike claustrophobic atmosphere of the ship's magazine. He was suddenly acutely aware that it wasn't just his war. Coverack people were at war too. International conflicts now affected everyone. Families no longer waited in comparative safety for news of their soldier sons fighting in a foreign field. Everyone was in the front line, so to speak. When it came to his turn to talk, Sam decided to gloss over the episodes that might have given his mother cause to worry. Instead he recalled amusing incidents of shipboard life, imitating the accents of his mates. It was the same every time he came home. He couldn't wait to tell his parents what had been going on, yet when he got to Coverack it all seemed irrelevant for one reason or another. He was home and all he wanted was to merge into the motley routine of family life and resume his "pre-Andrew" fly-on-the-wall existence. He could not now envisage his ever again tiring of the slow tempo of Coverack, despite the fact that only a couple of years ago he couldn't wait to leave.

Sam started giving the edited version of his last "trip". He couldn't help noticing that his mother's black hair was now streaked with grey and that his father was obviously very tired. They were well into their fifties and clearly getting older. When he got to the Malta convoy bit, his mother told him about the fright she had when Mr. Bray the Coastguard shouted to her from the window of the C.G. Duty Room next door saying, "Mrs. Exelby, your Sam is on the *Pathfinder*, isn't he?" On being told he was, Mr. Bray said, "She's sunk a submarine." Mary thought he had said the *Pathfinder* had been sunk by a submarine and screamed. The Coastguard was taken aback and said, "But it's good news!" and repeated what he had said in the first instance. Of course, Mary was much relieved and asked why the ship was mentioned as it was unusual to give the name. Mr. Bray told her it was because the Captain had been awarded the third bar to his D.S.O. and that was most unusual. Thus Sam got to learn of the fact that the *Pathfinder* was famous at last - and now he had left her! He chose that moment to tell his parents about going to HMS *King Alfred*. He told them of his doubts about his ability to cope but they brushed his fears aside, saying they knew he would manage and Mary couldn't help adding thankfully that she was pleased he wouldn't be going to sea again for a while.

In an attempt to bring a note of levity into the conversation before going to bed, Sam told his mother about the misty rain which was closing in over the village when he went to the Post Office. and advised her to get a washing machine to avoid being dependent on the weather.

"What do you know about washing machines?" she asked Sam.

"Well, Mum," he began, "it's funny you should ask me that, because I saw one when we were tied up in the Clyde alongside an American destroyer."

"Don't tell me they've got washing machines on board ship," said Mary.

"Ess, my dear, they 'ave, sure 'nough," drawled Sam in the Cornish voice he reserved for English listeners.

"Gus 'long with 'ee," replied his mother, entering into the mood of the moment.

"They have, Mum, honest," said Sam in his normal tones.

"Tell me about it," said Mary.

Sam went on to explain that a U.S. Navy ship came alongside in an effort to promote goodwill, as there had been trouble ashore between the British sailors and the "Yanks". It had all started in a pub when a matelot asked an American what his medal was for. The American explained that it was for crossing the Atlantic Ocean. Whether that was true or not, no one seemed to know but the Royal Navy sailor said if he'd had one each time he crossed the herring pond, there wouldn't be room enough on his chest for them, adding that the Americans hadn't been in the war five minutes yet and they've already started dishing out medals for doing damn all. "That did it," said Sam. "In a matter of moments fighting broke out between the American sailors and the British ones and before long the whole street in the dockland area was full of allies knocking hell out of each other." He went on to explain that there was considerable resentment between the two navies as the Americans were much better paid and consequently were a more attractive proposition than poor Jack when he was ashore. "The saying goes, Mum," Sam quoted with tongue in cheek, "they're overpaid, over-sexed and over here." To his surprise Mary said she had heard the airmen billeted in the village saying the same thing, so his daring talk didn't have the effect he thought it would. He decided to carry on with his description of the first washing machine he had ever seen. One afternoon when Sam was on duty on the Quarter Deck of the *Pathfinder*, he heard a strange "pipe" being relayed by the loud hailer on the American ship. The sailors were told to "Muster abaft the after smoke stack for ice cream and candy." It was as much as he and Alan, who was on duty with him, could do to refrain from laughing out loud but they were mindful of the reason for the destroyer's presence alongside so they restrained their mirth and watched what went on with interest. After the sailors had received their ration of ice cream and "nutty" some of them brought their dhobi along to the stern of their vessel and loaded it into a drum-like contraption which started revolving noisily, rather like one of the latest cement-mixing machines, spewing water on the deck as it went round. Sam told his parents that he just stood and stared at the grey-painted machine until Alan Emmet, the Quartermaster, broke the spell with "'Ere, boy, I believe that contraption is a washing machine. 'An'some, idn it?" "And that," said Sam,"was my first acquaintance with a washing machine."

Mary smiled, and ever practical, asked Sam if the clothes were clean. Sam told her he didn't know but added that the American sailors were always smartly dressed when they went ashore so he assumed the machines were efficient.

"I don't suppose we'll ever have one," said Mary, "so there's not much point in thinking about it."

Sam agreed and they began to talk about the latest news from Alex, who had written to say he was going to the Blue Hills in India on leave and hoped to visit a gold mine.

"At least that's better than fighting in the jungle," said Mary, "but I don't like the idea of Alex being underground."

"He'll be OK, Mum," laughed Sam. "I expect he will wangle a bit of dowsing while he's there to keep his hand in."

At that point George Exelby intervened and announced he was tired and going to bed, so Sam declared he was ready to turn in too and they started getting ready to go upstairs.

Mary produced a clean pair of pyjamas for Sam. He was delighted, suddenly remembering that he hadn't worn pyjamas since his last leave, and giving his mother a kiss, thanked her and proceeded up the stairs in front of his parents, telling them he was going to sleep for a week, but wouldn't mind having a cup of char in bed in the morning! As he undressed, looking forward to the feel and sweet smell of his old pyjamas, Sam heaved a great sigh of relief, saying to himself, "Bugger the war, I'm back in my own little bed and I'm going to enjoy it." He was asleep before he had time to experience the luxury of clean sheets and a soft mattress but his right arm was hooked across his body and his hand clutching a non-existent stanchion. He remained like that until his mother brought in the most delicious cup of tea he had ever tasted, some ten hours later. In the way that mothers have she knew he needed to catch up on his sleep and risked his anger by not calling him early as he had requested. The morning sunlight was flooding the room but the seagulls were still uttering their mournful "east wind" cries so he knew the blow wasn't over but that the mist would have cleared. He wanted badly to go down to the village to see what had happened during his absence but Mary insisted that he finish his breakfast first. He suspected she had given him her whole week's bacon ration together with two eggs from their own hens but he knew it was useless to protest. He had dressed in his old clothes, putting his "Guernsey" on over his pullover to keep out the east wind. When he arrived at the bomb site he was surprised at the short length of flattened rubble. For the first time he became aware of the size of the tiny Coverack thatched cottages. It was difficult to believe that five houses had occupied such a small area.

As he stood surveying the scene of destruction his fellow villagers stopped for a few minutes to enquire after his health and relate briefly their personal experiences of the bombing by the four Focke-Wulf 190s. Sam was mildly surprised at the lack of hostility uttered concerning the Germans as such. They were angry at the decision of the pilots to machine-gun children playing on the beach, calling into question their manhood, but accepted the destruction of the houses philosophically. On reflection Sam concluded that they were so accustomed to the damage often caused in the village by the forces of nature that the bombing was yet another local disaster, but to attack defenceless children was cowardly and incomprehensible. Sam was proud to hear that his mother was much admired for the way in which she had set about patching up the wounded and the calm way in which his father had used his local knowledge and building expertise to organise the Rescue Squads who came from Helston and Falmouth to help. Of course, his parents had not said much about their part in the aftermath of the raid.

The first day of his leave being Saturday, Elsie was free, and he took her for a long walk across the cliffs in the afternoon. She had been out in the boat with her brother when the Focke-Wulfs came over. Fortunately they were not hit by the machine-gun bullets but their former home, next to Granny Trengilly's quayside house, had been completely destroyed. In common with many people who have had a horrific experience, Elsie was reluctant to recount it but she made much of the fact that her "baby" brother Joe Barker was very annoyed about the afternoon of the raid because when they got back to the harbour he hid a fine turbot he had caught under the sternsheets before rushing up the hill to join their parents. When he was allowed to return to the quay he discovered that someone had stolen his fish. As it was summer he assumed it must have been "one of they emmets who don't know no better". Whoever it was, he or she came in for much more condemnation from Joe's point of view than the pilots who had so nearly killed him! It was good to walk along his beloved clifftops with a pretty girl and listen to her version of recent events in the village. When they got to their favourite hideaway spot they sat with their arms round one another, enjoying being together again. After a while they sauntered back towards the village aware of the fact that war or no war, as soon as they came into view, certain telescopes would be trained on them in the hope of seeing something that would provide a titbit for village gossip, so they walked sedately with a few feet between them, just to confound the voyeurs. They agreed to meet again the next afternoon when Elsie had finished her Sunday School work. She had decided she wanted to become a qualified teacher and was enjoying the valuable experience of instructing the young Wesleyans who had been put in her charge.

After tea Sam went out with his Dad on the usual round of "duty" calls to see his grandparents and aunts and uncles and other relations - his male cousins were all literally at sea. Despite rationing, his relatives always offered food and drink in the time-honoured custom of the Cornish people. He wished he had the courage to show Granny Trengilly how to make "proper" kye. Her cocoa was always too weak and watery for his liking but he didn't have the heart to tell her. Granny Exelby was still dispensing stale caraway seed cake to the grandchildren who called to see her. Sam asked if he could have a paper bag so that he could eat it "dreckly," which in the Cornish vernacular meant later on. Sam was well aware that his Granny considered mature cake was better for the digestion than one freshly baked but he also felt the seagulls would appreciate it more than he would. They always lived up to the name "shitehawks" which the matelots knew them by. He noticed the flicker of a smile on his father's face as he tucked the paper bag in his pocket. On their way back he told his father he was going to the Fishermen's Club for a while and that he wouldn't be late coming home. He had no need to add that he would be disposing of the seed cake when he crossed the cliff road.

Most of the local lads in the Club knew already that Sam had come home on leave. News, however unimportant, travels fast in a small community. In later life Sam was to discover that local gossip-mongering was known as "le téléphone arabe" in French. Living in a relatively isolated community he admired the imagery it evoked and the neatness of the turn of phrase, prefering it to "bush telegraph". He felt somewhat an intruder as he made his way to a seat near the fire which was burning with blue-yellow flames due to the salt in the wreckwood being patriotically used for fuel instead of precious coal which was needed for the war effort. A snooker match was in progress and the visiting team from St Keverne was winning by a small margin. It would never do for the neighbouring villagers to beat Coverack on their home territory. The atmosphere was tense. "All right, are 'ee Sam?" whispered Bill Reseigh, who had just come off duty as a Coastwatcher at Pen dhu. "Ess," replied Sam in the way only Coverack people seemed capable of pronouncing. The trick was to draw breath sharply past the bottom teeth while pushing forward the lips as if one is about to bestow a kiss on a bonny baby. While in full "hiss" as it were it is necessary to close the mouth abruptly. This makes the sound carry well, even in a room where several conversations are taking place at the same time. In the rarefied atmosphere of the Fishermen's Club it sounded shrilly above the muffled roar of the breakers being driven on shore by the east wind but as it was a St Keverne man who was preparing a shot the Coverack men smiled approvingly at Sam as they thought his affirmative hiss was intended to spoil the player's concentration. In the event, Coverack finally won the needle match and the men were so concerned with the postmortem of the play that Sam was unable to glean any local news from them. On a subsequent night one of the titbits he gleaned was that Mrs. B. was now accompanying her husband on Home Guard duty because she didn't trust him to be out on his own at night, although he was a grandfather several times over. "Perhaps his being an ex-matelot has something to do with that," suggested Sam. His comment steered the conversation to the perennial subject of girls and Sam was treated to an update on those who had abandoned their usual girlfriends for "a bit of new". The news of the arrival of more female evacuees and some young WAAFs at the Radar Station explained the recent "desertions".

The wind stayed in the east all the time Sam was on leave so there was no chance of going out in a boat. In fact only two boats had not been pulled up out of harm's way when the storm began and they were now hauled up out of reach of the sea. The consequence was that Sam didn't have any more fish that leave round. His mother Mary compensated for it by preparing as many of his favourite dishes as she could under the constraints of rationing. Sam suspected she was being over generous with the meat although he had dutifully handed over the coupons and cash for his subsistence as the Navy termed it. During one cosy evening before the fire, after listening to ITMA, the popular comedy programme which had become a "must" in the Exelby household, they turned to Lord Haw Haw, which was considered by most of the villagers to be another comedy programme although they were fully aware that William Joyce, who had founded the British National Socialist Party before fleeing to Germany, was a traitor. After his parents had discussed the latest propaganda from Germany, Sam broached the subject of Cadet Training as he needed the benefit of his parents' advice. He told them of the doubts and fears which had come to mind as he was travelling home on leave and asked for their candid opinion. They understood his point of view but pointed out that he really had nothing to lose as he would be sent back to sea as an A.B. if he failed the course and no harm would have been done, except possibly to his sense of pride. On the other hand if he was successful he would have the chance of a lifetime as only moneyed people could become officers in peacetime. His father gently teased him about having to salute his son when he came home on leave while his mother was already seeing him with a gold ring on his sleeve. It was plain to Sam that they wanted him to have a go, possibly because it would add a little kudos to their own place in society, so in the end he said he was prepared to try. No more was said and Sam wisely decided to apply his mind to the practicalities of being a naval cadet as they manifested themselves. Meanwhile he was going to carry on enjoying the last hours of his leave.

CHAPTER FOURTEEN

MAKE WAY FOR A NAVAL OFFICER

The remainder of Sam's leave went by so quickly that he found himself standing on Gwinear Road Station waiting for the train to Paddington, feeling quite bewildered as he had not really managed to make all the farewells he had intended. There was the usual knot of dejected-looking service men and women on the platform and when the train from Penzance pulled in; they shouldered their kit bags and barged into the corridors knowing there would be no one getting off except the odd railway worker going home after the night shift. The train was nearly half full so there was plenty of room and Sam found a corner seat in a carriage for smokers. He had acquired the habit when at sea and very hungry. A mate told him a cigarette would appease his hunger and persuaded him to try one. The taste was pretty nasty but it did in fact stop the gnawing ache in his empty tummy so later on he tried another and before long was getting his Duty Free Woodbines at fourpence for twenty. Many years later, Sam's daughter was to come home from school after watching an anti-smoking film and beg him to stop as she was convinced he would die if he had another cigarette. In due course Sam managed to kick the disgusting habit but it was one of the hardest tests of willpower he ever attempted.

No one in the carriage seemed ready to start a conversation. Each one was no doubt reflecting on the pleasures of being on home leave and wondering what would happen on returning to duty. Sam closed his eyes and listened to the rumble of the wheels as the train went up the incline in the approach to Truro. Puff - Puff - Puff - Puff, Puff - Puff - Puff - Puff, Puff - Puff - Puff - Puff, Sam translated the four slow beats of the steam engine as "We shall soon see, We shall soon see, We shall soon see." Coverack was already fading in his mind as he realised the enormity of the task he was about to undertake. He had enjoyed his time with Elsie but she too was "put on the back burner" as he contemplated the future. Conceivably he had passed into manhood without being aware of it, and as he journeyed northward he sensed an indefinable feeling that in a curious way the umbilical cord had indeed parted. Although the future was uncertain he had crossed the Tamar with a new confidence in his ability to cope with life, even within the confines of Naval discipline which to some extent shielded him from the vicissitudes which those unprotected by an institutional organisation had to endure. Now he was a Cornishman abroad. He no longer suffered from the "hyreth" or longing to be back home in common with his fellow Celtic shipmates from Wales: he decided he was going to be "himself", knowing that any pretence would soon be exposed to ridicule by his fellow cadets from the upper classes. He would show them that it was not an essential qualification to be well born in order to undertake officer duties. After all, the Merchant Navy actively encouraged men from "ordinary" families to train as officers and no one would dispute the efficiency, nor the courage of Merchant Navy Officers. In fact, Sam's hastily conceived philosophy was almost certainly due to a sense of inferiority, but a paradoxical pride in his family and his Cornish homeland enabled him to resolve to hold his own, come what may.

Sam did not see Dick until he was on the platform at Victoria waiting for the train to Brighton. Naturally, both friends were apprehensive about what lay ahead in HMS *King Alfred* so in the time-honoured tradition of the Royal Navy no mention was made about the new venture; instead, they hid their true feelings by exchanging what nineteenth century writers termed "pleasantries" about their time at home. There were several would-be cadets on the train. Some were chatting quietly like Sam and Dick. The extroverts were making sure everyone knew they were superior beings by ostentatiously reading *The Times* and a few had sought solace in the "arms of Bacchus" as Dick observed, and were already loudly practising what they imagined to be the vernacular of the Ward Room, the drink they had consumed probably masking their inner nervousness.

As the train approached Brighton the aspiring cadets began gathering their belongings together and smartening themselves up. It was just as well they did for there was an immaculately turned-out Chief Petty Officer waiting for them on the platform, complete with green gaiters, indicating he was the Duty Chief. Gone was any illusion of superiority any of the cadets might have been nurturing. When you are a seaman, be it Ordinary or Able, you are conditioned to abandon all personal thoughts, desires, prejudices and inhibitions when a CPO takes over your life; your only wish is to do whatever he commands so that he doesn't single you out for public humiliation. Surprisingly, the Chief was relatively gentle and in just a few minutes the cadets were lined up, marched smartly out of the station and put aboard a couple of three-ton trucks together with their kit and bound for Lancing College. That was a surprise for Sam. A pleasant one. He had often wondered what life was like in a Public School, and he had also wondered why such a private place was called public. Even if he were soon sent packing, or on a draft as the Navy termed it, he would at least be able to describe his experience for the benefit of those who had not had that privilege!

The accommodation was not at all luxurious, quite the contrary: it was Spartan but a shade better than the barracks at Guz. The buildings were in a sylvan setting with spacious grounds which Sam was to get to know quite well when on sentry duty. The "dorm", as Sam's fellow cadets who were former Public School boys immediately dubbed the sleeping quarters, held about forty cadets in two-tier beds. Somehow or other the would-be officers treated the place as a "dorm" and indulged in pillow fights, apple-pie-bed making and other high jinks. They were visited after "lights out" by the Officer of the Watch accompanied by the Duty Petty Officer. One PO who liked to use his authority whenever the opportunity arose was often the victim of schoolboy-type humour. The cadets had him pulling down blackout blinds which had been let up just prior to his arrival, and there was usually a kit bag or some other obstacle placed just inside the door where he could not fail to spot it. He delighted in shouting for the owner to come and get it and "stow it in a seaman-like manner, laddie". Sam was able to do a pretty fair imitation of a kitten mewing and one evening he had the PO crawling on the floor calling "Kitty, Kitty", until one of the "laddies" could no longer contain his mirth and sniggered, resulting in the PO letting off a string of expletives and storming out of the room in high dudgeon. These rather foolish pranks helped to let off steam after a day's hard work trying to cram a revised syllabus designed to last three years or more into a period of less than three months.

Meals were taken in what Sam assumed was the Assembly Hall. There was a balcony at the end opposite the stage and the recent arrivals took their meals there, waited on by WRNS stewards. Rumour had it that the new cadets were placed there so that they could observe table manners from on high before graduating to the main dining hall. Sam never discovered if the "buzz" was true - note that buzzes become rumours in HMS *King Alfred*! Nevertheless, the would-be or reluctant officer cadets enjoyed the idea of being initiated gastronomically and "etiquettely", so to speak, and while on the balcony would pass comments in the hearing of the Wren stewards such as, "Surely you don't expect me to eat this muck?" The girls would loyally suppress their giggles and were known to slip extra helpings to those who enlivened dull dining-in evenings with their mess-deck humour while outwardly they aped the antics of the "chosen ones" in the hall below. In due course when the next class of new cadets arrived Sam moved downstairs with his class and that change in routine made him realise that it would not be long before he would take a test to see if he were fit to go on to the next stage of training which was to be held in what was intended, pre-war, to be an underground car park in Brighton - or so rumour had it!

At weekends it was possible to go "ashore". The cadets were all marked men in that they wore white bands instead of the usual cap tallies so their behaviour had to be that which was worthy of a naval officer. As their pay was still that of a lowly seaman they were not able to go to the establishments which befitted their new status. Sam had nearly half of his pay allotted to his mother so he had very little to spend. He decided to stay "on board" on Saturday evenings. There were two advantages in that manoeuvre. One, larger helpings at dinner as there were not many people remaining on board. Two, the recreation rooms were quiet and he could do some much-needed revision of the work he had noted during the week. It was natural for a Cornish Wesleyan to go to Chapel on Sundays. Sam's grandfather, Henry Exelby, had written to say he had contacted the local Methodist Church and they would be pleased to welcome Sam at their Sunday services. So in one respect, Sam felt obliged to put in an attendance. He persuaded Dick to go with him, after stating casually that Chapel girls were known for their eagerness to meet lonely sailors away from home, so the two friends went along on Sunday morning in the hope that they might be invited out to lunch. They were disappointed and had to make do with a spam sandwich at the local YMCA. Dick wouldn't go again, so as Sam had made contact and could report back to Grandfather Henry, he decided that a brisk walk in the country on Sunday afternoons would be more beneficial. Dick agreed, so they followed that routine when they were "on board" until they left Lancing.

Regarding the lecturers, instructors or whatever they wanted to be called, very few remained in Sam's memory. They were for the large part remote, unapproachable. One had the impression of being watched all the time, a sort of Orwellian situation where ordinary mortals went about their duties, fulfilling them to the best of their abilities in the hope they would not be singled out for censure, nor, for that matter, praise. Perhaps it was Sam's extreme youth that made him feel like that, for in later years after being in training college and university, certain lecturers remained in his memory throughout his professional life, albeit some were figures of fun. Nevertheless, they were personalities from whom one could learn much, not only on an intellectual level but by taking heed of the way in which they approached life outside the rarefied atmosphere of the lecture hall and tutorials.

Sam's Divisional Officer gave lectures, pontificating in his best Dartmouth accent about the duties the cadets might one day have to perform. He rightly laid emphasis on the fact that ratings always come first, stating that no officer should ever retire to the Ward Room after a hard day's work without first making sure the "troops were fed and watered properly", as he put it. Surprisingly, this officer never once invited his students to consult him on any matter, personal or professional. Nevertheless, when Sam was serving in Landing Craft, he remembered his Divisional Officer's advice and frequently found himself one of the last to arrive in the Ward Room, wet and cold after a day or, even worse, a night at sea in what was virtually an open boat, but inwardly satisfied that duty had been done and his flotilla crews had not been fobbed off with lukewarm food by uninterested cooks, nor prevented from getting their wet clothes dried by some shore-based Petty Officer whose one thought was to "shut up shop" and retire to his Mess without having done his duty in a seamanlike manner as he had been taught.

Paradoxically, the "them and us" statements made in lectures by certain officer instructors did not adversely affect the minds of the cadet ratings. The very title "cadet ratings" was a constant reminder of their vulnerability. They knew that they could be withdrawn at any time from the course to continue their wartime career on the lower deck. No doubt most of them knew what it was like to be given orders that had to be carried out, regardless of the fact that the person giving the order might well be in error, so officers were not exactly infallible in their eyes. They knew that in turn they themselves would make mistakes but hoped they would have the grace to admit it even if it meant losing face.

The establishment of HMS *King Alfred* was later described by an American Admiral named H.R.Stark, as "Britain's greatest experiment in democracy". Sam was one of some 22,000 cadet ratings who passed through the portals. The word portals could be applied to Lancing College perhaps, but they did not open on to luxurious accommodation. In contrast with some centres of learning the building really was quite Spartan and austere in the tradition of public schools. It was not quite as uncomfortable as a naval barracks but nevertheless it was declared to be a "holiday" by those superior beings who had been initiated into the officer class of the Royal Navy at Dartmouth.

Sam was not really bothered about what amounted to "class distinction" nor the basic "amenities" provided. He had been brought up in a mason's cottage in Coverack where one had to fetch drinking water in buckets swinging on a yoke which sat uncomfortably on young shoulders; where bucket lavatories were used after climbing a ladder from the rear door of the house to a primitive privy in the back garden on the cliff which rose at a steep angle behind the house. Suffice it to say that Sam and his fellow cadet ratings went about their daily studies without finding it necessary, or indeed politic, to comment on the "establishment"'s somewhat tenuous statements concerning social background, or on the prevailing domestic arrangements.

It goes without saying that some of the cadet ratings were much more experienced in matters of the sea than Sam. After all, he was to all intents and purposes a raw schoolboy sailor. There was a fair sprinkling of Leading Seamen and Petty Officers from the Patrol Service. Many of them were former Merchant Navy Officers for whom the problems of navigation held no terrors due to their practical knowledge gained over the years. These cadets acted as kind of leavening in the mixture of men who ranged from young ex-schoolboys like Sam to graduates from Oxbridge and the redbrick universities. There was an academic atmosphere in the theoretical lectures which was both pleasing and alarming to Sam. He wanted to learn and was disappointed and downcast when he was unable to follow the train of thought of the lecturer. One Instructor Lieutenant, RN, or "Schooly", gave a series of lectures on elementary navigation. He wore the stark white ribbon of the Polar medal which instantly made him a hero in Sam's eyes as he had devoured all the books he could find on polar exploration when at school, having been inspired by the stirring tales of a neighbouring Station Officer of Coastguards called Patrick Keohane. This jovial Irishman had been one of the sledge party which bade farewell to Captain Scott when he pushed on to the South Pole. In spite of his keenness to succeed, Sam found it well-nigh impossible to make notes and understand what was being said. In retrospect he discovered he was one of many who found the "Schooly"'s lectures virtually incomprehensible and in common with the other cadets he privately resigned himself to failing the forthcoming exam. On one occasion he plucked up courage to ask the officer for clarification but he remained bewildered and was afraid to admit it. That was a salutary lesson for the future when Sam had to deliver lectures and found himself irritated when his students sought explanations from him. It made him realise, on reflection, that he was at fault and that he was annoyed with himself, not his students, because he had failed to give a clear explanation. He adopted a "golden rule" to recapitulate not only at the end of a lesson but at the beginning of the next one in order to help the timid souls, who, like him, were unable to admit they could not understand.

An officer who did make an impression on Sam was an elderly Lieutenant Commander, RN, always smartly turned out in polished black gaiters denoting that he was a gunnery officer. He demanded instant obedience on the parade ground and in other drills such as operating the simulated TS or transmitting station which passed orders to the guns on a big ship and was the nerve centre of the ship's armament. He was always in evidence and never left anything to chance in spite of the fact that his Petty Officer Instructors were word perfect and had no doubt been trained by him. This Officer was an "Upper Yard" man. That is to say, he had impressed his Officers with his knowledge and efficiency when a rating and was selected for officer training. In fact he probably knew more about the Royal Navy than the former Dartmouth Cadet Officers but it was unlikely he would ever be promoted to Commander because of his age and background. He was a keen, conscientious officer whose main aim was to inculcate the minds of the cadet ratings with his keenness, efficiency and sense of responsibility. It was clear to the students that his bark was worse than his bite and they quickly learned that he was sympathetic to them. After delivering a technical lecture he was given to avuncular-style homilies on the way in which his charges should conduct themselves in off-duty hours. Sam always paid attention to this gratuitous advice, being grateful for any tips which might save him embarrassment when mixing with the "high-ups" as his father called them. The Lieutenant Commander wore the medal ribbons of the 1914-1918 war and appeared to be a contemporary of his father, so having been brought up to respect his elders Sam listened carefully although his brain might be reeling from the effort of trying to master the intricacies of arms drill or gunnery or KR & AI - King's Regulations and Admiralty Instructions. The "two-and-a-half ringer" as Lieutenant Commanders are called on the Lower Deck, because of the gold stripes on their sleeves, was prone to repeating his advice quite frequently and was seemingly unaware of it. However, he had been through the system as it were and genuinely wanted to encourage the cadet ratings to work diligently and consistently. His final observation was invariably, "There are too many cadet ra(t)in's ea(t)in', smokin' and drinkin' in the cadet ra(t)in's' an(t)eroom." This was delivered in a pleasant cockney accent, complete with glottal stops which silenced the Ts in the middle of words. This statement became a sort of verbal talisman in Sam's circle of friends. Often in a self-imposed study period when there was absolute quiet, someone would shout, "There are too many cadet ra(t)in's ea(t)in', smokin' and drinkin' in the cadet ra(t)in's' an(t)eroom." The tension caused by having to commit large chunks of naval signalling codes or whatever would be relieved by the ensuing laughter and then work would resume in silence. Sam looked forward to working in groups as at the end of each study session they would divide into small sections and test each other. This proved to be an efficient method of learning through mutual help over difficult items to be mastered.

In addition to the concentrated study at *King Alfred*, the usual naval routine, with which all the cadet ratings were familiar, had to be carried out. One evening it was Sam's turn to be a sentry in the nearby wood at the rear of the college. He was inclined to agree with the general consensus of opinion in that the sentries were posted as a deterrent to over-zealous matelots who wanted to visit the "Wrennery", which was out of bounds. Officially, Sam was instructed to challenge anyone beating a path through the wood at night towards the officer training school. On this particular night, it was dark as pitch and raining steadily. Before being marched to his post by the PO in charge of the guard, Sam was given a description of three escaped German POWs who were believed to be in the vicinity. Sam was warned that at the end of his sentry duty he would have to repeat the description to his relief in the presence of the Duty PO. Sam suspected that the description was fictitious and was a part of the "course" but that did not make it any easier to remember. He resolved to go over the description, repeating it softly to himself every now and again so that he would not be found wanting at the end of his guard. He had found during his schooldays that it was easier to recall what he had been told to learn if he said the words out loud until they were fixed in his memory.

Meanwhile, the rain continued unabated and dripped relentlessly on Sam who had been detailed by the PO to remain beneath a broad oak tree which was situated in the centre of a small clearing in the copse and intended by the sympathetic commander of the guard to afford him some sort of shelter. Unfortunately it did not. The rain found its way under the upturned collar of his oilskin and slowly spread down his back, chilling him to the bone. Even his green canvas gaiters could not keep the water from wetting his ankles. Sam was really miserable and longed to be back on the *Pathfinder* where at least there was some point in being on watch in an exposed position as the safety of the ship was dependent on lookouts spotting the enemy. Sam could not believe that anyone in his right mind would venture out on such a night. After standing with his rifle and fixed bayonet slung over his shoulder for the first half hour of his watch, Sam decided that enough was enough and climbed into the tree, wedging himself into a sitting position in the fork of the oak which was about six feet from the ground. As he suspected, it was a bit drier there, and at least he wasn't standing up. He cheered up a little and had a go at reciting the details of the escaped Jerry prisoners. Then he lapsed into a semi-somnolent state until he was aware of people approaching the clearing, their feet squelching in the mud. He rightly guessed it was the Officer of the Watch and the Duty PO who were about to place the relief guards. It was too late to make an undignified descent so he remained stock still, hoping for inspiration.

The two officers stopped a couple of yards in front of the tree. The night was blacker than ever and the rain blurred what little vision there was. The PO assured the OOW they were in the correct spot. There was a moment's silence. At that point Sam jumped down from the tree shouting, "Halt, who goes there?" The PO was so surprised he took a step backwards and fell on the sodden ground while the Officer of the Watch backed away with Sam's bayonet a few inches from his chest. Sam unhooked his torch from his belt, shone it on the officer's face and immediately said innocently, "Oh, I'm very sorry, Sir. I heard people approaching and decided to climb into the tree in case they were the escaped Germans and they tried to overpower me."

Sam never did ascertain why he had formed this plan of action. It was no doubt born of desperation, but to his surprise it worked. The OOW pulled the PO to his feet, recovered his composure and inquired why Sam thought that was the best way of dealing with the situation. Sam told him he had been brought up in the country and knew most people never looked up when passing through a wood, especially at night, so to be sure of succeeding in apprehending the POWs by himself he had decided to observe before making a move. The Officer seemed a bit dubious but accepted Sam's explanation, adding that it was "... not a bad idea". After noting Sam's name he made him repeat the description of the POWs and then revealed it was in fact "an exercise in testing the retention of important information over a period of time". Meanwhile, Sam's relief had appeared on the scene and stood grinning in the background. As Sam turned to follow the OOW who had decided to light his way back to the Guard

Room, he winked at the new sentry who promptly gave the V sign. At that point, Sam realised that it had stopped raining!

He had certainly had a quiet guard with "not a mouse stirring" - until the OOW arrived, that is! For the first time Sam understood the strength of feeling behind the lines spoken by the soldier in *Hamlet*, "For this relief, much thanks. 'Tis bitter cold and I am sick at heart." Now he could relax and think of the cup of kye the Wren cook had promised him when he came off watch. Curiously, Sam did not dwell on the events of that night. He was more concerned with "the shape of things to come".

When Lancing Liberty men were piped, Sam was often at a loss to know what he ought to do. There was so much to learn that he felt he could not spare the time to "go ashore" into busy Brighton or even walk through lifeless Lancing. He was very conscious of the fact that he was just a schoolboy sailor and that he was competing with men of the world, some of whom were twice his age. He knew that though his Maths and Physics were probably better than theirs he lacked experience in applying his knowledge. Sam and others like him had to learn everything from scratch. As a trained seaman he was paid half a crown a day and a shilling of that was deducted and sent as an allowance to his mother. The more affluent ratings could afford to visit the fleshpots of Brighton and even go up to "Smoke" if the there was a convenient train to Victoria. In fact this state of affairs did not concern him greatly. He was quite content to go off with Dick Davis for a stroll in the country or to get fish and chips in Lancing. The one attempt to vary routine by attending the local chapel had ended in failure. There was no evidence of female "talent" there to entice him back. He was aware that Elsie no longer occupied the most prominent position in his mind when thinking about his beloved Coverack and he had hopes of getting off with a pretty girl when ashore.

On Sunday mornings, Duty Weekend Cadet Ratings were "invited" to Divisions, which was a parade where everyone wore Number Ones, including a dazzling white lanyard. It gave the Captain an opportunity to inspect the men and engage in a virtually one-sided conversation when he stopped in front of a rating to ask him why he was wearing a non-regulation item of clothing or to congratulate him on his smart appearance. Sailors have always loved to wear "tiddly" smart uniforms made by naval tailors and they were prepared to run up bills in order to cut a dashing figure when ashore. The trouble was that in an effort to please, the tailors often added little touches which were not strictly "regulation" and that sometimes incurred the displeasure of inspecting officers. Due to lack of space and the geography of the college the cadet ratings bowed to the inevitable and regardless of their faith or lack of it, went to divisions in their best uniforms rather than be found skulking on the mess deck and having to answer awkward questions at to why they were not at church. They were also aware that non-attendance might be interpreted as anti-social behaviour by someone in authority who didn't really understand the meaning of the freedom of the right to worship, so it transpired that the college chapel was usually full on Sunday mornings.

The naval chaplain at Lancing had the reputation of being outspoken to the point of being regarded as uncommitted to the Church. As a Padre he was an officer with the equivalent rank of Commander but in theory as a man of the cloth he was expected to mix with all ranks, listen to their problems and make an effort to help them arrive at a solution. In addition he was naturally expected to encourage ratings to come to church and inveigle them to carry out voluntary duties such as altar servers, readers, sidesmen, ushers, etc. It was noticeable that whenever the chaplain came into the cadet ratings' anteroom, many of those present suddenly found the urgent need to be somewhere else and would silently disappear. Of course there were a number of men who would greet the chaplain sincerely and who were prepared to help him in any way possible. All this palaver was quite new to Sam who had by tradition started life as a Wesleyan and was told at the tender age of nine in 1932 that he had now become a Methodist. However, notwithstanding his relative ignorance of the procedures of the Church of England, Sam enjoyed the services in spite of not knowing exactly when he should stand, sit or kneel. Local dignitaries were invited to attend the services in the college chapel and there was always a good sprinkling of them at the front with the officers. The cynics among Sam's acquaintances stated the locals only came for the pink gins which were offered them in the Ward Room after worship. On one occasion Elsie and Doris Waters came. Someone pointed them out to Sam. He had heard them many times on the wireless but didn't know what they looked like. They were among his mother's favourite performers and she was quite envious when he wrote and told her he had seen them at Church. He was to see them perform sometime later on the hatch of the troopship Highland Chieftain in Bombay, prior to sailing to Singapore after the Japanese surrender.

It was not all work and no play at HMS *King Alfred*. There were enjoyable interludes for Sam. The brother-in-law of Sam's brother Alex wrote to Sam inviting him to come for a weekend at his farm in nearby

Washington. Sam was pleased at this turn of events and as soon as he could get a twenty-four-hour pass he went to the farm, travelling by bus. He was warmly welcomed and delighted to be offered a tea of home-made bread and jam with farm butter and even some illegal Devon-style clotted cream to spread on the Devonshire splits made by David's mother, who was a true "Devonshire dumpling" as the Cornish often described those happy, hard-working Devon farmers' wives who kept everything ticking over in the farmhouses despite the seemingly insurmountable difficulties of wartime domestic agriculture.

From that time on, Sam made a number of visits to Washington while he was training to be an officer. David Varcoe worked hard all the week on the farm and Saturday was his one period of relaxation when his elderly father would take over the essential routine tasks which never end on a working farm. It was quite natural for David to take Sam with him to his local, the White Hart, for a few beers and to catch up with current gossip and exchange banter with the local girls. Sam got into the habit of taking his civilian clothes with him when he went to the farm. It was a delight to walk into the pub as an ordinary person and join in the conversation with David's friends. He probably looked a bit odd as his blue sports coat no longer fitted him as it did when he left school. He had not only filled out but grown a little taller so his grey flannels were at "half mast" and his cuffs half-way up his elbow. Nevertheless David's friends accepted him easily enough when he was introduced as a friend from Cornwall. Sam could talk their language about crops and animals, having worked on William Williams' Vounder farm near Coverack when he was a boy. William's wife Dorothy was an old school friend of his mother.

It was relaxing not to have to discuss matters pertaining to the course at *King Alfred*. Sam didn't have to watch his "Ps and Qs" in case he was being observed by somebody who was quietly assessing his leadership potential. Whether or not the authorities planted observers to report on the cadets in unguarded moments, Sam never found out, but he remained convinced there was an Orwellian atmosphere prevailing wherever cadets gathered in off-duty hours. After each happy weekend at Washington Sam found himself secretly envying David's country life. Conversely he later discovered that David wanted to be in the forces but had been told he could not be released from his war work on the farm and the specialised grass cutting he did with the farm tractor at local military installations. Both young men were realistic enough to accept that they were not able to change direction and almost certainly were glad that in a way their destiny was out of their hands. Being young they lived for the present and were eager to sample whatever life held in store for them. Of course, during their sessions in the White Hart when the watery beer loosened their tongues, they enjoyed commiserating with one another and rolled happily back to the farm loudly proclaiming what they would do to set the world to rights. They diplomatically ceased their proclamations on approaching the farm as David's Methodist parents would not have condoned such rowdy behaviour!

One of the most interesting aspects of the cadet training took place at Portslade, where elementary ship handling was taught. The "ships" were in fact redundant MFVs. These former motor fishing vessels had their wheel houses fitted out like the bridge of a minor warship, including engine-room telegraphs and voice pipes to the Quartermaster below. The officer who instructed Sam's class was Sub. Lieutenant Capes, RNR, a bluff Yorkshireman who, it was rumoured, was a skipper of a trawler which was part of the Icelandic fleet. Sam admired the way in which Mr. Capes patiently showed the cadets how to come alongside without causing damage to the ship or the jetty by assessing the strength of the wind and tide and allowing one or both to do some of the "work" when practicable. He began to realise the practical importance of knowing about parallelograms of forces which he had learned in his Physics lessons in Helston and indeed when he was doing elementary navigation in the Air Cadets. It was good to feel the wind on his face and the "ship" moving underneath him, albeit in fairly calm water, though the wind could play nasty tricks especially when approaching the jetty when it could "funnel" between the other ships tied up alongside. Of course, Sam had never handled a twin-screw vessel before but his experience as a Bosun's mate on the *Pathfinder* combined with using the analogy of what he used to do with his paddles when coming into the harbour at Coverack stood him in good stead. He was able to help Dick work out what to do by showing him how one used paddles when rowing by sitting on a chair and using his hands as oars and then substituting the oars or paddles for the ship's propellers. It was a crude analogy but it worked for them both. Of course it all depended on the type of ship one was handling and in spite of his confidence, Sam was to remember always his poor handling of a Tank Landing Craft when coming alongside in Singapore Harbour. He was not the Dock Master's favourite skipper after he carried away a substantial length of railing by approaching the jetty too fast in a stiff breeze, although in mitigation he did point out to the Dock Master that he was more accustomed to conning B Class MLs at that stage in his career!

The situation in the Brighton half of HMS *King Alfred* was quite different from Lancing College. The cadets led a sort of troglodyte existence in the former car park. It was quite unsuitable for sea training, as indeed was Lancing. There was a huge open-air parade ground, where Sam discovered to his amazement that he was capable of bellowing orders. There was a certain Instructor Petty Officer who delighted in ordering a cadet to tell his squad to "Quick March" and then the PO would not allow the cadet to give the next order until the squad was almost out of earshot. It was necessary to give the executive word "Turn" as the right foot came down so that the squad could then take one pace with the left foot before commencing the turn on the right foot, completing it in four movements as laid down in the drill book. Sam was terrified when he was subjected to the treatment, as he had never commanded a squad before and for a horrible moment could not remember on which foot he would have to give the order to turn about. To make matters worse his eyes started watering and he could not see the marching feet clearly! However, Lady Luck was on his side and after what seemed an eternity the PO said, "OK lad, bring them back," and to Sam's astonishment the squad heard him and did a smart about turn, thus avoiding the PO's customary sneering remark, "For God's sake say something lad, even if it's only 'goodbye'!" when a hapless cadet became tongue tied. The training class knew what to expect when this particular PO was on parade and would listen hard when marching away, one of their number calling out "About turn" if the stamping feet drowned the student cadet's command. Sam never discovered if he had been helped in this way. He liked to think that he had managed without it, but his initial success gave him the confidence he needed and he had no scathing comments from the "little Hitler" as the PO had been dubbed by his victims.

Although all the cadet ratings were familiar with rifle drill it was deemed an important part of the curriculum, but most of the cadets wished the training officers would reduce the time spent on drill and use it for more important subjects such as navigation. Sam managed to get his hands on a sextant only once, when the class went above ground and took sights on the front in Brighton, yet in theory when he left *King Alfred* he was supposed to be competent in watch-keeping as well as ship-handling - under supervision, of course. He knew the theory but that is of no use if one hasn't actually taken a sight. It is incredible that Royal Navy Officer Instructors at HMS *King Alfred* were ostensibly charged with training men to be officers yet did not have the resources to ensure the curriculum could be implemented. It would appear that there was no form of independent inspection which would have highlighted such a glaring omission as practice in the use of navigational instruments. Many years after the war Sam used to smile when he heard some of his contemporaries praising the "good old days" and stating, quite inaccurately, that "... young sailors these days don't know anything about the sea." It is almost certain that the expensive experience of poor instruction at HMS *King Alfred* led to the postwar Royal Navy concentrating on thorough and comprehensive training which was updated at regular intervals with refresher courses. One wonders whether the Second World War Royal Navy, mistakenly jealous of the "Britain's greatest experiment in democracy", conspired to create a second-class corps of officers, so to speak. That may not be as far-fetched as it first appears to be. There was a very strong lobby which strove to retain the status quo which had operated successfully up to the First World War when "cracks" in the class armour became visible and educated working-class servicemen achieved officer rank through merit rather than privilege. Sam was fortunate regarding practice in taking sights as an old salt from Coverack called Commander Genge had given him a Quadrant which had been used on a sailing ship in the nineteenth century. The Commander took an interest in Sam when he asked him for help in passing a test for a Sea Scout's badge and had given him the Quadrant as a keepsake when he moved from Coverack. Sam practised taking bearings on the Quadrant when he went on leave, despite the broken mirror used to align "horizons". When in the fulness of time he passed out as a Midshipman he proudly visited the old Commander and thanked him for his wise counsel given when he was trying to determine his future before leaving school. Sam did not have far to go to visit the Commander as he and his wife had moved to Saltdean, which was just along the coast from Newhaven where Sam was eventually posted.

Physical fitness was high on the list of curriculum subjects for officers in training. The war at sea had taught many lessons, indicating the need to remain mentally alert even when feeling physically exhausted. It had become apparent that officers, because of their extra responsibilities, were probably under greater strain than many of the ratings, so it was imperative that they should be in a good physical state before going to sea. Apart from the workouts in the gymnasium, survival swimming and gruelling parade-ground exercises, the cadet ratings had to go on long runs round the streets of Brighton. They could not be called cross-country runs: pavement pounding was probably a more accurate description. At the appointed time a crowd of cadets would leave *King Alfred* at a brisk trot and follow a predetermined track round the residential area behind the sea front. About forty minutes later the first bunch of runners could be seen returning to base. They were then followed by the mainstream of runners and then at intervals by stragglers who had not been able to keep up.

The casual observer outside HMS *King Alfred* probably assumed that a good afternoon's exercise had been accomplished. At first Sam enjoyed going on these runs, but then he discovered that in spite of the fear of swift retribution for disobeying orders, some of the cadet ratings had evolved a system whereby a knot of runners would leave the establishment at a steady pace, then go round the corner and repair to a congenial café for a cup of tea, despite the fact that they were clad only in singlet, shorts and white gym shoes. These "stalwart" skivers would remain in the café drinking and eating until the first of the genuine runners appeared on their way back to the barracks, and then they would follow them in with a show of puffing and blowing to allay any suspicions. Sam dearly wanted to become one of the sophisticated dodgers but he never had the courage to emulate them. No doubt some of them regretted later on that they had not achieved a sufficiently high state of physical fitness but at the time they were admired by their peers for their initiative and ability to avoid detection. It goes without saying that no one ever reported their misdemeanours to the training officers, not even the Petty Officer Physical Training Instructors who surely must have chosen to turn a blind eye to this blatant breach of discipline. Sam put it down to the fact that everyone has a sneaking admiration for a harmless rogue, especially when he cocks a snook at higher authority.

As time went on the course became more intense. Work on drill, signals, seamanship, navigation, administration, gunnery and so on was stepped up. What had at first seemed relatively easy became progressively more complicated. There was a lot of work to be done and Sam began to flounder. He didn't realise at the time he was not alone in feeling inadequate. He began to feel it would be a relief to be sent back to sea as a seaman. About three weeks before finals, the cadet ratings were ordered to enter into negotiations with a tailor to be measured for an officer's uniform. Fortunately a friend of Dick Davis known as "Ginger" Reynolds had been a manager of a branch of Hector Powe in Liverpool so the three of them went along to the local Hector Powe's shop. After "Ginger" had introduced himself the three were measured for their uniforms on the understanding that if they did not pass the uniforms would not be required and the cadets would not be liable to pay. The allowance from the Admiralty was £50. That was sufficient to buy a doeskin suit, a serge suit, a greatcoat, a cap and a couple of white shirts with separate stiff collars. It was all very bewildering to Sam as he had never even heard of doeskin. Logic told him it was a soft leather from a deer, which indeed it was, but it was also the name given to a soft woollen fabric from which suits were made. Fortunately Sam found the shop assistants to be accommodating and discreet so he was not embarrassed by his lack of knowledge.

Back in *King Alfred* there was feverish activity in the evenings. Only the confident and foolhardy went ashore. The remainder walked about with a preoccupied look, trying to memorise notes and diagrams together with unfamiliar phraseology. Sam found most of his acquaintances were only too willing to test him in return for being questioned themselves. This method of revising had already been proved a useful adjunct to conventional swotting as difficult points were often cleared up after discussion. All too soon the tests began and before long it appeared that at least half of the candidates were convinced they had already failed.

A couple of days after the completion of exams, lists were pinned on notice boards. Sam refused to look, being a Celtic pessimist, so Dick joined the throng round the boards and came back with the news that they had both passed. At first Sam wasn't sure whether he was pleased or disappointed but he found himself swept along in the tide of euphoria and was hustled through the streets to Hector Powe's with his friends to collect his new Midshipman's uniform. He couldn't help smiling at the suitability of the name hector, with a lower-case h, as he was feeling intimidated by all the attention his new-found status aroused.

When the little group of brand new officers had tried on their new uniforms and were ready to leave Hector Powe everyone began to feel self-conscious with the large cardboard box tucked under his arm, so it was decided to use the good offices of "Ginger" Reynolds and get him to ask the manager of Hector Powe to phone for a taxi. They returned to *King Alfred* in style and the business of decking themselves out began. When Sam finally emerged into the public arena, so to speak, he felt not only self-conscious but slightly guilty as well, for those who had failed were filing out, carrying their kit bags, on their way home for a spot of leave before being drafted to a ship in their old rank. His "brother officers" probably had a similar reaction but that did not make the embarrassment any easier to bear. Sam had difficulty in believing he had actually passed out. A Petty Officer, whom he knew as Jim, went by and wished him luck. In conversation with him on a previous occasion Sam had learned that he had spent some time as a Second Mate in the Merchant Navy and had much experience as a watch officer. In comparison with Jim, Sam felt an ignoramus. In his heart of hearts Sam knew Jim was a better man than he was and at that precise moment Sam would have willingly ceded his place to Jim, but of course it was not to be.

The following day there was a grand parade of newly appointed officers. Sam was presented with a Certificate stating that "Sam Exelby, Ordinary Seaman, after completing the preliminary period of his training in HMS *King Alfred* as a SPECIALLY SELECTED RATING, has been promoted to the rank of Temp. Midshipman, RNVR." It was signed by the Training Commander and an Instructor Commander and "Approved" by the Captain. The very same Captain, whose signature on the certificate was illegible, then gave the traditional farewell talk, urging them to keep up the traditions of an honourable service etc., etc. Sam was still young and naïve enough to feel a surge of pride at becoming a Naval Officer, albeit the lowest of the low. There was no gold ring on his sleeve. Instead there were the Red RNVR Midshiman's Patches on his lapel.

Officer Cadets passing out photo, HMS *King Alfred*, 1942
Sam is eighth from right, second row down

As various instructors stepped on to the podium to deliver their own brand of farewell homily, Sam found his mind wandering. What did he really know? He thought that he could probably anchor a battleship without too much difficulty. He never understood why he was taught to do that and had come to the conclusion it was included in the curriculum because some enthusiastic instructor had made a scale model to please the Captain. Similarly he knew he could direct the guns in a sea battle with enemy cruisers and battle wagons. He had been fortunate enough to be "told off" to attack a target on the simulator when a visiting "High Admiral" made a surprise visit to the section. More by luck than good management he straddled the enemy ship, then scored a direct hit, and was complimented, much to his bewilderment. He had learned the tactic on the beach at Coverack when shying stones at a tin can bobbing in the waves and was sometimes rewarded with a resounding clang when a hit was made after adjusting the strength of his throw. In addition, he had learned the drill for controlling a burial party and performing the slow march with funereal finesse. For some reason or other he had not been taught how to manage a burial at sea but he already knew something about that due to his time on the *Pathfinder*.

Sam was startled out of his reverie when the parade was called to attention and they were marched off to some staging erected for the purpose of taking a panoramic group photograph. The photos were paid for in advance and after a meal they were finally dismissed and instructed to collect the "mail". In each man's pigeon hole was a letter stating what his first appointment was to be. Some of the high flyers were being sent straight to Greenwich for courses in astro-navigation, others were going to a variety of ships. Sam was to go to HMS *Helder*, a stone frigate in St. Osyth near Brightlingsea in Essex, for training in Combined Operations. He knew then why he had passed. He was to be cannon fodder! As far as he could remember he had never even seen an assault landing craft but he privately heaved a sigh of relief as he knew he would probably be able to handle small craft, and being fairly fit he looked forward to the prospect of joining an arm of the Royal Navy which was gaining a reputation for "derring do", or at least that was what the propagandists were putting across to the general public. Of course, he couldn't see himself as a naval commando but he was happy to go along with what Their Lordships wanted; not that he could choose, anyway.

Leave passes and railway warrants were collected and before long Sam and his friends were outside *King Alfred*, having decided once more to splash out on a taxi to take them to the station. The green suitcases were loaded in the space at the front of the cab and the young officers piled in the back. In that confined space Bill Porritt decided he could no longer suppress the build-up of wind in his lower region and let off a "rip snorter" which drew cries of protest in time-honoured naval fashion. Bill was unrepentant and took the "heat" out of the situation by calmly stating he wanted to discover if "officers' farts were odourless". Everyone joined in the laughter which followed and added a few choice adjectives into the bargain. The taxi driver laughed loudest of all, probably in the hope that he might get a decent tip from the young, newly-created "gentlemen" if he admired their lavatorial humour.

When they pulled into Brighton Station the young officers piled out in the way that matelots do when they are going on leave, laughing and joking while slinging their kit about. At least they had no hammocks to contend with, but in their new status they felt obliged to add some small change to the fare the taxi driver wanted. They made their way noisily to the Victoria-bound platform and settled somewhat diffidently in a first-class carriage of the Southern Railway. No one else came into their compartment so they continued larking about, chatting in loud tones and enjoying the spaciousness of the carriage.

At Victoria they separated, promising to keep in touch but not exchanging addresses. They were too excited to think about such mundane things. Sam and Dick took the Circle Line to Paddington and the others went Euston and Liverpool Street. The journey down to Gwinear Road passed in a haze for Sam. Neither he nor Dick was in the mood for formal conversation. Both were rather overawed at the enormity of the task that lay ahead. After all, they were not even twenty years old. As if by agreement they settled down to read the evening paper and barely spoke. Sam was wondering how he would cope if one of his fellow first-class passengers struck up a conversation. He needn't have worried. The prosperous-looking businessman opposite him was engrossed in *The Times* and true to form seemed unaware of the existence of the lower mortals travelling with him. Sam couldn't repress a giggle when he remembered the anecdote one of the teachers at Helston told his class about the gentleman in a First Class railway carriage being informed he had dropped ash on his trousers, who responded with the astonishing statement, "Your back pocket has been alight for ten minutes but I haven't interfered with you!" Sam wondered if the businessman's aloofness might be attributed to his reading a lowly evening paper, but he wasn't unduly worried. He was on his way home, he was a "new person", but it was not long before he closed his eyes and reverted to his favourite train journey pastime of allowing the train to "talk" to him. It declared, "We're going on leave, We're going on leave, We're going on leave, _ _ _ _, _ _ _ _, _ _ _ _, _ _ _ _." His dream sequence was interrupted by the dining car attendant sliding the compartment door open to announce, "Dinner is now being served." Sam and Dick looked at each other and they both nodded assent simultaneously. They got up and made their way to the nearby dining car. It was a totally new experience for Sam but Dick had dined on trains with his parents a few times so Sam knew he was in good hands. Of course, neither one could really afford the meal but they had been paid before leaving *King Alfred* and decided to splash out in celebration.

When they entered the restaurant car and smelled food they realised how hungry they were. Fortunately the fatherly steward recognised their need and gave them extra helpings with each course regardless of rationing. By the time they returned to their compartment they were full of "bonhomie", so to speak. Sam promptly went to sleep, no longer plagued with doubts about his situation. The next thing he knew was Dick shaking him by the shoulder in order to say "Cheerio". He had been appointed to "Guz", as they both knew it. Dick was not looking forward to being a "snottie", as Midshipmen were called in the Royal Navy, in such an impersonal place as HMS *Drake* in Devonport, but he comforted himself with the knowledge that it would give him a breathing space before being given a sea-going appointment. Being young, the two friends were quite offhand in their leave taking, in spite of all that they had been through together, confident they would run across each other in the course of time. In fact, they never saw each other again. From time to time in the postwar years, Sam would make a mental note to set about tracing Dick Davis, but that was as far as he got.

Left to himself, Sam dozed off again and it was Plymouth before he woke up. He found it strange to be in a First Class compartment with only three seats on each side but did not take long to become accustomed to the capacious compartment and in a vague sort of way regretted there was no First Class carriage to carry him from Gwinear Road to Helston. When he finally set foot on familiar territory in Coverack he was again somewhat disappointed that no one seemed to notice he was now in fore-and-aft rig. On previous leaves some of his fellow villagers had insinuated that it was strange to see him dressed in the square rig of an Able Seaman despite the fact that he had been to the "Secatary" School, for most boys who had attended the Grammar School in Helston wore what they termed "livery", the superior fore-and-aft rig of a Writer or Artificer with a peak cap and black buttons. Sam wisely decided not to draw attention to his change in fortunes and simply smiled to himself at the gentle irony of the situation.

Naturally, when he got off the bus in Coverack, with his spanking new green "pusser"'s suitcase in lieu of a kit bag, Sam was proud to walk through the village. A few villagers greeted him with the usual, "Hello, Sam, home again?" in the tone of voice which seemed to imply, "You're lucky to be back so soon after the last leave!" Perhaps Sam was wrong in his interpretation but sensitivity was an integral part of his Celtic make up and he felt he was being controlled by his inner spirit or whatever one might like to call it. On the other hand, when he had phoned to say he was coming home, his mother was so overjoyed at the thought of her "baby" son arriving and in his new uniform to boot that she announced she was going to Helston to meet him. That was the last thing Sam wanted - it would be so embarrassing hearing Mary telling everyone about his promotion - so he mollified her by saying he would rather have a hot meal all ready for him when he arrived.

True to form, as soon as he opened the front door of the cottage in Sunny Cove, the delightful aroma of hot pasties greeted him. They had just been taken out of the oven and placed on top of the slab to keep warm, with a clean white cloth covering them to keep them moist. Mary was slightly disappointed when Sam took off his new greatcoat and revealed his red RNVR Midshipman's lapel patches instead of a gold ring on his sleeve. He explained that he would have to wait until he was twenty before "Their Lordships" would grant him a commission as a Sub. Lieutenant. Sam couldn't wait to get his new "clobber" off. The unfamiliar stiff collar was chafing his neck and he longed for the freedom his seaman's jersey gave him, so after he had finished what he always described on the first night of his leave as "the most wonderful meal I have ever tasted", he announced he was going to change and go down to the harbour for a while. His father stated he would like to go for a stroll as well, so after Sam had hung his uniform in the familiar rickety wardrobe in his tiny bedroom, he put on his old trousers and his seaman's jersey and joined his father who was waiting outside, somewhat selfishly leaving Mary to do the dishes. She was so happy to have Sam back "safe and sound", as she termed it, that in truth she did not realise her "men" had not shown their appreciation of another beautiful meal by clearing up afterwards. Later, by way of compensation, she was to enjoy Sam's description of his bleak Brighton billet. That little bit of gossip was to enable her to relate with glee to her local friends what strange ways the "up-country" folk have compared with the welcome given to service men and women stationed in Coverack.

When father and son returned from their companionable stroll through the blacked out village, Mary was sitting darning socks, her glasses perched on the end of her nose as usual. Sam often pictured this scene when he was away from home. He began making a cup of tea and his mother asked him how he had got on in the billet in Brighton.

"It's funny you should ask," said Sam. "I was about to tell you about Miss Harrison and her mother. Actually they lived in Hove, not too far from HMS *King Alfred*."

When the tea was ready to pour, Mary produced some saffron buns.

"Goodness me," said Sam. "Where did you get saffron?"

"I'm afraid it's Ersatz," replied Mary, proudly saying her newly acquired bit of wartime German, "but it's not too bad. It's not being imported in wartime but there are plenty of crocuses growing here - I can't think why someone hasn't started a business."

"It's probably because the drying process is too complicated," said Sam. "Anyway, I must admit this bun is some 'andsome and I'm still leary."

"I don't know how you can be hungry after that great pasty," laughed Mary, "but you can have mine. Saffron buns give me indigestion if I eat them just before going to bed."

"Oh, thanks Mum," beamed Sam. "You'll have a crown in glory."

"I don't think there's much chance of that," said Mary. "The Wesleyans have made it quite clear I committed a mortal sin by opening the tea room on Sundays. I don't know where they think the RAF boys are going to get a cup of tea in Coverack on a Sunday. I do it to stop them going down to the Paris."

"Well," said Sam, "you ought to give the Harrisons a few lessons in hospitality." Sam launched into his tale of woe about his billet which he shared with Dick Davis. He explained that they were compulsorily lodged with the middle-aged spinster and her ancient mother. That didn't exactly endear the two sailors to the genteel ladies. They slept in the dining room downstairs because of the air raids. There was a serving hatch opening into the hallway and it was used to pass the dishes through when meals were carried to the dining room from the kitchen at the back of the house.

When the two friends came in at night, the hatch would slide open with a bang and Miss Harrison would poke her head through, curlers and all, and say, "Mind you bar the door before you go upstairs. You can't be too careful these days." She never said "Good evening", or wished them "Good night", but slammed the hatch shut before the boys had a chance to reply. Sam went on to explain to his mother that they were not allowed to have a bath because the two ladies couldn't get enough coke for the boiler, so they had to do a "strip-wash". On Sunday mornings they were supplied with a bowl of hot water each for their weekly dhobi. That was the only time they were allowed in the kitchen, in order to get the extra hot water which Miss Harrison heated on the kitchen range. After doing the washing they were permitted to go out into the back garden to hang out the clean clothes to dry. Of course, as Sam explained, he and Dick found all these petty restrictions highly amusing. The two ladies must have heard some pretty imaginative tales about sailors as the old lady hardly ever appeared and Miss Harrison, who was obviously dominated by her mother, was always called back to their living quarters if she spent more than a couple of minutes chatting to the boys. It was as if mother was afraid her daughter would be violated by the nasty rough sailors! "Mind you," said Sam, "she did have quite an attractive light grey moustache!"

"Oh, Sam," chuckled his mother, "I hope you weren't rude to her."

"Of course I wasn't," replied Sam. "We both felt sorry for the two old dears and often slipped them a bar of nutty or some pusser's soap. At first they wouldn't accept our offerings, as if they were afraid we had some sinister motive in giving them a little present, but they eventually accepted, saying 'Thank you' over and over again until it was quite embarrassing."

"I'm some glad you did that," said his mother. "Perhaps they will be more hospitable to the next lot of lads who are billeted on them. I'm pleased you didn't write and tell me about the digs - I would have been worried sick."

"That's why I didn't mention it," laughed Sam. "Anyway, that's enough of that. How about another saffron bun, Mum, or are you going to be another Miss Harrison?"

"As a matter of fact I was saving the rest for tomorrow, but as it's your first night home you might as well fill yourself up. Do you think I ought to write Mrs Harrison to thank her for lodging you?"

"No fear," said Sam. "She might take it the wrong way. I think she thought we were 'working class', which we are, and to be honest she looked down on us and was really surprised when we behaved like ordinary mortals. No, Mum, leave it. There's no point. The Navy will thank her at the end of the war for her war effort!"

At that, they decided it was late and got ready for bed. Sam couldn't resist teasing his mother by adding that because the digs were not very comfortable, Dick and he went to the pub round the corner every night and came "home" singing rude songs out loud.

"Oh, Sam!" wailed Mary. "You didn't?" She looked at Sam's face and realising he was kidding, gave him a kiss and said, "Go to bed, you naughty boy."

"Yes, Miss Harrison," said Sam, and dashed up the stairs before she could retaliate.

The next day was occupied in "duty" visits to grandparents, uncles and aunts, etc. Sam was so pleased to be able to walk through the village in his old clothes and settle in to the comfortable Coverack daily life, being treated as one of the local lads instead of having to adjust to the mood of the moment as he had felt obliged to do at *King Alfred*. In the evening, Sam and his father went out again after a delicious supper of raw fry and bacon. Once more, Mary had worked a miracle and added a generous helping of bacon to the potatoes which George had grown in the back garden, with the help of some manure from the hen house. Sam felt it wise not to enquire where his mother had obtained the bacon. He knew that fishermen were allowed an extra ration as they went to sea in the early hours and it was felt they were entitled to a second breakfast when they landed the catch of the day an hour or so before noon. Privately he thought his mother had been given some extra rashers by one of the fishermen in return for treating an injured hand or looking after boils which the fisher folk were prone to get after handling "spiky" species which left their poisons embedded in the skin.

There was no one about, that night, except the Home Guard sentries strategically placed close to the grandly named Paris pub. The building was not a copy of some mythical "auberge": it had been rebuilt early in the twentieth century after a liner of that name had been wrecked on Lowland Point, which may have owed its Cornish name (Holan Point) to the existence of a Romano-British salt works. After the traditional, "All right un, Cap'n?" addressed to George, who replied with the usual, "Ess you," father and son went on their way, chatting amiably about recent village happenings. Just before they got back to the house in Sunny Cove, George told Sam how pleased he and his mother were to know that he had "passed out" as he put it. Always a man of few words, George had found it difficult to say what was in his mind, but when he placed his huge hand on Sam's shoulder and squeezed so hard that Sam feared he had dislocated it, Sam knew his father's underlying strength of feeling. Nothing more was ever said on the subject, but it was all Sam wanted to know. He knew his mother would be boring her friends about his achievement for some time to come, but he valued his father's praise more highly as he knew it had taken the long walk in the blacked-out village for his father to decide when to tell him how proud he was feeling.

One morning Sam's mother handed him a letter addressed to Midshipman Sam Exelby, RNVR. It was marked CONFIDENTIAL, underlined for good measure and headed "By Command of the Commissioners for Executing the Office of Lord High Admiral of the United Kingdom, &c." It read like a verse from Gilbert and Sullivan's *HMS Pinafore* but it was deadly serious and went on to state, "The Lords Commissioners of the Admiralty hereby appoint you Temporary Midshipman, RNVR of His Majesty's Ship *King Alfred* addl. Your appointment is to take effect from the 29th January 1943." It was signed by H.V. Markham, "By Command of their Lordships at Admiralty, S.W.1". Fortunately Sam knew it was only a formality and that he had to report to HMS *Helder* at St. Osyth on the River Colne in Essex, but his mother was very impressed and faintly disappointed when he told her she could keep it as a souvenir. Fortunately she kept it safe until some years later Sam needed it to prove a date, when she triumphantly produced it from the box in which she kept all the "treasures" belonging to her children. She knew that it was bound to be asked for in due course and she would be expected to produce it despite the fact that Sam, with the confidence of inexperienced youth, could see no use for it at the time.

True to established form, the leave in Coverack came to an end just as Sam was slipping back into the way of life he had known before he joined the navy. The old magic still worked: he felt at one with his fellow villagers and had no desire whatever to go back across the Tamar. Of course, Sam knew the ostrich-like mentality seeping into his subconscious had to be eradicated and so yet again he found himself speeding towards Brunel's bridge spanning the Tamar, having drifted through the process of packing and leave taking in what contemporary film directors are pleased to call a "dream sequence".

CHAPTER FIFTEEN

COMBINED OPERATIONS TRAINING

HMS *Helder*, the Combined Operations training ship, turned out to be a "stone frigate" which was a requisitioned holiday camp of wooden chalets in the village of St. Osyth, near Brightlingsea in Essex. Sam didn't quite know what to make of it but he knew the best plan was to wait and watch and get settled. No one told him what was going on but a pattern emerged as the programme began.

There was a strong emphasis on the physical side of the course, as might be expected. Route marches, assault courses over rough terrain, scaling high walls, each section culminating in the crossing of the local River Colne hand over hand on a wire hawser. Failure to manage the final effort meant dropping into the freezing cold water. The penalty was having to dhobi one's boiler suit in the evening, clean the rifle which had been submerged in the Colne and usually had mud embedded in the barrel, and of course boots had to be boned until they shone, ready for the next day. Sam, like many of his fellow officers, got first-hand experience of the ignominy of failure but in due course managed to complete each day's activities without falling into the river. Towards the end of the course officers were issued with revolvers, which were known to be pretty ineffective weapons in combat situations but were lighter than the .303 rifles and consequently made the final Tarzan-like activity less daunting for the fledgling officers.

Sea-Training Exercises went on in parallel with the assault courses and unarmed combat sessions. The latter were highly physical, of course, and Sam learned much which was to give him self-confidence for the future when facing tricky situations. Sam was highly amused when one rather stroppy PTI invited anyone who wished to come and throw him on his back. A New Zealander came forward and threw the Instructor over his shoulder with apparent ease. Everyone present was delighted as the Petty Officer had been literally throwing his weight about. He was, fortunately, unaware that the young Kiwi officer was a devotee of Jujitsu and capable of countering the moves of the rather supercilious PTI.

The landing craft were LCAs - assault "boats", powered by two Chrysler v-8 engines, plus a variety of LCMs which as the initials imply were Mixed or Miscellaneous and were used for carrying troops or half track vehicles or mobile Bofors Guns. A whole new code of signals had to be learned as landing craft could not be controlled by the "big ship" method of flag hoists or complicated commands in Morse. In spite of that, when Sam was posted to a Landing Craft Flotilla at a later date a stubborn Royal Marine Captain, refusing to compromise, rigged up a miniature mast on his LCM and used conventional flag hoists to control his flotilla by day, risking the wrath of senior officers. Fortunately for him, most of the senior officers were ignorant of the Landing Craft system of manoeuvring signals, though nominally in positions of authority, so he escaped serious censure and was much admired for cocking a snook at the new "establishment". Unfortunately the brave Captain of Marines was killed in the D Day landings and was greatly missed by all who knew and admired him.

Sam was perturbed regarding the new system of signalling in that he had spent a considerable time in learning the Naval Alphabetical Flags and the Special Flags together with the Pendants, only to find his hard-won knowledge redundant. He had some sympathy with Captain Bird who considered the current system adequate, but being essentially a "big ship" man the Captain probably did not appreciate at first the problems of communications from sea level, as it were, when in a Landing Craft which was rolling and pitching in breaking seas. There was a Day System and a Night System. By day, one needed a supply of flags, if in the Flotilla Leader's Craft. Flag A meant Line Ahead. By night it was a series of As in Morse with a blue or white light. Loose Formation was Flag A waved from side to side or AL in Morse at night. Sam could not help smiling at the signal for loose formation as that was generally the order of the day during training as the Coxswains were learners too and could not hold Line Ahead unless the conditions were flat calm. Deploy to Port was Flag P held vertically. P was a red triangular Flag and pretty obvious. Deploy to Starboard was a green burgee, again quite logical, and by night Port Deployment was signalled by a steady red light, and Starboard Deployment was a steady green light. There were many other signals to be learned and Sam wondered whether they would be practical in action, approaching an enemy beach with bullets flying about. His Flotilla Officer had a signal of his own which was used pretty frequently during training. When a manoeuvre was badly executed, Lieutenant Commander Rankin would semaphore "P as P". It did not take a genius to translate it as "Poor as Piss". Sam saw to it that he did not get too many of those unofficial reprimands! In the event when it came to real live landings, the Flotillas were later issued with American Walky-Talkies or Talky-Walkies as the non-British Allies termed them. Night Signals were transmitted by infra-red lamps which were read by using special goggles or binoculars. Everyone was much relieved that the "Heath Robinson" Codes were abandoned in favour of Plain Language radio communication and infra-red lights. The range of the Walkie-Talkies was only about three miles so there was little danger of the signals being intercepted by the enemy.

When Sam was considered reasonably competent by a senior officer he was put in charge of three LCAs which had Leading Seamen as Coxswains. Long hours were spent on the River Colne both by day and by night until everyone was pronounced proficient. Then followed realistic exercises with troops on board and the "enemy" tossing fairly harmless explosive amatol charges all over the place as they touched down after putting out kedge anchors so that they could quickly haul themselves off the shingle and retire for another load of "pongoes". Sam had experience of landing allied troops and found the language problem inhibiting on some occasions. One enthusiastic Czech soldier misunderstood the order to lower the door prior to landing and dashed off while the craft was in about a fathom and a half, or ten feet of water. Fortunately Sam's crewman on the stern of the landing craft managed to fish him out with a boat hook as the poor fellow couldn't swim with all the heavy equipment he was carrying. Night exercises were not popular as it was well nigh impossible to consult charts without showing the light of a torch, so one had to memorise the area of operations. Sam found his experience in small boats in Coverack a great advantage and didn't make too many serious errors. Part of his training consisted in having to act as "stoker", sitting between the two hot petrol engines and responding to the primitive engine-room telegraphs. It was not a pleasant experience but it had the desired effect, making Sam appreciate the difficulties his own stokers had when doing a landing. Of course, it would have been better if the landing craft had remote control engine-room telegraphs but at that stage they were still designed in the traditional manner. When it came to the "real thing", Sam had nothing but admiration for the men who controlled the engines while sitting in a confined space surrounded by highly flammable fuel tanks which would fry them alive if they were hit on the way in to the enemy beach.

Most of the young officers had become aware that they were being offered up as cannon fodder so that the long-awaited landing on the European mainland would be a success. It was a subject that was never mentioned but it resulted in everyone being determined to enjoy life as it came. There were some very lively nights in the Ward Room, sometimes ending in a "conga" which entailed doing a forward roll through the serving hatch into the kitchen and threading one's way through the corridors back into the Ward Room where the volunteer pianist was banging out the tune, accompanied by a handful of "portly" inebriated singers who had wisely decided not to join the line of young men doing the conga via the serving hatch! In retrospect it all seemed rather puerile behaviour but at the time it had the desired therapeutic effect of letting off steam after a gruelling day on the cold Colne. To be truthful, of course, most of the officers were not "gentlemen" in the naval sense of the word; the more senior regular officers there wisely withdrew or remained, seemingly unaware of what was going on, stoically drinking gin after gin to ease the pain! They had probably decided that HMS *Helder* was just a temporary measure to meet the "exigencies of the Service" and were waiting for the war to end so that they could continue their relatively peaceful lives in the manner to which they were accustomed. Sam did not philosophise about the situation. He joined in the fun without stopping to consider what his beloved teetotal mother would say. Each day ended in near physical exhaustion and after the "shenanigans" he was only too happy to seek oblivion in his bunk to gather energy for the next day's activities.

One strange effect of his training at HMS *Helder* was that the officers and ratings as individuals rapidly became blurred in Sam's mind. In later years he likened them to convivial fellow passengers such as one meets on a cross-Channel ferry - pleasant characters with whom to while away an hour or two, but not memorable. It was possibly due to the fact that Sam's sights were already fixed on his first operational appointment, despite his not knowing what it was going to be. One thing was certain: he would not be landed on the bridge of an ocean-going destroyer not knowing what was expected of him. At least he felt reasonably confident that he would manage to do the duties of an officer in a Landing Craft Flotilla preparing for a landing in France.

When the training was completed to the satisfaction of the instructors of HMS *Helder*, the Navy didn't surprise Sam, who by this time had learned to expect the unexpected. He found himself retained to train a fresh batch of sailors drafted into Combined Ops. His assignment was to take the "class" round the assault course and show the rather unwilling recruits how to scale walls, crawl under barbed wire, climb ropes and go hand over hand across the uninviting, chilly Colne. Sam was determined not to repeat the first disastrous attempt he made at crossing the stream. He still remembered vividly how his wet, muddy hands were so slippery and cold that he was obliged to let go and fell flat on his back, complete with a pack on his back and a rifle slung across his chest. His tin hat chin strap almost choked him as he struggled to force his way through the muddy water, soaked to the skin, back to the bank in order to have another go at crossing by wire. It was a salutary lesson. Whether it was fear or pride that drove him on he didn't know, but he made it and it was not until he returned to his cabin later on that he discovered his hands were torn and still bleeding. Before making the second attempt he had rubbed his hands fiercely on his dungaree trousers in order to "burn" them dry, so to speak, then he grasped the wire hawser firmly and went relatively slowly, hand over hand, resisting the temptation to slide down to the lowest point. By doing that he was able to allow his feet to hang in mid air without kicking wildly as he did at the first attempt. It was the kicking movement that made him let go in the first instance. He got to the centre and by a superhuman effort pulled himself up to the post on the other side of the river. Practice makes perfect, as the saying goes, and indeed subsequent crossings became easier but still demanded every ounce of strength that Sam could muster. He was not quite sure why he was expected to do the Tarzan act because he considered that if he ever found himself in a situation where he had to cross a river on a wire, he would not be able to do it while being sniped at by the enemy. He did acknowledge that it was a good toughening-up exercise and wisely decided not to enter into a discussion on the Training Syllabus. When he himself was called upon to initiate the sailors to the assault course, he found himself copying the simulated wrath of his previous instructors in order to goad the trainees into making the necessary effort to cross the river! Of course, he felt he had to demonstrate the technique but as an instructor he didn't carry a pack or a rifle, and wore a balaclava instead of a steel helmet, so he managed to get across without dropping into the "drink".

At HMS *Helder* it was essential to have sound footwear for the daily route marches. Sailors are given a regular allowance of money so that they can keep their kit in good order. Inevitably it transpired that some of the sailors had not maintained their boots properly, and after a few miles of carrying a pack and .303 rifle, complete with steel helmet plus a respirator strapped to the chest, matelots could be observed limping badly as the column marched through local hamlets. Sometimes a middle-aged, sympathetic housewife would come out and place a chair on the pavement, inviting a "wounded" sailor to sit and rest. As officer in charge of the training class, Sam had to go and explain that the situation was of the sailor's own making. On one memorable occasion a worthy female villager, probably imagining her own son in a similar situation, refused point blank to allow the man to continue the march. Sam, mindful of the need to maintain good public relations, was obliged to leave his man resting on the chair and go to the village kiosk and arrange for a 15 cwt. truck to collect the hapless matelot. He did not inform the caring lady that his man would be brought before the Officer of the Watch and charged with "wilfully incapacitating himself" in order to avoid carrying out his duty! In practice, the "skates", as the law breakers were termed in the navy, were given a stern warning and required to produce a sound pair of "pusser" boots within so many days, or face a serious charge. Sam himself saw to it that his own boots were "tapped" by Henry Mundy, Coverack's redoubtable shoemaker, who was currently spending much of his time as a very efficient Sergeant in the village Home Guard, and who knew how important it was to have boots which could stand up to any kind of maltreatment such as a fiendish assault course devised by Combined Ops. professionals!

The sea training was overseen by permanent instructors but it was in Sam's interest to "spot" potential coxswains. He began his quest by asking simply if anyone present had handled a small boat before coming into Combined Operations. Of course, it was traditional among the sailors to volunteer for nothing as Petty Officers had a habit of speaking in hyperbole and had been known to call for volunteers who could play the piano and having got them, promptly sent them on a mission to lift a grand piano on to the stage! However, Sam did get a few willing hands and gave each man a trial run in the armoured cockpit of an Assault Landing Craft (LCA). It was tempting to grab the wheel when the would-be coxswain made a mistake but Sam resisted his natural reaction and lived to regret his patience when there was an almighty crash due to an order being misinterpreted when the flotilla was executing a starboard turn at speed. Of course, LCAs were only capable of doing ten knots or so when fully loaded with infantry and all their equipment, but the damage was considerable, and Sam had an uncomfortable interview with the Commander afterwards. Collisions were expected in a training flotilla, but Sam was informed forcibly that he should have anticipated the possibility, seeing that he had an inexperienced seaman at the helm. Sam agreed ruefully, after being informed by the Commander that in the days of sailing ships helmsmen often mistook larboard for starboard and so the word port was introduced to avoid such a calamity. There was no real excuse for the "cock-up", as the Commander rather indelicately put it.

Training in LCMs was easier. An LCM was a medium type landing craft designed as a "maid of all work". Training a seaman to be a coxswain of an LCM was less difficult in that one could stand on the stern beside the coxswain and grab the helm if need be. The craft caught the wind easily and needed a lot of rudder to manoeuvre successfully, especially when loaded. In truth it was like handling a large floating matchbox, so when loaded with a Bofors gun the "pongoes" had to be warned not to train their gun outwards as when the barrel was abeam the craft became unbalanced and would swiftly heel over and capsize. Sam didn't want another embarrassing interview with the long-suffering Commander so he hammered home his warnings in true Navy fashion, adding that even if they were attacked by enemy aircraft the gun was not to be fired but remain locked in position. Mindful of his *King Alfred* training, he wisely refrained from using colourful adjectives which would have added weight to his words. In a sense his reticence was unnecessary as he carried Czech and Polish soldiers much of the time and his warnings went largely unheeded. Bearing this in mind he usually went to the Bofors himself and locked it in the fore and aft position, miming the warning that the gun was not to be touched by shaking his head vigorously and drawing his finger across his throat in dramatic fashion.

After about six weeks in the role of instructor Their Lordships deemed it time for Sam to move on. He was fully expecting to be sent to an operational unit where training would be more intensive as it would be working up in readiness for a landing. In true Navy fashion it was not to be. He was appointed to a base in the Albert Dock in Liverpool. On arrival he learned his new duties consisted of "watches" of twenty-four hours followed by twenty-four hours off duty. He wondered how he was going to be able to stay awake for twenty-four hours at a time. He gathered his work included mooring landing craft as they were unloaded from Liberty Ships which were bringing them across the Atlantic in large numbers. They were to be moored in "trots" in the dock prior to being checked by shipwrights and mechanics before being sent to the south coast in readiness for the invasion of Europe. Sam had to ensure that the sentries on the jetty were ready to prevent any would-be saboteurs from getting on board to cause damage and that the landing craft remained afloat. Although in theory the boats were ready for use, it was well known that in some instances they were not seaworthy, having been constructed in haste in American shipyards by people employed on piece work and therefore not exactly devoted to producing a high standard of workmanship.

Sam was accommodated in a requisitioned girls' boarding school in Dingle which was situated near the terminus of the Overhead Railway which transported workers to various parts of the widespread docks. He was amused by a printed notice on the wall of his bedroom which read, "If you require a Mistress during the night ring the bell." Sam was reliably informed by a fellow officer that when the Navy first occupied the school, bells were ringing non-stop until the novelty wore off and the wires were disconnected! The twenty-four-hour shifts did prove to be very tiring as Sam had thought, in spite of the fact that a camp bed was provided in the duty office for use during the "small hours" when, in theory, there was little demand for his services. There were occasional sporadic bombing raids during the "small hours" when shrapnel from the anti aircraft guns sometimes went through the fragile decks of the landing craft. Sam had to organise pumps to clear the inrush of water and get the duty shipwrights to plug the holes after he had put extra lashings from the bollards and the craft alongside to prevent them from sinking before temporary repairs could be effected. It was Sam's introduction to what the Americans were to call "friendly fire". His fellow sailors had less complimentary expressions to describe the actions of the local anti-aircraft batteries!

On occasions Sam needed to go through the Mersey Tunnel in a 15 cwt. truck with his duty crew to deal with landing craft on the other side of the river. When he first did the journey he was shocked to see crude slogans daubed on the walls of the buildings saying, "Stop the war." His Petty Officer attributed the protests to local Irish immigrants. Sam had not considered that possibility but he could understand how poor people who had lost the little they had, and could see no way out of their plight, were unable to take any more and just wanted to be left alone in their misery. One of the Coverack residents had shouted to his father, "Why don't they go and bomb the English?" after her house had been so badly damaged by the low-flying FW 190s that George arranged for her to go and stay with Sam's grandmother Kate Exelby until the fisherman's cottage was made habitable again. Although the bombing of a seemingly sleepy Cornish fishing village was inexcusable in the eyes of the residents, Sam learned later that the Wrens' ops. room attached to the hotel on the headland was involved in directing Atlantic convoys to avoid concentrations of U-boats, so in German eyes there may have been some justification for the attack.

At first Sam did very little in his off-duty hours, except sleep and eat. As time went on, however, he took to going on cycle rides, visiting local "beauty spots" such as West Kirby. He was pleasantly surprised by the proximity of attractive places near the busy, battle-scarred port. Of course he was impressed by the grandeur of business houses such as the Liver Buildings and he often stood on the nearby pier to admire the seamanship of the Birkenhead Ferries as they came alongside in the swiftly flowing Mersey. He, himself, was to experience the hazards of berthing while battling against the tide! When he was "flush", which only occurred shortly after pay-day, he would visit the Adelphi Hotel with some of his colleagues. It was rumoured that a half-crown tip was expected if you handed in your uniform cap for safe keeping before finding a table, so Sam and his equally impecunious friends kept their caps securely tucked under their arms in the way of naval officers visiting the lower deck when off duty. Of course, the young officers only visited the hotel for the rather dubious kudos gained by being able to state they "knew" the Adelphi when conversing with toffee-nosed types in the Base Wardroom!

In the fulness of time, Sam began to feel competent in his ability to manage the trots, organise sentries, deal with emergencies and generally supervise the Combined Operations sector of the Albert Dock and find his way round the jetties, but then the inevitable happened. He was warned that in a couple of weeks he would be appointed to Preston Docks where he would be in sole charge with a Petty Officer and a dozen hands. The set-up was similar to the one in Liverpool but obviously on a smaller scale. At first Sam thought he was being given the "heave-ho" as they say in the Navy because someone didn't approve of the way he managed the Albert Dock when he was on duty. He confided his thoughts to a fellow Midshipman named Galloway but Douglas assured Sam that it wasn't so, as he had heard a buzz in the Ward Room that the Lieutenant in charge of the Dock had decided Sam would be able to do the job in spite of his youth and inexperience. Sam and Doug had been ashore together a few times, including a "prestigious" visit to the Adelphi, and although they were not close friends they got on well and trusted each other, so Sam was content to let the matter rest. He received written confirmation of his transfer a couple of days later when Lieutenant Ellis spotted him as he was entering the lecture room to hear Lieutenant Bruce

Belfridge give a talk entitled "Escaping from the enemy". The Lieutenant had a green stripe between the gold rings on his sleeve, indicating he was in the Special Branch. Sam was fascinated by the array of "gimmicks" which were issued to service personnel when they were liable to be taken prisoner so that they could effect an escape, and he began to wonder if Bruce knew something he didn't, as all the Combined Ops. Officers were present. The emergency ration kit, the size of a flat box of 50 cigarettes, contained a variety of concentrated foods which lacked bulk but were capable of sustaining anyone having to draw on reserves of strength in his efforts to evade capture or indeed escape from the enemy. There were even tablets to purify water for drinking, glucose sweets for energy and a small magnetic compass disguised as a black coat button. In true Naval fashion, the lecturer concentrated not on escaping from the Germans, which one would have expected, but on how to evade the Japanese. Everyone began to wonder if they were going to miss the landing in Europe and be sent to the Far East in the very near future. The possibility was made all the more real when the assembled officers were even advised on how to deal with a tiger should it be going along a jungle trail which they were following. It transpired that the best way was to step smartly aside and allow the beast to go on its way. Everyone laughed rather nervously at the thought. Sam, being Sam, never forgot how to identify human excreta in the jungle! It was stated that a man would simply sit on his haunches and evacuate in a "straight" pile. A woman, being of a nervous disposition, would be continually looking to the left, then the right for fear of being surprised in the act, so to speak, so the result tended to be coiled. Sam was never in a situation where this knowledge was of use to him, but in certain company, such as Royal Naval Association dinners, he found it unfailing in its attraction to his "RNA shipmates"!

After the lecture, the Base Commander took Sam on one side and told him he would be going to Preston at the end of the following week. He was to be responsible for the security of some hundred landing craft of all types. Most of them were being kept in a huge dock shed at the side of the basin where they would be hidden from enemy reconnaissance aircraft. Some were to be kept afloat for use when other barges, as the Commander termed them, would be sent to the dock via the River Ribble for maintenance and repairs prior to being stored in readiness for the landing in Europe. Sam was tempted to ask if they might indeed be destined for the Far East in view of the lecture he had just attended but on reflection he wisely refrained from being facetious. He learned that the technical work in Preston was being overseen by an Engineer Lieutenant who was in charge of a team of mechanics and shipwrights. Sam's main duties were to set sentries, look after the safety of all the landing craft and generally keep the place in good order. He was to liaise with the Dock Master regarding movement of craft on the Ribble and with the Docks Police concerning security measures taken. He was warned that as the craft were being stored on land there was a considerable fire risk and in view of the invasion being imminent, action might be taken by enemy agents or indeed dissident Irish immigrants who were employed in the area. Sentries were to be armed with live ammunition and there was a Guard Room for the duty watch which would work 24-hour shifts. The "troops" were billeted on civilians in the town and accommodation had been found for Sam in a street close to the dock basin. The Engineer Officer was already installed at the same address. An office was provided for Sam and it had a small bedroom attached for use when it was deemed necessary to remain in the docks over night. The Commander assured Sam he would soon get accustomed to the new routine and that if problems arose he could get in touch with Liverpool on a direct line, adding a rare compliment that he was pleased with the way Sam had managed his watches in the Albert Dock. The final remark was enough to convince Sam that he was not the victim of a plot to get rid of him but a genuine move to fill a new post. If he had known the significance of his appointment he would have kissed the Commander goodbye!

The appointed day came swiftly and Sam took leave of his fellow watch keepers at lunch time over a glass of India Pale Ale in the Ward Room at Dingle. Doug Galloway made him promise to look him up in Blackpool when he had some spare time; the others just uttered the usual platitudes of "ships that pass in the night" and they all expressed a wish to meet Sam again in the future, which was indeed uncertain, but being young they were confident it would happen one day. Fortunately the leave taking was not prolonged as a Petty Officer reported to the Ward Room that he had arrived from Preston and was ready to transport Sam to his new post.

The journey by road did not take long. Sam was struck by the fact that once they had left Liverpool they passed through some beautiful country-side. It gave the lie to the textbook descriptions of industrial wasteland in the North. After a while he quizzed the PO regarding the work at Preston. He was not very forthcoming, merely saying that there was plenty to do and the ratings were a pretty reasonable lot on the whole. Petty Officer

Holland was a "scouse" with a thick Liverpool accent. Sam guessed he did not approve of Combined Operations and would rather be at sea on a "proper" ship, so when Sam remarked that he found life in Liverpool quite strange after being on Atlantic Convoys, Henry Holland loosened up a little, and by the time they had arrived in the Landing Craft Shed the two of them were on friendly terms. Petty Officer Holland introduced him to the sailors who were in the Guard Room, showed him round the Basin and then took him to his billet where he was offered a welcome cup of tea and a home-made parkin by Mrs. Predin. She was a cheery, plump lady who made him feel very welcome, telling him not to be shy but ask for anything he needed, adding that she would do Sam's washing if he gave it to her every Monday morning before going to work. She then took Sam next door where he was to sleep. Mrs. Parker was a tall, upright old lady who greeted Sam in the way his Granny Exelby spoke, except that she had a strong Lancashire accent. She lost little time in telling Sam that she had worked in t'mill when a lass and that "young people nowadays don't know what real work is like." It was just like being back in Coverack, hearing the young being criticised for not "loustering"! Sam was left to unpack and informed that dinner would be at 6.30.

So this was Preston. Sam realised he knew very little about the town. His mother, being a Charles Dickens fan, had made sure he was aware of the novel *Hard Times*, which portrayed Preston in the name of Coketown. Dickens visited the manufacturing town in 1854 to get an impression of industrial unrest and the life of the workers in a cotton town of the north of England. He had described it as "... a town of unnatural red and black like the painted face of a savage". Sam had certainly noticed the red brick buildings as he travelled through the town but he did not find them unattractive and when he saw the River Ribble for the first time it was definitely not "purple with ill-smelling dye" as in the time of Dickens. However he could not dwell on such matters as he needed to get ready for the evening meal and wanted some time to reflect on the job which was to start early the next morning.

At 6.30 sharp, Sam said "Cheerio" to Mrs. Parker, who grudgingly gave him a key, "... in case they keep you talking till after my bedtime", and went through the gate which had been placed in the dividing hedge at the back of the house to facilitate easy access between the two houses. Sam knocked at the back door and Mrs. Predin called out cheerily, "Come in, Sam." She introduced him to her husband, Stanley, who had just arrived home from his work in the Town Hall, and to Engineer Lieutenant John Marshall, RNVR, who was in charge of the technical side of the Base. Sitting beside John was Mrs. Predin's son, a fair-haired lad of about 14 named Clifford, who acknowledged Sam with a cheeky grin but said nothing. Beside him sat his sister, Grace, who nodded shyly but like her brother didn't speak.

Sam sat down and waited to be served. Stanley and John were discussing the latest match at Preston North End and Sam realised with delight that while in Preston he might get a chance to see Tom Finney play. He joined in the conversation and was told that he would probably see Tom, who sometimes came down to the docks in the course of his work. While Stanley and John continued their conversation, Sam had the opportunity of observing Grace more closely. She was a petite, dark-haired, hazel-eyed vision of loveliness in the full flush of late teenaged beauty. When she smiled, her eyes would sparkle and half close, seemingly giving a promise of hidden delights to whoever dared win her favours. Unfortunately, she ignored Sam. His fellow billetee was a smooth-talking, blond-haired, blue-eyed Welshman. He monopolised the conversation at the dinner table, leaving Sam mute and miserable, yet giving Sam the opportunity of observing Grace at close quarters without her being aware of his scrutiny. Surely, thought Sam, this lovely girl couldn't be interested in this chap, who must be at least ten years older than she was, and they would have nothing in common, yet he had the knack of drawing her into the conversation and she replied animatedly when spoken to. Sam was in his late teens himself and soon to be promoted to Sub. Lieutenant when he attained the great age of 20. Without knowing it, he had already decided that he had to get to know Grace. It was a *coup de foudre.* He was bowled over, yet totally powerless. He had never been in that situation before and when the meal was over he beat a hasty retreat, muttering that he had an early start in the morning. When he got into bed he could not get Grace out of his mind and determined to work out a strategy which would get Grace to acknowledge his presence and enter into conversation with him.

The next day Sam had of necessity to concentrate on the job in hand. He had been ordered to get the landing craft ready for active service. To date he had had very little experience of negotiating rivers but he soon learned how to manage the currents and the shallows and enjoyed most of all whizzing round the basin, if that's the right word to describe moving about in a sort of "floating shoe box", which was how an unkind merchant seaman described an assault landing craft. Sam was mindful, of course, not to rock the coasters and small cargo boats which were tied up near the unloading bays. Almost every time he took to the water he had to handle a different type of landing craft and he revelled in the challenge. If only the lads in Coverack could see him now! He knew they would be jealous of the opportunities which came his way. In addition to the seamanship side of his work he had to organise a rota of sentries - he had been warned by the docks police there was a strong element of anti-British Irishmen in the local workforce, so it was incumbent upon him to put in force patrols to deter saboteurs from damaging the craft in his care. It was not easy to impress the matelots of the need to be vigilant as on the surface Preston appeared to be a relatively quiet haven, far removed from the dangers of ports such as Liverpool. The Commander of Albert Dock had advised him to make sure his sentries were thorough in their patrols round the huge covered area which housed the landing craft being made ready for shipment.

Sam knew all about sentry duty, having done quite a bit himself, including the guarding of the cadet establishment at Lancing, and had been apprised by his more experienced mates of the dodges which could be worked in order to make life easier for the duty guard. In view of this, Sam adopted a method of turning up at the Regulating Office at irregular intervals during the night and turning out the duty Petty Officer to go on the rounds of the dock complex.

One night, during a surprise visit, the sentry on duty was missing. Sam wondered if a saboteur had "done him in" as the Petty Officer had suggested. A preliminary search of the area revealed nothing and Sam was worried. He told the PO to cover the same ground again while he remained at the spot where the sentry was supposed to be at that particular time. It was a black, quiet night. Sam stood stock still, wondering what he should do next. He became aware of the sound of someone breathing quite heavily. He thought the worst and imagined his man was lying unconscious nearby. But where was he? The ground beneath the landing craft had already been checked so Sam climbed on to an LCS (Landing Craft Stretcher) to get a better vantage point. He looked down and there was his man. He was fast asleep with his rifle tidily placed on the thwart beside him. Gingerly, Sam picked up the rifle and placed it under the tarpaulin covering the stern and engine of the LCS, then he climbed down and stood waiting for the PO to return. When he arrived he quietly told by the PO what had happened and together they awakened the slumbering seaman, who, of course, vehemently denied he had been asleep but couldn't account for the "missing" rifle.

This episode upset Sam not a little but he knew what had to be done and in due course the hapless sentry was sent to the NOIC (Naval Officer in Charge) at Liverpool for sentencing. This sleeping sentry saga served to enhance Sam's reputation for being "a bit of a sod" but ensured there were no further sleeping sentry incidents while he was in Preston. It was part of the price to be paid for being the officer in charge.

Winter nights on the River Ribble were very cold during 1943-1944. The hut allocated to the Combined Operations Naval Party was not only cold but damp also. This combination rendered the allocated fuel ration totally inadequate. One dark night - all nights were dark during wartime, except when an often unwelcome moon was shining - Sam arrived unexpectedly as was his wont, and told two mystified standby guards to follow him. During the previous forenoon Sam had spotted a handcart lying idly by, looking as if it belonged to no one in particular, so he wheeled it in between two "beached" landing craft where it could not be seen easily and placed two "spare" shovels in it. The seamen dutifully followed Sam to the hidden handcart and he motioned them to pull it along behind him. At the end of the landing craft shed stood a coal wagon awaiting the shunting engine. Without further ado the seamen nodded knowingly and began loading the handcart with coal, and when it was full the trio returned silently and in triumph to the Guard Room. The handcart was swiftly emptied and returned to its original position and the standby guards were soon having a good warm in the middle of the night. Later, when the buzz got round that the "Snotty" had purloined some extra fuel Sam's standing was enhanced, though he was still regarded as a "bit of a sod" and the matelots did not interpret his escapade as a sign of weakness or of pandering for popularity. They accepted it as an indication that Sam was aware of the irritating domestic problems of life in Preston Docks and was prepared to take a risk to remedy the situation.

Sam had been allocated a 15 cwt. truck for land transport. It was used for getting stores from the depot at Bamber Bridge, checking on the billets which the sailors had been given and paying courtesy visits to the local police who were always ready to help with security as were the Docks Police. As a general runabout in the basin and on the river, Sam used an LCS. It was a fairly fast wooden craft with provision for carrying six men on stretchers placed transversely between the thwarts or seats. Sam had not seen an LCS before he came to Preston and was surprised that he did not see many when on the invasion beaches of Normandy later on. Perhaps someone decided they were too expensive. When he took out members of the local Sea Cadet Corps on exercise on Sunday mornings - he had been prevailed on to help out by Detective Sergeant Campbell when visiting the Police Station on a goodwill mission - the Sergeant, a former Merchant Navy Officer, was an instructor to the SCC, and naturally wanted his boys to have hands-on experience of a "real" RN boat. Fortunately the LCS did resemble a boat rather than a floating shoe box so the boys were happy to go out in her as a treat after Sam had put them through their weekly rifle drill. In fact Sam was not very much older than the senior Cadets and got on well with them. The instructors were pleased to be relieved of some of the Sunday morning training duties and supplied Sam with coffee and cakes when he had finished while the boys had lemonade made from crystals which the Sergeant had managed to obtain from a friendly shopkeeper.

Sam's newly found confidence spilled over into his private life and encouraged him to approach Grace. To his delight she agreed to go to the cinema with him. As luck would have it, one of her favourite stars, Margaret Lockwood, was appearing in person to publicise *The Man in Grey* with James Mason and Phyllis Calvert. They sat side by side in the warm dark. Couples were snogging all round them. Greatly daring, Sam sought Grace's hand and held it. She made no attempt to withdraw it and he sat entranced through the rest of the picture. He didn't know what it was about but he enjoyed it immensely. The seemingly impossible had happened. That was all that mattered. This was the innocent beginning of a romance which was to last until some time after the war.

The Royal Navy has the unhappy knack of uprooting sailors and drafting them just when they are beginning to settle happily in their surroundings, be it on board ship or in a shore establishment. Sam's romance with Grace went from strength to strength. Her parents did not disapprove of the friendship and they were allowed to plan their spare time more or less as they wished, even to the extent of doing a spot of baby-sitting for some neighbours. Those evenings, alas all-too-few for Sam's liking, were a delight. The children scarcely ever disturbed them and if they did, Grace had the knack of comforting them and getting them back to sleep with the minimum of fuss, so they had the evenings to themselves. They would sit in the dark, patriotically saving fuel as urged by the Government, holding hands and whispering endearments to each other. It was utter bliss.

Sam decided he had to get to know Grace.

Their new-found happiness was rudely shattered one fine autumn morning when Sam received a signal ordering him to go on leave and report to the Commanding Officer of a Light Scout Car Company at Ballantrae, Ayrshire, in a fortnight's time. In spite of various panic phone calls, Sam could not discover why he was being sent to an Army unit, so he reluctantly set about preparing to obey orders and wondering how he was going to break the news to Grace.

In the event he took her to the cinema and under cover of darkness whispered his news. She remained very quiet, holding his hand with a strength he never knew she possessed. They walked home with their arms around each other and remained kissing outside the back door until Mrs. Predin rather pointedly opened the door and invited them in "out of the cold". While sipping a cup of hot cocoa, Grace told her mother the news and after a while Mrs. Predin stated she was tired and going up to bed, leaving the unhappy couple alone in the kitchen. Sam felt a milestone had been reached as this privilege had not been granted before.

The next day, Sam reluctantly set about getting his unit in order ready to hand over to his successor and at the end of the week was rather touched when one of the Wiremen presented him with an engraved cigarette lighter on behalf of the unit as a memento of his time at Preston. It was especially welcome as the man had made the lighter himself in the workshop used by the maintenance crew. Farewells were said and Sam remained at Grace's home for a couple of days before going down to Coverack as she had wangled some free time from her job in the Town Hall, her boss being sympathetic to the fact that her sailor boy was being drafted unexpectedly. Long hours were spent walking round the town and sitting in cafés, talking about the coming separation and making the most of the time together. All too soon, Sam found himself on the station platform saying goodbye to Grace and repeating a time-honoured promise, expected from all sailors about to depart for foreign shores, to be true to her. The train came in and after one last lingering kiss, Sam got in the carriage, bagged a seat and stood leaning out of the window waving goodbye to the diminutive figure on the platform. When she was out of sight, Sam stowed his kit in the rack, sat down, closed his eyes and suffered the pains of being lovesick for the first time in his life. He came to some time later when the train pulled in at Crewe where he and seemingly most of the passengers had to change for Penzance.

After a long wait at Crewe, Sam boarded the westcountry-bound train and managed to barge his way to a seat. He closed his eyes and once more revelled in the unaccustomed emotions experienced by all young men in his situation. As the train rattled on he remembered that he had read a book in Grace's house about the Jacobite soldiers who made a stand in Preston in 1715 when General Wills attacked them because they had proclaimed James III (the Old Pretender) to be their King. After an initial victory the Scots surrendered, knowing their cause to be lost, but in mitigation, excused their apparent lack of enthusiasm by declaring, "... the Ladys in this towne are so beautiful and so richly attired that the Gentlemen soldiers minded nothing but courting and feasting." Sam, for his part, smiled to himself at the thought of stopping the war and returning to the town which harboured one certain beautiful lady!

The leave in Coverack went by very quickly as leaves always did. The bright spots were when Grace's promised daily letters arrived. She never failed to write every day, nor did Sam. One afternoon, Sam could no longer stay away from the harbour so he went down to the cove and borrowed a motor boat. That was never a problem for a native of Coverack. In a village you are who you are, no pretensions, no swaggering to give the impression you are more important than you really are. You are a villager, known to everyone since you were born and accepted, to put it in Coverack terms, as "one of we".

Sam went out to sea, taking Ed Rickard with him. Ed was a retired farmer who lived near Sam's parents in Sunny Cove. The old man loved the sea but was nervous about going out on his own as he was a bit unsteady on his feet. The pair had a wonderful afternoon's sport. They went up and down about a half a mile off shore, returning with nigh-on five score of mackerel - Coverack men still counted in scores - and they gave them away to the villagers who Ed knew would not have had any free fish for a while. Naturally they kept some for themselves and left plenty in a box under the thwarts as bait for Art' Rawe, Coxswain of Coverack Lifeboat, who had lent them the Bessie. Of course, Mary was delighted when Sam brought some fresh mackerel home for tea and she set about cooking them. Sam had settled down at last to the slow, satisfying rhythm of village life when he realised with a jolt that he had to leave next day and go off once more into the unknown.

Sam's leave in Coverack had been relatively uneventful in that he followed the now established pattern of shaking off the veneer of English social mores which he had appropriated since joining the Royal Navy. On this occasion he had to admit to himself that he would have preferred to spend all his leave in Preston but he wouldn't dream of disappointing his mother by so doing. She had sensed a difference in Sam's demeanour and assuming it was because he had found out that Elsie and her family had left Coverack to live in Camborne, she sympathised with him. This gave Sam the opportunity to let his mother know he no longer corresponded with Elsie and he explained his unaccustomed long face was because he had fallen for Grace and that he was missing her company. At this point Mary admitted to her son that she always knew his friendship with Elsie would be transient and that when he had had the opportunity of meeting other girls he would find a kindred spirit among them in due course. Encouraged by his mother's attitude, Sam shyly showed his mother a photograph of Grace which he carried everywhere with him in his wallet. She studied it for a moment and sent Sam's spirits soaring when she smiled broadly, declaring Grace to be a beauty and that she hoped to be able to meet her one day. Emboldened by his mother's subtle remark, which was calculated to get Sam to tell her more, he "confessed" that he had already spent a few days of his leave at Grace's home. Much to his surprise she told him she would have been surprised if he hadn't. Of course, Sam had not considered the fact that his mother had already gone through a similar experience when his brother Alexander began to spread his wings on leaving Coverack. After this quiet talk, Sam found himself slipping more readily back into the easy-going, unhurried way of life in Coverack.

Of course, the war was having a visible effect on the village. Evacuee children swarmed all over the place, playing unfamiliar games and calling out to each other in Cockney and Plymothian accents. There were always a a few off-duty airmen and WAAFs from the local Radar Station moving about, together with some WRNs from the wireless interception station on the headland. Because of the nature of their work they did not draw attention to themselves. Most of them were linguists and had been made Chief Petty Officers after training. It would attract unwelcome interest if the village had a disproportionate number of senior NCOs stationed in such a remote place, so they wore civilian clothes and gave the casual observer the impression they were out-of-season visitors enjoying the relaxed atmosphere of village life. Sam had not yet become accustomed to the long, ugly scar in the cove where five houses had been before the Focke-Wulfe raid, nor the gap on the hill above his home which had been the home of his father's ARP warden, Mrs. Hannah. Sam had been relieved to know that Mrs. Hannah's sister in law was looking after the two motherless children while their father continued his war service as an RAF Officer. He still knew nothing about his next appointment, except what he had heard on the grapevine, that it was something to do with the newly formed Special Boat Squadron, which was hush-hush and so not talked about - for the simple reason that no one knew what it really was. People were always evasive about the work of the Special Boat personnel and quite naturally did not discuss matters which involved clandestine operations as one never knew who might be listening. Service men were almost paranoid about security, yet it was well known in the Andrew that if you wanted to discover where your ship was going, you only needed to ask a "dockie" and the shipyard worker would provide an answer which more often than not proved subsequently to be accurate!

Almost before he knew it, Sam found himself doing the usual round of "Goodbyes" and taking a final walk round the village with his father in the blackout. As usual, the next morning Mary was tearful and his father stoical. Sam assured his mother that he wasn't going back to sea - "just spending a week or two with a crowd of pongoes" was the way he put it, adding for his mother's benefit that "pongoes" was naval slang for soldiers.

When he had settled in the carriage after changing at Gwinear Road, Sam closed his eyes and reflected on his new relationship. It was so much more meaningful than any he had experienced before. Grace was just the person for him, quiet, unassuming, intelligent but modest, never boasting nor seeking praise and adulation, which was not common with girls who were as attractive as she undoubtedly was. Glances Sam intercepted when walking along the street with her told him he was envied by other males on the lookout for a chance encounter. Maggie, Grace's mother, was known as "Madame" to her music pupils. She was ebullient, had a beautiful voice and was highly qualified. In addition she had an infectious sense of humour though Sam sensed a certain amount of reserve as far as his relationship with her was concerned. Stanley Predin, Grace's father, clearly loved his daughter dearly but was not given to outward show of affection. He was a typical World War One veteran, just like Sam's father, taciturn, given to introspection, never revealing any of the feelings he had regarding the horrors he had experienced. Sam knew Stanley had been badly gassed. He was given to drinking endless cups of tea as he sat in the corner by the fire and quaffed his beer in the same manner when Maggie graciously provided it for him. Sam got on well with Stanley. The two men tacitly understood that there was no point in declaiming what a horrible thing war was; they felt it better left unsaid, but their eyes met on occasions when the war was being discussed and they both knew there was no point in describing their feelings as only people who had undergone the trauma of action could possibly know what it was like and their sense of chivalry spared their loved ones from the horrors they had witnessed. Of course, Sam realised that the war at sea did not compare with the murderous trench warfare Stanley had experienced, but the two men acknowledged a common bond and warmed to one another. Grandma Parker was a lovely lady, outspoken almost to the point of rudeness, due no doubt to the harsh conditions she had endured as a "four-loom weaver" before she invested her hard-earned savings in a small business and got out of the poverty trap so many of her contemporaries endured in the interwar years. She was acutely aware of the fact that hard times could be just around the corner and was an inveterate hoarder. When she became aware that Sam had access to commodities that were in short supply to civilians, she gave out broad hints that she could "do with" a little extra chocolate, or a bar of soap, or a bath towel, etc. etc. Sam gladly supplied these when he could and he later learned that Grandma didn't use them but duly hid them in the cupboard under the stairs for a future emergency!

Introspection was Sam's way of dealing, sometimes profitably, with his personal feelings on being parted from those he loved. Similarly, when affected by the euphoria of anticipation when returning after a lengthy period of absence, he would attempt, not always successfully, to apply his mind to the implications of the next step in his personal life or in his career, in order that the time should quickly pass. The journey to Scotland, not surprisingly, turned out to be tedious, the monotony only broken by changing at Crewe as always, and every now and again Sam delved into his hand luggage to find another delicious snack which Mary had prepared for him. As usual, when he produced a pasty, his travelling companions questioned him about its contents. Sam knew the drill by heart and regaled them with stories about the miners needing pasties which could be dropped down a shaft without breaking, and how the devil never came to Cornwall because he was scared he would be put in a pasty, as in lean times anything edible would be used to fill it. At last Sam found himself on the platform at Stranraer being jostled by passengers anxious to board the ferry for Larne. It had not been easy to stop in Preston en route. Grace was so near, yet so far. He consoled himself by starting a letter to her, giving his address as Preston Station! For the moment, all was forgotten as he hurried to the RTO's office where he had been instructed to report. The Transport Officer, a harassed-looking, middle-aged Army Lieutenant, was desperately trying to placate two young slightly inebriated private soldiers who had lost all their kit. Sam stood patiently, waiting for a chance to speak, when a soldier came up to him, saluted smartly and asked if he was bound for Laggan House. Sam assured him he was and thankfully left the RTO's Office and accompanied the driver to a 15 cwt. army truck which was parked outside the station.

The kit was loaded on board and they took off at breakneck speed into the dark Scottish country roads. Sam found it was not easy to converse with the driver, who was probably hurrying to be back in time for tea. The noise of the engine, combined with the thumping of the tyres on the bumpy road, made talking difficult, and each time Sam managed to ask a question in a casual way concerning what went on at Laggan House he received a non-committal reply, which, as it was intended to do, told him absolutely nothing.

On arrival Sam was greeted by a bespectacled, middle-aged Army Lieutenant who introduced himself as the Adjutant of the Light Scout Car Company. The Lieutenant got an orderly to show Sam to his "cabin" which was a cold, camouflaged Nissen Hut containing a Tortoise Stove, just like the one which was used in the school at Coverack. It made Sam feel more at home, if not a little homesick, at this strange turn of events. The stove had a blackened, rickety chimney going up through the rounded roof, and Sam rightly guessed it would smoke like mad, just like the one in Coverack when it was east wind. The orderly, with a slight grin on his face, politely told Sam to make himself at home and left, telling Sam that dinner was at 1930 "in the big house". "Curiouser and curiouser" said Sam to himself in the idiom of Lewis Carroll's *Alice in Wonderland*, and wondered if one day he would be emulating Charles Dodgson and relating his encounters with the "brown jobs" manning the Light Scout Car Company. Daydreaming would get him nowhere, so Sam began unpacking. When he had stored his kit in the plain wooden locker placed by the door of the Nissen Hut, Sam began to explore his surroundings. There was a wicker basket of kindling wood beside the stove and a pile of logs just outside the door. It was clear that warmth was of paramount importance to anyone living in the cavernous hut. The dull grey concrete floor was bare, except for a long, narrow length of coir matting leading from the entrance. Sam moved his bed close to the Tortoise and positioned the mat so that he could step on it when he got out of bed in the morning. At the end of the hut opposite the "front" door was a partition, behind which was an ablution section with urinals and toilets and an exit door. When he turned on the tap marked Hot on one of the wash basins, he discovered the water was stone cold, but there was an electric kettle on a shelf in the lobby of the block, so Sam filled it with ice-cold water and was soon having a much-needed wash and shave, which made him feel more "human", as his mother was wont to say when she had a wash in the evening after a hard day's cooking and serving in the café. Sam had determined to make a good impression on behalf of the Royal Navy in this alien atmosphere so he changed into his number one suit and made his way to the 16th-century Manor House which had been requisitioned for the Officers' Mess.

The brightly lit lounge of Laggan House was cosily furnished with comfortable looking easy chairs and heated by a blazing hot fire at the far end, round which some subalterns were kneeling, holding out long, bright metal forks on which were speared large slices of white bread. The Adjutant spotted Sam as he made his entrance and came across the room to tell him dinner had been postponed for an hour as the evening's Guest of Honour had just phoned to say he had been "unavoidably detained". The friendly Lieutenant advised Sam to make himself a piece of toast as a pre-prandial snack if he was hungry. Sam was indeed very hungry. He had long since demolished the large pasty his mother had packed for him. He had saved it until last in order to enjoy it all the more, but that seemed hours and hours ago and to make matters worse he was thirsty to boot. He had managed to get a cup of GWR tea at Bristol Temple Meads and another LMS cup when he changed trains at Crewe. Both drinks were "stewed" as Sam's mother would have described them and served to make Sam thirstier than ever, so Sam gladly went to the fireplace, toasted a thick slice of bread and poured himself a most welcome cup of tea. Ever since he had endured tea made with condensed milk when on board the *Pathfinder*, Sam always put three spoons of sugar in, otherwise the tea tasted bitter. The young officers gathered round the fire watched in awe, not realising that in the Royal Navy sugar was not rationed, and they marvelled at Sam's audacity in taking more sugar than he should have done. Of course, he was unaware of the gaffe he had made and the young officers were eager to find out more about the "blue job" who had landed in their midst. Sam had the distinct impression that they didn't believe him when he replied casually, "Haven't a clue, old boy," in response to a question concerning why he had been sent to Ballantrae. When, in turn, he asked what went on at Laggan House, all he could deduce from their evasive answers was that they were engaged in manoeuvres. Sam decided, as on previous occasions, it would be politic to await developments rather than probe unnecessarily.

While they were chatting he studied the uniforms of the assembled officers. As it was a "dining in" night they were all in their dress uniforms, blues, reds and greens plus a sprinkling of kilts. Sam was not familiar with the tartans the Scottish soldiers were wearing and began to wonder why such a motley crowd had been assembled. He learned later that most of them were actually in the Royal Armoured Corps and a goodly sprinkling of technical officers from the Royal Corps of Signals who were in a sense the key figures in the Light Scout Car Company. The RAC Officers preferred to retain the dress uniforms of their old cavalry units , apparently. Whether or not this was in order, Sam never found out. The important point was that they were on the whole a jolly crowd and because he was a bit of an oddity they did their best to make him feel at home.

The dinner was quite a grand affair with a General as the principal guest. Sam never did find out his name, nor exactly what his role was in the local military hierarchy. He was preoccupied in trying to understand the army protocol but he did remember to stand up instead of remaining seated, as is the custom in the Royal Navy, when His Majesty was toasted. It was a glittering occasion, all the officers wearing ceremonial dress with shiny brass buttons and the older officers wearing their First World War medals.

When dinner was over and Sam was in the lounge talking to a young subaltern whom he had met while "toasting", the Adjutant came to ask him to report to his office at 0900 in the morning. By now, Sam was feeling decidedly sleepy due not only to the tedium of the long journey from Coverack but also to the effects of the pink gins which the generous "pongoes" had given him - no doubt with the intention of making him feel welcome in his new surroundings. Many of the soldiers were unfamiliar with the rank of Midshipman RNVR and came up to ask him what the red patches signified. Sam resolved there and then to have the gold ring put on his number-one uniform to avoid awkward questions. He had recently been promoted and Grace's father, Stanley, had kindly arranged for a tailor in the Town Hall to sew on the gold braid, but there had been no time to alter the number-one uniform before he left. After trying to stifle yawns, Sam declared he was ready for bed and took his leave. He left the brightly lit mess and strode into the blackout. Before the meal he had taken the precaution of getting a mental "fix" on the relative position of his Nissen Hut, which was just as well as there were six of them in a row. His was the third from the right, so keeping his eye on the silhouette, he stumbled along the path of granite chippings and down the stone steps, guided by the low, whitewashed wooden posts which were quite effective as markers in the inky blackness. While making his way there he remembered his father telling him about one of his army comrades who was not terribly bright, being sent to whitewash the "Last Post". He smiled to himself and his momentary lack of concentration sent him sprawling as he reached the door of the hut.

Sam knew he was in for a cold night, so after brushing the dust off his precious number ones he hung them in the wooden wardrobe and turned in with his greatcoat draped across the army blankets and was quickly in a warm, deep sleep, with a beatific smile on his face as the last thing he saw before lights out was Grace's photo which was propped up on the makeshift bedside table. He was awakened by the Reveille Bugle broadcast on the Army Tannoy. He hurriedly washed in cold water while waiting for the electric kettle to provide hot water for a much needed shave. He dressed and made his way to the Officers' Mess.

Breakfast was, as is usual in the services, an informal affair. Everyone was in a hurry, preoccupied with thoughts about the day's work ahead. There was not a great deal of chatter, just a low buzz of conversation punctuated with incongruous polite requests to "pass the marmalade" etc. The meal over, Sam made his way to the Adjutant's office and was highly amused to receive a "Present Arms" from the sentry outside. He gravely returned the salute. The young sentry had understandably mistaken Sam's snottie's red tabs on his khaki battle dress for the red tabs of an army Staff Officer, although he must have been mystified to have to present arms to such a youthful bigwig.

For the first time, Sam discovered the Adjutant's name, which was displayed on the polished wooden plaque screwed to his office door. Up to that moment he had simply called him "Adj." in common with the other officers, except that some who were obviously well known to him addressed him as "Bob". So Lieutenant Bob Hesketh began the morning's proceedings by stating sympathetically that he was sure Sam had been wondering what he was going to do at Laggan House and that now he could tell him he was going to be engaged in "Sonic Warfare". The Adjutant knew this would have little meaning for Sam so he went on to explain that Sonic Warfare was a method of deceiving the enemy by making sounds which would give the impression of the approach of a large force of tanks, vehicles, men, landing craft or whatever. This would then cause the enemy to deploy troops etc. to meet the impending assault and meanwhile the genuine attack would take place at a point from where defending troops had in theory been withdrawn in order to meet the diversionary movement created by the use of Sonic Warfare. "If I can coin a phrase," Sam began, "that sounds like a Harry Tate outfit to me, with the accent on 'sounds'." The Adjutant roared with laughter. "That was almost exactly my first reaction, Sam - and by the way, seeing we are going to work together, you might as well call me Bob." He then went on to explain that this method of creating a diversion had already been used with some degree of success on land and now the Navy wanted to get in on the act, so to speak, so Sam had been chosen to be in charge of the naval section about to be trained by instructors from the Royal Corps of Signals.

At this juncture, Sam felt he had to point out that he knew nothing about electronics and even less about the theory of sound, having only studied it to Cambridge School Certificate level, and wondered if he could be returned to base as a mistake had been made in appointing him to such an outfit. Bob laughed again and said, "Don't give it another thought, Sam. I tried that one and got nowhere - just 'play it by ear' to coin a phrase." Having made his objection known, Sam decided to do no more about it for the time being and settled down to hear the rest of the description of Sonic Warfare. He learned that according to the Top Secret signal the Commanding Officer of Laggan House had received, the Special Boat Unit was sending four groups for training by the army. Each group would consist of an Executive Officer, a Seaman Petty Officer and eight ratings, to include men with experience in Wireless Telegraphy, Radio Direction Finding (the acronym RADAR - radio detection and ranging - was not in general use at that time). The signal added that Radio Mechanics would also be drafted when the training reached an advanced stage. At this point Bob declared that there was an agreement to give the ratings a simple academic test when they arrived and those found to be unsuitable would be returned to barracks. Sam brightened at this piece of information and suggested to Bob that he himself would soon be on his way back to Liverpool. "Afraid not, old boy," said Bob, taking a typewritten sheet of paper from the pile on the desk in front of him, and beginning to read out loud. "Criteria laid down by the Admiralty for Officers sent for training in Sonic Warfare.

1. No one over the age of 30.
2. Each officer to be keen, alert, and fit for sea service.
3. Each one to have an aptitude for assimilating technical knowledge."

Sam couldn't resist a cynical laugh at the last criterion. "That lets me out, then. I am useless at assimilating technical knowledge and have never had an aptitude test."

"Don't worry, old chap," said Bob soothingly. "You know what B.F.s there are in Headquarters Staff - they probably picked out your name with a pin." Sam grinned and decided it would be best to give in gracefully. He could always make a mess of the exams and be returned to Liverpool when he failed. Not to be deprived of his enjoyment in telling Sam about his new appointment, Bob went on to say that a memo had been received stating that owing to the highly secret nature of the operations in which the Naval Combined Operations Scout Unit would be involved, the Admiralty had stipulated officers should also be capable of dealing direct with officers from Military Intelligence. Sam politely refrained from laughing out loud. He was conscious of having come a long way since leaving Coverack as a very immature schoolboy sailor, but he had never thought of himself as being capable of reaching such heights so soon! At any rate it would be an interesting tale to tell when his children asked, "What did you do in the war, Daddy?"

Sam was shaken out of his reverie by the harsh sound of the Adjutant's chair scraping the polished wooden floor as he stood up, announcing he was taking Sam to the lecture room to introduce him to Sergeant Ernie Baines, who was to be his technical instructor. The diminutive, bespectacled Royal Corps of Signals Sergeant looked more like a schoolmaster than an army Sergeant. Sam learned later that he was, in fact, a science teacher in civilian life. He was obviously taking his job very seriously as all professional teachers do, and after the introduction followed by general small talk concerning the journey to Scotland and the advantages of being in such a pleasant place as Ballantrae, the Sergeant launched into a synopsis of the syllabus, using terms which Sam had never heard before. Then without more ado he handed Sam a list of text-books dealing with elementary electricity and radio that he thought would "come in useful", adding that he would have to wait until he visited Stranraer before he could find a bookshop which stocked the books. At this point Sam stated he knew nothing about electricity. The Sergeant assured him there was no need to be concerned, adding with a wry smile on his face, "You will know all that's needed by the time I've finished with you - Sir!"

Sam left the lecture hut with Bob and they crossed the lawn in front of Laggan House, round to a collection of Nissen Huts which Bob announced were the quarters where the matelots would be housed. Sam asked to be shown round so that he would be familiar with the layout before the "troops" arrived. The huts were the same as the one in which he was housed, except that they were built at right angles to an ablution block which backed on to the park land surrounding the country house. While doing the tour of the "heads", which were bucket lavatories in lieu of flush toilets, they came across the Sergeant Major of the Light Scout Car Company. He was a huge man, seemingly all muscle, a forbidding figure, and Sam wondered how the naval ratings would get on with this fierce-looking embodiment of a British RSM. He was to learn later that during bayonet fighting drill, which was compulsory for the Navy as well as the Army, the RSM invited the relatively timid matelots to pretend they were stabbing him when they plunged their bayonets into the straw-filled dummies, urging them to shout, "This is for you, Bib!" Apparently when introducing himself to the trainees, he would shout, "I'm RSM Charlton, known to everyone as Bib. In case you don't know why I'm called that, I'll tell you. It's because I'm a Big Ignorant Bastard. What I say goes. There's no argument!" There was no argument after such an introduction as that, but on the other hand the trainees discovered as time went on that when talking to him privately, man to man, so to speak, he was quite fatherly and sympathetic. Of course, when it came to administration and personal problems, it was Sam's responsibility. "Bib" stuck to his remit of preparing the units for active service, which might well include having to engage in hand-to-hand combat with the enemy. It seemed highly unlikely that the sailors would find themselves in such a situation but no one could categorically claim it would not happen, so "Bib" made sure they were prepared - and that included Sam and the other officers, who in fact had a harder time of it than the troops. Sam managed it without too much trouble: his assault course training had well prepared him for such eventualities and he was glad of the opportunity to let off steam after the claustrophobic atmosphere of the lecture hut.

After lunch the two COSUs arrived in a couple of three-ton lorries which had met them at Stranraer Station. Sam looked in vain for the seaman Petty Officer in charge but in true Navy style, someone had blundered and he had to be content with a rather young-looking Leading Seaman called Stoddard, wearing what was obviously a recently acquired "hook" on his left sleeve. The other Killick was a thick-set, weatherbeaten, three-badge Leading Seaman named Smythe, who looked as if he had already enjoyed more than one tot at noon, despite having travelled by train where there was no "Up spirits". "Not an auspicious beginning to a new venture," thought Sam; then, remembering the danger of prejudging his men, Sam introduced himself and added that after their long train journey they deserved a "make and mend" which would give them a chance of settling in their Nissen Huts and relaxing before starting work in the morning after breakfast. He said nothing about the nature of that work but cautioned them to remember they were in an army establishment and the "pongoes" would judge the Navy according to their behaviour, so he didn't want to hear of any clashes and said he would deal with any problems which arose and that they were not to take the law into their own hands.

Sam had saved Bib to the last. He wanted the sailors to associate him with the navy so that his traditional welcoming speech would remain in their minds as a contrast to the Army "indoctrination". He announced that while they were in Ballantrae, they would be in the charge of RSM Charlton who was in charge of the physical side of their training and would show them the ropes. Bib had been hovering nearby while Sam was addressing the matelots and on being introduced, sprang smartly to attention, and saluted Sam, then bellowed, "Royal Navy, Royal Navy, Shun! Shoulder your kit. By the left, Quick March!" Sam managed to suppress a grin at the look of horrified surprise on the faces of the startled sailors as they picked up their kit bags and marched off with their now redundant hammocks bouncing unsteadily on the top of their bulging kit bags. He then retreated in as dignified a manner as he could muster to the sound of Bib calling out, "Left, Left, Left Right Left, come on, Royal Navy, I'm going to have to teach you matelots to march as well as the Army while you're here. Left, Left, Left Right, Left!" Sam would have wagered at that moment that every man Jack of them was wishing he was back in the Naval barracks from which they had come.

In the evening, after dinner, Sam went down to the Naval Nissen Huts to do his own version of "Rounds". He removed his cap before entering as a sign that it was an informal visit and that he was not checking on the tidiness and cleanliness of the sleeping quarters. He had a chat with the two Leading Seamen and revealed that they were there to do special Combined Ops. Training prior to joining a special Boat Unit after Christmas. He added that he couldn't tell them much more as he didn't know himself with any degree of certainty. Everyone present was curious to know what was happening but Sam reiterated that he couldn't say and advised them to get their heads down and have a good sleep before starting a new chapter in their naval careers, adding that it was all new to him as well after serving in destroyers and landing craft, but he was grateful that they were all nice and snug in sleepy Ballantrae for a while at least! He then went from group to group for an informal chat in order to learn their names and something of their background.

The next morning, Bib presented Sam with the two units outside the lecture hut punctually at 0800 after breakfast. Sam thanked him and indicated that in future the two Leading Seamen would muster the "troops", thus giving him time for his other duties. Bib thanked Sam politely but the disappointed expression on his face told everyone present that he had been looking forward to knocking the sloppy sailors into shape. After telling the sailors they were to have a morning of instruction, with a ten minute "Stand easy" half way through when they would be able to get a cup of char from the NAAFI canteen, Sam told them to file into the lecture hut where he introduced the now bewildered sailors to the mild-mannered Sergeant Ernest Baines of the Royal Corps of Signals.

The Sergeant began by telling his class they were there to learn the theory of electricity and how to operate what he termed "Special Equipment". He asked if anyone present was conversant with electrical theory so Sam introduced him to the four radio mechanics who were part of the naval contingent whom he had met the previous evening. The Sergeant told them that a colleague would come later on and take them to the workshop where they would start work with the Army Radio Mechanics in order to familiarise them with the equipment.

Sam found the next hour or so quite fascinating. The Sergeant explained the way in which electricity worked, frequently turning to the analogy of the movement of water in pipes. His illustrations on the blackboard were superb and even the obviously "bolshy" seamen in the class began to show an interest. After "Stand Easy" Sam was relieved that all the sailors were back in time for "Out Pipes" when cigarettes were stubbed and the lecture recommenced.

By the end of the day, Sam had compiled several pages of notes and wondered if he would ever have time to learn them. He was cheered by the news given by the Adjutant that a Sub. Lieutenant Mountjoy would be arriving before dinner. He could do with an ally in this alien environment. The two of them were going to be introduced to the Training Major that evening. The Major would outline exactly what the course entailed and what, in his view, was the role of the Royal Navy in Sonic Warfare.

"Enfin," muttered Sam, unaware that a bit of forgotten French had suddenly surfaced.

"What's that?" said Bob.

"Oh, nothing," said Sam swiftly. "I'm just pleased to have someone to help out with the daily routine."

Norman Mountjoy arrived on time and Sam took him to their Nissen Hut so that he could settle in and get ready for the meeting with the Training Major. While unpacking Norman quizzed Sam about the work at Laggan House, so Sam told him the little he knew and off they went for the all-important revelation by Major Cockcroft. In the event, the Major just reiterated what Sam had already been told. The Major was due to go on leave the next day and hurriedly excused himself as he had some packing to do.

"Plus ça change," said Sam.

"What's that?" asked Norman.

"Oh, nothing," replied Sam. "I was just thinking aloud. It seems to me that there's nothing new. We've been told, in effect, to get on with what we are doing and wait to be told what it is we are doing."

"You're right, Sam," said Norman. "We are only Subs. and we shall only be allowed to join in when the s..t hits the fan and then they won't want to know."

Sam laughed. "That's right, Norman. Remember Tennyson's 'The Charge of the Light Brigade'? How does it go? Oh, yes: 'Their's not to reason why, Their's but to do and die'."

"Not if I can b....y well help it." replied Norman. "Come on, Sam, let's have a gin before dinner and b....r the Pongoes!"

So off the two young lads went, intent on getting to the bar before the gong went for dinner. It had done Sam a lot of good to have an ally in the "alien camp"!

The following morning the lectures continued apace, with no regard for the thick heads of Norman and Sam after their evening of necessarily mild debauchery on Sub. Lieutenants' pay. The Army were not entitled to Duty Free drinks! It was with some relief that just before "Stand Easy" Sgt. Baines announced that the class would be shown the apparatus they were to use and that in the following week they would be going on exercise and so needed to be familiar with handling the controls in the dark. Although it would be a welcome relief from note taking, Sam was not at all happy at being made responsible for handling delicate machinery. It was strange that from the time he could talk he had always regarded boats as being of the female gender and so amenable to being handled by a male. Other inanimate objects also took on human attributes which were less easy to control and so they were stubborn males. Sam knew full well that these objects did not irritate him on purpose. After all, how could they? Nevertheless he was inclined to think they did when he was unable to manipulate them to his own satisfaction. In a strange sort of way, Sgt. Baines seemed to divine Sam's thoughts, for in answer to a question from Leading Seaman Stoddard as to how they could effect repairs in the dark, given their limited knowledge, the Sergeant declared that a good hefty kick often did the trick, but he immediately stated that he would deny he ever said it if anyone followed his advice and shattered an amplifier! Slowly but surely the Sergeant was winning over the reluctant sailors to his way of thinking and when they came face to face with the amplifiers, loudspeakers, RCA cinematograph machines and wire recorders, they began asking questions and were eager to discover how to handle the equipment, especially when they learned that it was all "Top Secret" and unique in the history of warfare!

The Sergeant's "sound" advice had given Sam, too, a little more confidence and it was indeed to stand him in good stead later on, not only concerning the delicate apparatus used in Sonic Warfare at sea but also when out in the English Channel using the newly invented QZ machine as an aid to navigation. In the early stages of use, the QZ was assembled in three sections and by a process of trial and error it was possible to ascertain where the fault was situated in the event of a breakdown. Sam soon learned that a reasonably gentle punch in the right place, rather than Sgt. Baines' "good hefty kick", would bring the desired co-ordinates into focus from the "chains" being broadcast from the masts on shore. It proved to be a very useful piece of equipment in due course and was a great help in determining one's position when in thick weather with no visible stars. Many, many years later in his role as an Auxiliary Coastguard, coming to the aid of "lost" fishermen whose Decca systems had ceased to function, Sam would smile to himself when he advised them to adopt the practice of keeping an approximate position marked in pencil on the chart, for he knew full well they would doubtless ignore his comment as they were too busy handling their trawls and expected the expensive navigational aids they were renting to provide continuously accurate information while they got on with the real business of fishing!

To return to the training at Laggan House. Sam's sailors did not take kindly to the idea of prancing about the Ayrshire countryside in pitch dark, even if they did have Light Scout Cars from which to operate the diversionary noises. To be fair, the loudspeakers mounted on the cars did produce the sound of approaching tanks, and so on, very realistically and when on occasions Sam had to monitor the sounds from a couple of miles away, he could not tell that he was hearing "diversionary noises", but there again, he was not really qualified to express an opinion and pointed out to the instructors he would rather witness the sounds coming from seawards before making a comment. Naturally, it was not possible to do that. It had yet to be decided what type of craft were to be used and how the equipment was to be mounted. It was quite evident that landing craft would be unsuitable as they were too slow and too low in the water. He told the soldiers that after a mile or two the water shipped by LCAs or LCMs would render the delicate electrical apparatus useless, even if there was enough power generated to run it. That argument was soon settled by the proposed provision of portable generators which would be carried on deck. Again Sam declared that would be quite impossible on landing craft and suggested Fairmile Motor Launches would be more practical, although the hulls were wooden. Sam's comments were noted and there the matter rested, no doubt awaiting decision by the armchair sailors in Whitehall or wherever!

As described earlier, the basic aim of Sonic Warfare was to produce sound effects which would give a listening enemy the impression of tanks and vehicles lagering and preparing to launch an attack. This was done by playing a sound track on 35 mm. film or wire recorders, the sound being amplified and broadcast by large, powerful loudspeakers mounted on half-track vehicles or 15 cwt. trucks. Naturally this was expected to draw enemy fire but perhaps more importantly cause advance enemy scouting parties to report back that reinforcements from another sector were soon to be needed. In theory that would weaken the defence of the sector on which the main allied attack was to be launched, thus saving casualties. Again in theory, this type of deception could be carried out by different sonic units along a wide front and was calculated to cause confusion. The enemy resistance would be further weakened by the fact that their troops would be moving behind the lines, so to speak, in order to withstand an expected attack, thus allowing the main thrust of the allied attack to take place against a weakened enemy.

Secrecy was of paramount importance. The huge loudspeakers were suitably camouflaged so that, in theory, troops not in the Sonic Unit would be unaware of the significance of the "boxes" mounted on the vehicles.

This was necessary so that in the event of being taken prisoner, soldiers would not be able to divulge the use of the diversionary tactic. The cars would have to penetrate to within a short distance of the advance posts of the enemy, "play the programme", withdraw swiftly before being rumbled and move to another preordained position in order to continue the deception. This activity was not without some risk, so the soldiers were trained to set up shop in silence and at speed, play the programme, pack up swiftly and withdraw as silently as they had come. A small group of lightly armed soldiers from the Light Scout Car Unit accompanied them to protect the sonic unit from a surprise attack while operating. All the men involved were trained in what Bib termed "hand-to-hand fighting" as well as being able to carry out the duties involved in operating the equipment. This ensured, in theory, that in the event of casualties the unit would be able to complete the operation. Sam learned that in principle these tactics were in keeping with General Wavell's pronouncement on deception - "attract the enemy's attention to what you wish him to see and distract his attention from what you do not wish him to see."

Sam and Norman Mountjoy, together with their band of reluctant naval heroes, were somewhat disillusioned by the demands of being part of a Sonic Warfare Unit, especially as what they were being obliged to do seemingly bore little resemblance to being part of the Royal Navy's traditional style of warfare, yet they were constantly being reassured by the head of Training, Major Cockroft, that the new Combined Operations Supremo was cognisant of the fact and required the Scout Unit to be fully conversant with all aspects of the training schedule. Sam and Norman had their doubts about this and the "troops" clearly thought that they had been sent to "a f.....g madhouse". They were not at all keen on taking part in RSM Charlton's bayonet practices and resorted to the time-honoured naval practice of needing urgently to pay a visit to the "heads" if they knew a training session was imminent. Bib was up to their little tricks, so instead of storming in to the bucket toilets and driving the "skates" out, he and a couple of Corporals went along behind the huts, lifting the trap doors through which the buckets were withdrawn every morning for emptying, and thrust a bunch of stinging nettles through the hole and up to the seats on which the skulking sailors were sitting. Some, having decided to be authentic, had dropped their trousers, just in case their privacy was invaded by an NCO. The resulting yells told Bib what he wanted to know and the matelots came rushing out, to be escorted by the RSM and his trusty Corporals to the field for their "hand-to-hand fighting" practice! Needless to say, Bib usually had a "full house" after that little episode.

Of course, the sailors had already undergone bayonet practice as part of their naval training. This activity was still deemed necessary, possibly because memories of the Naval Brigade which operated in the trenches during the Great War of 1914-1918 were still fresh in the minds of senior Naval Officers. Rupert Brooke's "The Soldier" might just as well have been entitled "The Sailor" as he was commissioned in the Royal Navy and saw action in Europe with the Brigade, only to die from septicemia on board a hospital ship while he was on his way to the Dardanelles. Bib Charlton had no illusions about the need for knowledge of bayonet fighting, no doubt believing it was "good for the soul". He would shout, "Come on you b.....s, stick him in the guts. That's me, Bib, the Big Ignorant Bastard in front of you. Give it to me, lads! Thrust, twist and withdraw!' This exhortation always had the desired effect and even the most timid matelot in the unit was observed advancing at speed on the row of straw-filled dummies uttering blood-curdling cries. Sam learned quite a bit about his "crew" while present at this stage of their training. He, too, felt it was good character training, even if it was not relevant. After all, they were at war, and Bib, who had seen plenty of action, knew better than most that some sort of unorthodox stimulus was needed to drive ordinary men to the state where they would want to kill another human being.

The night exercises not only involved practice in operating the prepared programmes from the Light Scout Cars but included crawling through muddy fields and gorse-strewn heathland prior to carrying out dummy attacks with rifle and bayonet on "enemy outposts". Towards the end of their training they were obliged to advance on their bellies towards the "enemy" while live bullets whistled a few feet above their heads. It was not a pleasant experience, but necessary, nevertheless. The manoeuvres took place after dark, and during the day Sergeant Baines continued his lectures. Some of the sailors became quite adept at doing running repairs in the semi-darkness of the cars, such as splicing the film when it snapped. It was a pity that tape recorders as such had not been invented for the film was used only because of the sound track which was printed at the right hand edge of the film strip. There was no photography involved! The wire recorders were not very reliable and if the wire snapped it often meant the whole recording had to be scrapped as a repair was very difficult to achieve without interrupting the flow of sound when it was played back. Sam and Norman had a great deal of sympathy for the "troops" and they both longed for the time when they could go back to sea, even if it did mean playing "silly buggers" with the equipment as Norman described Sonic Warfare in his lighter moments.

It goes without saying that there were "drips" or rumblings of discontent among the sailors. One Saturday evening on a run "ashore", Able Seaman "Florrie" Ford was unable to contain his frustration any longer and after having a few pints of the local brew in Ballantrae decided he would have a wrestling match with a petrol pump while walking, or perhaps lurching would be a more appropriate word, back to Laggan House. Sam received a telephone call from the local policeman, asking him to go to the country garage to deal with an inebriated seaman. Sam knew enough about drunken sailors to avoid a confrontation with one, not that he was especially afraid of getting into a tussle, but because he knew that if he were struck it would be a court martial offence for the sailor, who obviously was not in control of his senses. It so happened that the duty Killick was the youthful, diminutive Leading Seaman Stoddard, but nothing daunted, the pair set off in a 15cwt. Army truck for the garage. As the local Bobby had described, A.B. Ford was wrestling noisily with the inanimate petrol pump, much to the barely contained amusement of the policeman. "Tell him to cut it out," said Sam. Stoddard cleared his throat and shouted, "That's enough Florrie, your run ashore is over now!" To everyone's surprise, after looking at the Killick, then at Sam standing beside him, shining his torch so that the seaman could see who they were, Florrie gave a sheepish grin, meekly stood up and tried to get into the truck. It needed the combined efforts of Sam and the Leading Seaman to get Ford over the tailboard, whereupon he collapsed in a heap on the floor of the truck and stayed that way until they got back to Laggan House. The garage proprietor was very grateful at this turn of events and after Sam had apologised for the "unfortunate incident" as he delicately put it, the garage man decided not to press charges as the sturdy, hand-operated petrol pump was not damaged in any way. He even paid tribute to the discipline of the Royal Navy, which did not go down well with the Army truck driver who had been raked out of the NAAFI to take Sam and Stoddard to the garage. The local man even praised the courage of the "wee laddie" who had faced the drunken six-footer who had already begun to snore noisily while the group were talking. The policeman was pleased he did not have to put the sailor into one of his cells, nor write a report, so after bidding everyone "Goodnight" got on his bike and cycled off in the dark without lighting his bicycle lamp. Sam also decided it would be politic to forget the incident after having a conversation with Leading Seaman Stoddard, and when he had sobered up, Able Seaman Ford just carried on as usual, only too grateful for getting off the hook, so to speak.

"Florrie"'s luck in not having his misdemeanour officially counted against him was the talk of the lower deck for a while. The "sleeping sentry saga" at Preston had somehow become known and Sam's reputation for being a bit of a sod had followed him. In truth, Sam was learning fast how to deal with men who were almost twice his age, yet behaved rather like recalcitrant children on occasions. On reflection he had reasoned that much of the resentment at being made to play "silly buggers" would most probably evaporate if strict discipline were relaxed for a while. He had decided while riding in the truck to recover A.B. Ford that if the occasion arose he would try to defuse the situation without invoking the full weight of traditional naval discipline. His ploy worked, for the "troops" were puzzled by the way in which the situation was handled and began to go about their duties with a more relaxed air, except, of course, when RSM Charlton was on the warpath. Sam always hated himself after he had lost his temper and dealt harshly with people. As time went on his lapses became less frequent and he acquired a method of acting as if he were very annoyed, which had the desired effect without his judgement being clouded by losing his temper. Many years later this ruse worked well when he had to deal with unruly teenagers who were not intimidated by the prospect of unpleasant consequences resulting from their bad behaviour as were the wartime sailors.

Norman and Sam were just as frustrated as the men in their charge. They relieved the tensions caused by their unaccustomed roles on the tree trunks which had been stacked outside their Nissen hut for sawing into logs to feed the ever hungry stove, which never actually made the hut feel cosy despite using up all the wood which Sam and Norman prepared for it. They usually had a frenzied session on Saturday afternoon, prior to "going ashore" to Stranraer for the evening. During the week they spent the long dark evenings in the mess, engaged in banal conversation and consuming large quantities of beer when funds were low and pink gins when they were "flush". They were not keen on the official dining-in nights when senior officers held sway while the juniors dutifully waited for the moment when they could chat freely with their peers without fear of committing a gaffe before their out-pipping superiors. At least, after they had discussed the happenings which went on in the army mess, that seemed to be the drill as far as the two sailors could ascertain, both having come from circles where elitist protocol was not practised. In the manner of all service training courses the work continued unimpeded by mildly uninterested trainees and so slowly and surely the students began to gain confidence, sometimes in spite of themselves. They became adept at setting up the apparatus under simulated active service conditions and in dealing with minor problems such as faulty Onan generators which supplied 110-watt power to the American-made RCA film projectors and wire recorders. Splicing the broken film strip which carried the sound track was not a big problem but when the slender wire of a recorder snapped it was usually one of the properly trained technicians who effected the repair. Sam was not happy about the prospect of keeping the equipment running when at sea, especially as the vulnerable generators would almost certainly have to be lashed to ring bolts on the upper deck where they would be immersed in spray for much of the time. Likewise the loudspeakers would no doubt pack up after being exposed to the weather conditions prevalent in the English Channel. Both Sam and Norman felt there would be no chance of operating the equipment from a landing craft and they knew that Coastal Forces skippers would not be overjoyed by the presence of the Sonic Warfare equipment on their sleek craft. As they had surmised, when they were sent to Newhaven the powers that be saw reason and provided Harbour Defence Motor Launches (HDMLs) and B Class Fairmiles for the operations. These craft proved to be quite suitable for what their crews dubbed "The Fred Karno's Outfit", which rolled off the tongue more readily than Combined Operations Scout Unit (COSU).

What concerned Sam most of all was that he did not consider himself to be competent enough to be in charge of the technical/tactical side of a unit. He knew he would have to rely on the expertise of the Radar Mechanics. Luckily most of them were former Grammar School pupils like himself, with whom he was on good terms. Before the end of the course, Their Lords Commissioners of the Admiralty suddenly decided, in their wisdom, to give another appointment to Norman Mountjoy. Sam never found out if Norman had requested a transfer. There was a farewell "do" in the Mess and the next morning Norman went off to a landing craft flotilla. Sam was informed by signal that he was in sole charge of the two COSUs. He felt left out and bewildered but he knew he had to cope so kept his doubts and fears to himself. There was indeed little else he could do. He could hardly complain to the Training Major, who, in any case, had already left for one of his frequent and mysterious weekends.

Another week went slowly by. Christmas was approaching and everyone was hoping for leave. No one in the COSU was disappointed. Sam had instructions to send both units home for a week's end-of-course leave plus Christmas Day and Boxing Day. Indeed, Sam's unit was already on leave, having been sent a day early by the Adjutant's Office when a "Most Secret" signal was sent to Admiralty on the 26th December 1943 by Major Cockcroft, the Training Major, who had inexplicably been clobbered for duty over the Christmas period, stating, "Training completed at Ballantrae". Sam was to read much later, in the records lodged at the Public Record Office in Kew, that this Boxing Day signal was part of the planning for Operation "Glimmer" which was in turn part of the larger Operation "Fortitude" on which the main "Operation Overlord" depended for success. It is just as well that at the time no one knew a signal had been sent to Admiralty a month earlier on the 9th November 1943 stating that there were only eight sets available to the Admiralty out of a possible eighteen. Not a good beginning for a new operational unit. Everything was so hush-hush that even the officers concerned were kept in ignorance. It was apparently left to the chair-borne planners to mastermind the provision of apparatus for those at the sharp end. "Their's but to do and die" seemed to be the order of the day.

Blissfully ignorant of the machinations of the secret planners, Sam went gleefully on leave, dividing his free time into two, spending a couple of days with Grace and her family, helping to cope with the Christmas shopping which went ahead everywhere in spite of shortages. A sort of camaraderie had developed whereby people shared their knowledge concerning where items in short supply could be obtained, provided, of course, one was prepared to queue in the biting wind for long periods in order to purchase a packet of tinsel or whatever. Sam and Grace didn't mind being sent on these errands as long as they were together, and they accepted the situation cheerfully. Sam delighted in walking around the shops hand in hand with his girlfriend, acting as official parcel carrier. It was all he had dreamed of in the run-up to Christmas. Two perfect days went by at the rate of knots. He managed to buy a small gold cross for Grace to wear while he was away. She was allowed to wear it after Sam had reassured her mother he was not of the Catholic faith but simply wanted Grace to have a keepsake. Such was the climate of religious awareness in Priest-town. At the end of the two euphoric days, Sam found himself saying his farewells once more on Preston Station and reluctantly boarding the train for the Westcountry as the guard was waving his green lantern and blowing his whistle. As he had a First Class ticket he managed to get a good seat and before long he was catching up on his lost sleep. He awoke just before Bristol and set about demolishing the sandwiches Mrs. Predin had prepared for him, then he dozed off again, waking as he crossed the Tamar, having been unaware of stopping at Exeter and Plymouth. As he passed through the corridor on his way to the toilet to have a shave he found the unfortunate servicemen who had to stand in the corridor surprisingly cheerful as he squeezed past their bulky kit bags. After all, it was Christmas and they were back in Cornwall. What more could anyone ask, except a seat on the train?

On arriving at last in Coverack, Sam fended off the usual comments of "Home again, Sam?" as he walked through the village by replying with such comments as, "Ess, they can do without me for a bit", or, "They've stopped the war till I get back", tailoring each comment to suit the villager to whom it was addressed, as he knew his answer would be reported and commented on as part of family gossip and village entertainment. Everyone he met had known him all his life and knew there was no malice in his replies, which were his way of getting back into the familiar repartee so beloved by his fellow villagers.

True to type, Mary had already prepared the family Christmas puddings and the cake. George had plucked and "drawn" a plump capon which had been specially chosen from the chicken "run" situated on the edge of the back garden. George had never been able to bring himself to take out his penknife and cut the throat of a bird which he had reared from a chick, so just prior to the execution he would ask John Lang the village milkman to accompany him up the steps of the near cliff at the rear of the house for "a few minutes". John always knew what was coming next. George would enter the pen, grab the chosen bird and hand it, without saying a word, to John who would nonchalantly slit its throat, tie its feet together and hang it on Mary's clothes line so that the bird's blood would conveniently drip on to the ground below, thus avoiding any mess to be cleared up later. It was a sort of barnyard ashes-to-ashes ritual. Mother earth absorbs all her creatures with a final embrace, even the humble fowl. When the bird had given its final flap, George would take down the still warm body and make it ready for Mary to cook. Sam had often witnessed this familiar activity and indeed had sometimes plucked a bird himself, but like his father he balked at slitting its throat. Indeed he had gone through a long phase when he could not even bring himself to eat roast chicken, but this occasion was special. He was home for Christmas and in any case his mind was so preoccupied with his lovely dark-haired Lancashire lass that he spent the whole family Christmas in a pleasant but non-alcoholic haze. His parents were strictly teetotal, having been brought up in the Wesleyan tradition. At Christmas, George always bought a small bottle of Ginger Wine and that year, Sam, having reached manhood, was invited to join his father for a drink before the Christmas dinner began at one o'clock. Sam was flattered by this promotion and readily agreed but had to admit to himself that he would have preferred a pink gin, or even an IPA. He had taken to drinking India Pale Ale when funds were getting low at the end of the month. With true Cornish caution he would never allow himself to run up a Mess Bill which he couldn't meet. His parents, of course, assumed he was teetotal so they had no worries on that score. With true nonconformist propriety, Sam had to admit privately that he felt guilty about succumbing to the lure of the "demon drink", for his father had told him that even during the bitter winters he had experienced in the trenches in France and before an attack, he had never once taken his rum ration. He knew in his heart of hearts that his father was a better man than he could ever be, so though he did not especially enjoy the taste of Ginger Wine he readily accepted a second glass, knowing it would give his dear father great pleasure and perhaps make up, in a small way, for the fact that his elder siblings Emily and Alexander could not be there with them. Mary did not join her husband and son. Sam had the impression that she disapproved of his father's annual "indulgence", the word Wine having a sinful connotation in her mind.

So Christmas Day passed slowly and pleasantly. In the afternoon they listened to the King's broadcast and felt for him when he stumbled over words which his stammer would not allow him to pronounce easily. The evening before, they had listened to the Nativity Play which was broadcast from the church of the controversial Bernard Walke, Anglo-Catholic Vicar of St. Hilary. Mary was not concerned with the strange happenings that had occurred at St. Hilary: she was a devotee of dramatic productions on the wireless although she had never seen a professional play in a theatre, and she just wanted to hear the re-enactment of the birth of Christ. Mary had sat, entranced, in the kitchen, making last-minute preparations for the morrow while the play was on. She usually produced one play a year in the Lambygh Hall in aid of the British Legion, but she had never had any formal training except acting in costume plays when she attended the Grammar School in Helston after winning a three-year scholarship.

In the eyes of her less fortunate villagers this limited experience qualified her to organise village drama. They always willingly co-operated by helping to make costumes and lending props for the everyday "domestic" type of sketches which Mary knew would appeal to her friends.

The three Exelbys spent Christmas evening playing the games they had always played in the festive season - Halma, Snakes and Ladders, Consequences, I Spy and a few hands of Whist. When they tired of playing they sat companionably chatting and reminiscing until Mary decided to leave the two men and go to make a few chicken sandwiches for supper. George went to sit at the harmonium and began playing Christmas carols, singing softly in his tenor voice while Mary accompanied him from the kitchen in her rich alto. Sam had not inherited any musical ability from his parents so he was content to sit before the fire with his eyes closed, listening to his parents and wallowing in the sheer joy of being fortunate enough to be at home for Christmas and at the same time wondering how his brother Alexander was spending Christmas in Burma and if his sister was knocking back a few whiskies in the Sergeants' Mess or on duty in a draughty gun site at Pilning near Bristol. It was perhaps just as well that the thought of the inexorable approach of the invasion of Europe in which he knew he was to take part did not cross his mind while he was in Coverack. He was home. That was all that mattered for the time being. On Boxing Day he accompanied his parents on the annual visit to Grandfather Jim and Granny Catherine Exelby. This was the one day in the year when the front parlour was actually used as a purely family sitting room, the only room in the house which had a carpet. It was kept in pristine condition, ready for special occasions such as Christmas, weddings, funerals and visiting Wesleyan preachers. When Sam and his parents had settled somewhat uncomfortably on the solid, upright, best wooden chairs, Granny Exelby was ushered to her easy chair and her arthritic knees wrapped in a warm woollen rug by the ever attentive Cap'n Jim as he was known in Coverack circles. Grandfather Exelby then reverently took his flute from the fireside cupboard, placed his music sheets on the metal stand which had already been assembled in the centre of the room and standing with his back to the log fire burning brightly in the grate, began to play "O come all ye faithful". Sam found he was still fascinated by the way in which the old gentleman's ginger-grey beard fluttered in the "down draught" generated by the expelled air required to play the complicated notes. In later years when thinking of his childhood Christmases he would wonder how his Grandfather had acquired the knowledge needed to play the instrument. Jim had large, calloused hands yet he manipulated the minuscule silver keys with apparent ease. As the tune progressed on this wartime Boxing Day, his cheeks got redder and redder due to the exertions of blowing downwards into the tiny aperture of the flute. Catherine began to rock in her chair and when the second verse began she accompanied Jim in her quavering alto voice while George and Mary hummed the tune softly in harmony to show their delight with the "performance". Sam listened while looking out to sea towards the Manacle Rocks. He had never been able to understand why the front parlour, though reverently dusted every Saturday throughout the year, was so rarely used when it had such a stunning view. When the music ceased Sam continued to look out to sea. There was not a ship in sight. Peace had come down at Christmas.

During the remaining few afternoons of his leave Sam did the Christmas rounds of his relations and friends, returning home each evening to spend time with his lonely parents who wanted to see as much of their "baby" son as possible while he was on leave. Duty done in the late afternoon, Sam would walk back to Sunny Cove taking large gulps of the salt-laden air, expelling it slowly from his lungs in the hope that the smell of cheap port and sherry he had consumed would not be detected when he entered his mother's kitchen. In almost every "teetotal" house he visited, when a suitable lull in the conversation occurred, a bottle would be slyly produced from the back of a handy cupboard and with a cheeky grin on his face, the host would declare, "Better 'ave a drop of trade before 'ee do go, Sam," to which he would reply in a conspiratorial tone, "Ess you, but 'ee wen't tell mother, will 'ee?" Everyone would laugh, then the glasses would be set out and filled and each one present would be given a thin slice of Christmas cake to go with the drink. Sam was aware that if he refused to accept the Christmas cheer in any house, his friends and relations would be very disappointed, so he manfully accepted all that was offered, knowing that when he returned home with a full stomach he would be expected to eat a substantial meal which his mother had prepared while he was "gallivanting" as she described his afternoon visits. He consoled himself by privately vowing to go on a diet when he left Coverack. Of course, he never did.

CHAPTER SIXTEEN

NEWHAVEN AND NORMANDY

It was not without trepidation that Sam stepped off the train at Newhaven Harbour Station and went to report to the Officer of the Watch. He was allocated a "cabin" in the requisitioned London and Paris Hotel and told that Lieutenant Branson was expecting him and would make contact in the Ward Room after dinner. "Chimmo", as Sam learned to call his Commanding Officer, was a friendly character with a seemingly perpetual grin on his face. He was a regular officer and wore the ribbon of the Polish Medal for Gallantry, so Sam knew there must be steel beneath the charming exterior. He was told that three other officers would be joining the group which had been allocated the title of Combined Operations Scout Unit - COSU for short. The "troops", as Chimmo put it, were already quartered in a requisitioned row of houses on the opposite side of the tiny harbour and would be mustered on the jetty at 0800 the following morning under Petty Officer Dick Richards. The new CO then proceeded to question Sam regarding his knowledge of the "troops" who would be under his command, being careful not to talk about the technical nature of the work in the hearing of the officers present in the Ward Room. The latter were mainly officers from the MTBs and MLs in the harbour and the staff of HMS *Aggressive* which was the shore establishment of Coastal Forces.

Promptly at 0800 the following morning, PO Dick Richards brought the COSU group to attention and reported to Sam that all were present and correct. Sam did a smart about turn, marched a few steps forward and saluted his new CO, repeating the time-honoured phrase. Chimmo told Sam to stand the unit at ease as he wanted to address them. Sam did so and Chimmo told the sailors he was their new CO and that he expected them to be a credit to the Royal Navy and to work hard, etc., etc. It was the usual pep talk of a new Commanding Officer but Sam could see that his troops were quite pleased at having a young and obviously enthusiastic officer in charge of them.

There was plenty of work for the units in the succeeding weeks. COSU had been allocated a workshop for the servicing of the equipment which had been brought to Newhaven in lorries belonging to the Light Scout Car Company at Ballantrae. The Radio and Radar Mechanics got the amplifiers on the test benches and tuned them ready for action and checked that everything else was in good working order. Sam set up the necessary administration section for each unit. He inspected the private houses where the sailors slept, making sure that they understood no damage to private property would be tolerated. They were responsible for cleaning the houses and generally taking care of the buildings. Sam was at pains to explain that at the end of hostilities the houses would be handed back to their owners who would expect to find them in good order. He pointed out that if the sailors' own houses were taken over by the Admiralty, they would expect the occupiers to treat the accommodation as if it were their own. A Leading Seaman was put in charge of each house and he was answerable to Petty Officer Richards regarding the state of the property. Sam knew that Richards would demand a high standard and was hopeful that there would be no damage done.

Meanwhile, Chimmo and Sam made contact with the officers and crews of the Harbour Defence Motor Launches who would be taking them to sea. It had been decreed by the Admiralty that these vessels were to be used to carry out the work of deception. Of course the HDML personnel were mystified as to their role in the forthcoming operations but accepted the imposition with good grace and tolerated the presence of the COSU ratings while they installed the equipment below deck and bolted the generators to the tiny quarter decks. The unwieldy speakers were lashed temporarily to ring bolts on the fo'c'sle. Sam knew they would almost certainly impede the traversing of the two pounder guns and after shipping them had them unshipped and taken back to the workshop to await sea trials on exercise before making any special arrangements. He knew that the two pounders were pretty ineffective anyway and ordered the Leading Seamen to have canvas covers with lengths of cod line spliced on to eyelets round the base for lashing the four-foot speaker cubes to the deck, protecting them from the elements. The speakers would have, in theory, to be able to be trained on a given bearing but it was obvious that the HDMLs would have to maintain the ship's head on the given bearings as they had no means of aiming the speakers. So much for the boffins who had thought up the scheme. Chimmo Branson was well aware of the limitations of the equipment and managed to persuade the HDML officers to "wait and see". Naturally all this activity did not go unnoticed in the harbour and when curious onlookers received fatuous explanations from the COSU ratings they dubbed COSU as another "Fred Karno Outfit" and lost interest after a while.

Preparations had reached an advanced stage when three Sub. Lieutenants were appointed to COSU. They had received a rather hurried training and after familiarising themselves with the equipment went to sea on the first exercise. Joss Broome worked with Sam and Bill Porritt and Keith Chandler went on the other HDML with the second unit. In the way that naval parties attached to the Special Boat Units had of expanding personnel, two Lieutenants appeared a week or two later and spent much of their time "having the odd noggin" in the Ward Room of HMS *Aggressive*, appearing on the jetty with bewildered looks each time the HDMLs put to sea. In the course of time they took to hanging about in the workshops, learning "on the job" as it were. They hardly ever went to sea and the four Subs. were quite amused at the Lieutenants' statements regarding the necessity to go up to "Smoke" from time to time. They assumed that the "business" they had to attend to wore skirts. Chimmo tolerated the two RNVR Lieutenants and didn't appear at all concerned by their seemingly "surplus to requirements" role in COSU. Sam had become accustomed to the bizarre behaviour of "up-country people" who descended on Coverack during the summer months. He had taken some out pollacking in his uncle Alexander Trengilly's rowing boat and subconsciously decided quite early in his young life that there was little point in trying to analyse the antics of those known collectively by his fellow villagers as their "betters", or sometimes just "they", pronounced in a pejorative vein. He was pleased, however, to be accepted as a fellow officer and they never made him feel uncomfortable by adopting a superior attitude because he was not one of their own kind and Cornish to boot! Sam was to discover later that they did have an important role to play in the fortunes of COSU and that they were indeed true gentlemen in the best sense of the word. It transpired that Cowper-Coles was working on Top Secret plans regarding the implementation of Operation Fortitude in all its aspects, hence his furtive trips to London. It was better that the junior officers of COSU did not know of these plans so that in the event of their being captured the enemy would not be able to extract the information from them. When CC, as Cowper-Coles became known to his fellow officers, had the job of getting Sam's effects together after he had gone missing on a landing in Normandy, he wrote a most sympathetic note to Sam's mother, but fortunately Sam had only been wrecked and turned up smiling in time to prevent the news, together with his kit, being sent to his mother. Regarding the other Lieutenant, Pete Fell, he just nonchalantly saw to it that exercises and operations were organised as efficiently as possible simply by being there and asking pertinent questions in such a fashion that no one could be offended. After observing what was going on he would calmly make suggestions as to how improvements could be made in the organisation, then he would disappear, remarking that something had "cropped up". He was, of course, confident that his colleagues would see the logic in his ideas and adopt them as far as practicable. Pete had obviously been appointed by someone who knew he would become a kind of "éminence grise", quietly controlling the youngsters at the "sharp end" of the "outfit", which was his term for the Sonic Warfare party.

The winter of 1944 wore on and night exercises became the norm. The little flotilla of HDMLs left Newhaven Harbour after dark, returning at dawn by permission of the Royal Artillery guarding the entrance to the port with their high-angle guns which doubled as anti-aircraft defences when the German planes flew across the coast. It was necessary to have the code ready to flash back to the soldiers when requesting permission to enter harbour. Unfortunately the Army did not always have an up-to-date code, which was changed twice daily, so though they knew the HDMLs perfectly well, the little ships were kept rolling in the swell while the Artillery duty officer ascertained that the Morse letters being flashed at the fort were the correct ones.

One dark night, Sam and Joss obtained permission to put their operational efficiency to the test. They carried out an exercise off a part of the Sussex coast known as the Seven Sisters. It was known that there was a Royal Observer Corps post near the cliff top and it was felt that these volunteer observers might well be able to give an account of what they had seen and heard after a full programme had been played at full blast from seawards. The skipper was not very happy about lying off while Joss and Sam went ashore, and indeed got rather heated after he bumped the bow on a shelf of rock as he came in close to allow the two officers to get in a float and paddle shorewards. Nothing daunted, the two friends scrambled silently up the cliff as they had been trained to do and found the sandbagged Observer Post about 100 yards inland from the cliff edge. When the two Balaclava-clad sailors suddenly appeared out of the darkness the pair of unarmed, middle-aged men in the dugout were badly startled, believing, they said afterwards, they were about to be abducted by a German landing party. They were visibly relieved when Sam calmly announced they had just come ashore from a "patrol vessel" and were trying to ascertain if they had been aware of any activity from seawards that night. Sam and Joss were disappointed when told that "nothing untoward" had happened and they could only recall hearing the engine noises they always heard when on night duty. They did point out that they were only interested in aircraft movements and tended to ignore sounds from seawards. That helped a little to soften the frustration felt by the two friends as they made their way back to the waiting ML. They duly reported what they had learned from the Observers and found it harder than ever to maintain their enthusiasm for the work they had been appointed to do.

It was the custom to put a jug containing equal quantities of rum and orange juice, sweetened with demerara sugar, on the stove about an hour before they were due to enter harbour. This concoction ensured that the officers, who were more often than not wet and cold after a night on the open bridge, went to sleep quite quickly when they turned in after their morning tot, so consequently they did not take kindly to being kept waiting while the "pongoes" sorted out their signals. Sam and his colleagues, having been seamen themselves, knew that similar concoctions were being prepared on the mess deck every night but they obligingly turned a blind eye to it and co-operated fully when Petty Officer Richards would declare in his broad Aberdeen accent that a jar of rum had been stove in "when we were off the Seven Sisters, Sir," his rolling Rs accentuating the final syllables. One could only concur after such a convincing performance, but on signing the declaration of damage, Sam would remark, "We've had a good spell of fine weather recently, haven't we, Dick?" The PO would grin and say, "Aye aye, Sir." Dick was a trawler man and a very fine seaman. Sam, having come from a fishing family, identified with him, and the two regularly went ashore together, Sam wearing his civilian clothes so that neither would feel uncomfortable in each other's company. The other officers, being ex-Public School, usually went their own ways, but Sam, and Joss, who was also ex-Grammar School, could not afford their expensive forms of entertainment and usually only accompanied them when they went for a boozy run ashore in Brighton after a particularly hard week of night exercises.

The nightly sorties did not give Sam the same kind of satisfaction that he had experienced when landing troops from his LCA. There was little in the way of feedback and after an hour or two running a programme at full blast with the speakers pointed on shore, the unit wondered if they were in effect just wasting their time. It was especially frustrating for the HDML crews but their officers wisely allowed them privileges they wouldn't have had otherwise so they enjoyed the relaxed discipline and accepted the activities of "Fred Karno's Navy" with good humour.

In the accustomed manner of Their Lordships, Chimmo Branson was appointed to what turned out to be "consultant" to D Day planners. After a few days, Lieutenant Commander Hugo Brassey, RNVR, arrived in his place. Hugo was a bluff, devil-may-care type who had spent years on the coast of Queensland. Sam liked him instinctively, and though the new CO knew little about the purpose of COSU he quickly assimilated the tactical knowledge required. To Sam's delight he asked him to accompany him to a forthcoming conference at the Admiralty as his "Technical Adviser". Sam enjoyed immensely his visit to the Holy of Holies in Whitehall. At first he was overawed by the presence of the top brass but as the discussion about the forthcoming Operation Fortitude got under way Sam realised that although the RN Commanders sitting round the table and indeed the Chairman himself who was a Captain RNR knew exactly what they intended to do, they had scant knowledge of the "nuts and bolts" of the covert operation. Hugo had quickly assessed the situation and when a pause came in the discussion he decided to jerk the conference into reality. A civilian psychiatrist who had been asked to give expert advice on the psychology of deception, stated that in addition to the sounds of approaching fast landing craft, tanks and armoured cars warming up on board landing ships and so on, there should be sounds of human voices as well, shouting phrases like "All aboard for the *Skylark*". Sam tactfully bent his head close to his notes to hide his grin but Hugo jumped in "feet first" at this point and interrupted, with a beatific smile on his weather-beaten face, saying in a loud voice, "If you don't mind my saying so, Sir, that is a load of balls." There was a short, stunned silence. Hugo then proceeded to explain that if the Germans were going to be fooled by the noises coming from seaward and consequently call for reinforcements to meet the supposed invading force, the noise had to be loud and menacing enough to galvanise the lookouts on the coast to inform their officers that the long-awaited invasion was beginning there and then and that help was needed at once. The hapless psychiatrist sat open-mouthed at Hugo's outburst and didn't utter another word throughout the discussion, though doubtless he subsequently drew a fat fee for his worthless contribution. The other members of the conference ignored him and Hugo referred them to Sam who informed them of the decibel strength needed to carry out such an operation in Channel weather, which was most unlikely to be fine. Sam explained that he and Joss had listened on shore to programmes being relayed from sea in rough weather and that if there was surf running the sounds heard by watchers on shore would be unlikely to persuade them that an invasion was imminent. Ideally, he continued, sound transmission would be most effective when there was an onshore wind and relatively high humidity. Data compiled by the Americans had indicated that wind angle and wind gradient were the controlling factors and that night time would produce the best atmospheric conditions. As he spoke, Sam glanced at Hugo who was grinning and mouthing, "Bullshit baffles brain." Sam took that to mean he had better stop talking, so he added simply, "We were all pleased to learn that operations should take place under cover of darkness!" The assembled "brass" chuckled at that and the Chairman thanked him for his contribution to the debate and just smiled knowingly. Sam had the impression that what he had said was being dismissed as relatively unimportant but at least he had made the point regarding future ops. He did not know until literally hours before leaving for Normandy that COSU's part was just a tiny fragment of the overall deception plan and was intended merely to confirm an elaborate system of false messages purporting to be the radio traffic of troops moving towards the south coast of England and culminating in the troops embarking for the Pas de Calais. Nor did he know that false radar echoes would also be beamed at the shore while the "real" troops effected a landing in Normandy.

Sam's presence at the conference had an interesting spin-off when he was ordered some time later to take some secret documents to OIC (Operations Intelligence Centre) near Admiralty Arch. Hugo had given him a welcome break from the routine exercises in the Channel. An official, locked briefcase was attached to Sam's left wrist by a thin steel chain and he wore a Webley and pouch of ammunition on a webbing belt. A fairly obvious target for an enemy agent! Naval tradition dies hard so naturally Sam complied with the regulations but put his greatcoat on, leaving it unbuttoned, to hide the revolver. The long sleeve hid the small padlock on his wrist. Sam then took the train for Victoria from the Harbour Station adjoining the London and Paris Hotel in Newhaven and found himself alone in the First Class carriage. A taxi bore him to the recently built OIC, where he was escorted through the corridors by an armed Royal Marine guard who took him to the Combined Operations Office. Sam unlocked the padlock on his wrist, handed over the precious case, obtained a signature for it and was escorted back to the entrance by the Royal Marine. Hugo had told him he could while away a few hours in London before returning to Newhaven so he set off on foot for Lyons Corner House. He felt rather self-conscious striding along with the Webley revolver concealed beneath his greatcoat. While it was a common sight in wartime to see Army officers wearing side arms, it was unusual to see Naval officers looking warlike. Nevertheless, Sam was ravenous so he walked swiftly to the restaurant and confidently ordered a Steak Baleine. He was expecting a juicy red piece of beef and was bitterly disappointed when the elderly "Nippy" put a plate before him on which was a solid, brownish square of anonymous flesh. Sam's French vocabulary had not extended to the word for "whale"! Nothing daunted, and being very hungry, Sam began eating. The whale meat was quite palatable in a fishy sort of way. Needless to say, Sam never forgot the French for whale after that little episode - and he did discover that whale, washed down with a pint of wartime Devon cider, was not as bad as he at first thought it would be!

When one is preparing for a momentous event it always seems a long way off at the beginning. There is no immediate sense of urgency, but then all at once reality becomes imminent and urgent and one realises there is much to be done and not enough time in which to achieve it. That's how it was when Sam was informed, in confidence, that the run-up to D day had begun. Night exercises were more frequent and because of the extra usage involved, the RCA projectors and the new wire recorders which provided the sound tracks started breaking down more frequently than hitherto. In addition the weather in the English Channel became unusually rough for the time of the year and the seas breaking over the little ships prompted Sam to add extra waterproofing to the Onan generators in order to keep them going. He wisely refrained from telling his superiors that he had been agitating for better covers ever since they had been placed aboard the MLs. The most difficult problem was the protection of the large loudspeakers lashed to the fo'c'sle as the MLs had to keep up their speed and the electrical connections often parted at a crucial moment, despite the fact that the stout canvas covers were only removed at the last moment to allow the sound to be broadcast unimpeded when they were in position for the final approach to the enemy coast. Sam frequently found himself working on the bow, in the dark, being regularly dowsed with freezing cold water. These drenchings made him look forward to the ritual they had devised as an antidote to the effect of Channel weather. When the ships were about five miles off Newhaven it had became the custom to mix the "grog" in a large jug and put it on the stove so that when they were safely alongside they could each partake of a tumbler of hot, home-made Coastal Forces toddy before turning in at about five o' clock in the morning. Though vastly different from the Palm Toddy which Sam was to try later when in the Far East, he found it induced sleep almost instantaneously, due, so he declared subsequently to interested listeners, to the heat of the drink. He tactfully omitted to state that the drink contained about 50% pusser's rum "saved" after breakages caused by rough weather in the Channel! If they were not too tired after a night at sea the officers were able to obtain an early breakfast in the dining room of HMS *Aggressive*, which in peacetime was known as the London and Paris Hotel. On one such occasion, the room was almost full of officers who had just come ashore from their MLs and MTBs. They were in a skittish mood, having carried out a successful operation against German E boats. Someone, probably not long out of Grammar School, began firing pats of precious rationed butter at the ceiling to see if they would stick to the mouldings. When Sam and his colleagues sat down there was no butter left on any of the plates so they could not join in the rather indelicate "fun", much to their disappointment! Of course, a strongly worded warning inevitably followed this exhibition of high spirits, fuelled no doubt by Coastal Forces toddy, because it so happened that at about eight o'clock when the Captain of the base came in to breakfast and sat in his usual chair, one of the pats of butter stuck to the ceiling above him, melted and dropped fairly and squarely on his sparsely covered head and dripped down his face. In due course it became abundantly clear what had been happening at the early breakfast, hence the Captain's stern comment about wasting rationed food which civilians would be glad to have, plus a statement that such behaviour was not becoming to a naval officer. The Captain did not add the traditional words "and gentleman" to the time-honoured phrase, which left the guilty ones in no doubt as to the Captain's opinion of young RNVR officers. Of course, he was right to castigate the unknown pranksters, but being a one-armed veteran of World War One, he most probably understood their behaviour after surviving a night of highly dangerous activity.

As spring approached it had become obvious to everyone in Britain that 1944 was going to be the year in which the allies would land in France, and this was confirmed to COSU by the increase in signal traffic. Early in April Lieutenant Chimmo Branson was sent to C. in C. Rosyth for "discussions". This move was puzzling but in retrospect Sam thought the "discussions" were probably about the plans for wireless deception tactics involving the spurious movement of troops towards the area in the

South East of England from which they could be assumed to be getting ready to land in the Pas de Calais. These "movements" were intended to be monitored by the German Wermacht and were dubbed "The Phantom Army of Kent" when in the course of time all was revealed. A week after Chimmo had been summoned to Rosyth another signal was received stating it was now too late for COSU to co-ordinate training and they were to remain at HMS *Aggressive* and not go to HMS *Newt*. As far as they were concerned, COSU had not been aware they were going to move! Then came even more mysterious Top Secret signals giving information about Anti-Radar Balloons which at 400 feet would give an echo roughly equivalent to that of a cruiser, the idea being to provide alternative and confusing points of aim for individual ships. These, it was decreed, were to be 500 yards nearer the enemy radar station than originally planned and bearing 2 - 4° off centre and were declared to be more likely to be effective in groups of 3 or 4. Fortunately all this information went over Sam's head. He had no idea what it was all about! He put it down to the signals having been sent to COSU in error and diplomatically refrained from making inquiries.

Later Sam realised that Lieut. Cowper-Coles, who had been appointed to the unit a few weeks before, knew exactly what it was all about but such was the level of security concerning the new methods of deception that he did not enlighten the junior officers regarding his true role in COSU. His duties, when the crunch came, prevented him from going to sea for the Normandy landings and his evident relief when the little fleet returned to Newhaven was quite touching to those who observed it. The junior officers had simply assumed it was partly a guilt complex because he had somehow managed to avoid going on the operation, but in truth it was vital for the success of the operation that the Lieutenant stayed ashore to co-ordinate the Navy's role in Operation Fortitude. Cowper-Coles' concern was genuine. He knew there was a distinct possibility of his friends in the HDMLs being blasted out of the water at long range by a German shore battery or a German cruiser. What COSU were in fact doing, in their innocence, was following General Wavell's "Golden Rule" of deception, "to attract the enemy's attention to what you wish him to see and to distract his attention from what you do not wish him to see." Chimmo Branson and CC, as Cowper-Coles was known to COSU, were actually summoned by signal to a Top Secret meeting ten days after D Day to discuss the results of Operation Glimmer in which COSU took part. The idea was to record impressions and learn lessons for future operations of deception. Sam learned, at a much later date, that the effectiveness of the "screens" provided by COSU was checked in detail by examining captured enemy radar plot records. It appeared that only about 20% of the German 15th Army radar stations were active, due to allied bombing. However, the evident success of the feint operation led to the same tactics being used again off Cap de la Hague on the Cotentin Peninsula. Perhaps it was just as well that those "at the sharp end" were unaware of their being led "like lambs to the slaughter" by the "boffins" in their laboratories on shore.

Sam was heartened when he went to Coverack on leave a while after D Day and his mother showed him a cutting she had saved from the front page of the *Daily Mirror* dated the 7th June 1944. The title was "Landings along broad front are going well." There was a map showing the chief centres of activity between Cherbourg and Le Havre and a statement that the latest German radio reports "suggest new Allied landings further north near Boulogne and Calais." Sam's comment was non-committal but he was delighted to know that Operation Glimmer had apparently been justified, though he did wonder, on reflection, if the account had been leaked to the British press to help persuade the harassed Germans that troops were in the Pas de Calais area. He decided it was all too complicated for him to think about and tried to put it out of his mind by enjoying his freedom at home.

When one considers the magnitude of the task of organising the invasion of Europe it is not surprising that there were omissions and alterations which the individual units had to overcome. COSU was no exception. On 6th February 1944 a signal was received stating that MLs could be used if landing craft were not available. This caused some cynical comments as Sam and his colleagues had been going out into the English Channel in HDMLs on night exercises for several weeks. A couple of weeks afterwards another signal arrived stating details of HDMLs not included previously would be communicated as soon as possible! This was followed in March by the information that the forces at Newhaven would be used as one of the diversionary forces. The officers in COSU began to wonder what the powers that be thought they had been doing for the previous three months, but of course they were all accustomed to "cock-ups" and just carried on in the hope that all would be sorted out in time for what their enemies called "der Tag".

There were a couple of interesting personal diversions for Sam during the frenetic runup to D Day. One morning Sam was hurrying along the jetty when a voice called, "What are you doing here, Sam?" It was Frank

Willoughby from Camborne. He was a sort of elderly cousin twice removed, as the saying goes. He must have been at least 35! Sam never did work out what the exact relationship was but he was glad to see a familiar face and they had a brief discussion about the latest news from Coverack as Frank was a frequent visitor to the village. The two Cornishmen arranged to meet in the Ward Room of HMS *Aggressive* the following evening - Frank was a Lieutenant, RNVR - but Sam didn't see him again until a few years after the war. It was literally a case of "ships that pass in the night" as Frank's boat left Newhaven at dusk that day. A few days after that Sam saw another familiar man strolling along the jetty. It was Pat Tyrell, a fellow pupil at Helston. Pat was one of Sam's schoolboy heroes. He ran away to sea when he was in the fourth form but was dragged off a passenger ship at Southampton before it sailed and on his return to school Pat had to face "Dreaded Dranny", the Headmaster. He was given a severe beating and everyone felt sorry for him when he displayed the weals on his hands. Dranny had drawn blood. In those days no one dared question the authority of the Headmaster so nothing was done about it and Pat became a hero in the eyes of his fellow pupils. Now, Pat had achieved his ambition and was an Able Seaman in the Royal Navy. Just as Sam never met Frank again until after the war, he didn't see Pat until several years later when they met on Flora Day in Helston, the day on which Cornish men and women traditionally seek out old friends.

By early June Newhaven harbour was so full of landing craft, MTBs and MLs that one could walk across the water from one side to the other by clambering over the small ships moored there. The whole area was teeming with troops and vehicles and no one could enter Sussex without a pass. The HDMLs were fitted with an extra radio aerial and tall posts were fixed on either side of the tiny bridge with a crossbar above giving each HDML the appearance of a floating goal mouth. There was another addition. A launch manned by Wrens came alongside with a barrage balloon. Sam was fascinated to see a diminutive Wren come aboard holding the wire of the balloon without any safety lanyard attached. Fortunately there was little wind so an obliging AB made the balloon fast before it carried the young lady aloft over the town of Newhaven. That was not all. A couple more Wrens then hauled what appeared to be a large wire cage on board and told the skipper that the cage would have to be slung beneath the balloon on receiving a signal. The balloon had to be made fast to the cross bar of the "goal posts". Sam could not resist laughing when the skipper declared he would have no more "gubbins" aboard his ship! There was more to come but fortunately they were both unaware of that and a diversion occurred which banished thoughts of going to sea looking like a Christmas tree. A dockside "buzz" was repeated by a seaman who had just come from the Regulating Office, to the effect that some Windmill girls were in the Ward Room and were going to give a performance that very night. There were mixed feelings about that. On the one hand all the sailors wanted to see the girls, who were famed for not wearing clothes when they were on stage, but was it just a sop because the powers that be had decided it would be good for morale as there was soon to be a mass slaughter when the invasion began and the "troops" were to be given a glimpse of Nirvana before they perished? It did not take the men long to decide that whatever happened they were not going to miss the show, and bribes were being offered by Duty Men who wanted to swap so that they could attend. Rome had fallen a few days before and news of the terrible losses at Cassino in May had filtered through. Now it was the turn of the men in what had been dubbed the "island fortress" by enthusiastic journalists.

There was no time to philosophise. The immediate need was to go to the show. Sam had never seen a naked lady, unless the Freetown topless females could be counted as such, so he eagerly joined the queue for seats after dinner that evening. Some of the girls were being entertained in the Wardroom and he tried to imagine what they would look like on the stage. To be honest he was not particularly impressed. There was no one there who was as pretty as Grace and he wondered absently whether or not he should tell her about the farewell concert. His doubts did not prevent him from enjoying the show. There was very little dialogue apart from loud comments by a sort of Master of Ceremonies whose innuendoes were much appreciated by the sailors and greeted with equally loud bawdy comments. All good things come to an end and in seemingly no time at all the jetty was crowded with sailors returning to their craft.

The next morning a United States Army Sergeant reported on board for duty, carrying what appeared to be an Army Type 22 Radio Telephony Set. No one knew he was coming but it now became clear why the extra wireless aerial had been fitted. The Sergeant said he would be keeping "in touch" with his comrades while crossing the Channel. There was a gale blowing outside the harbour and the Sergeant anxiously asked if the weather was going to improve. No one could give him that assurance, of course, but it was obvious the Sergeant was not looking forward to the crossing, though he tucked in heartily when offered some lunch. A good maxim is, if you are going to be seasick, be sick on a full stomach. No one mentioned that to the American.

The die was cast. After a delay of 24 hours the craft began leaving Newhaven in the late afternoon of June 5th 1944. The larger tank-landing craft had been anchored off for a couple of days and from the look of the soldiers hanging over the side when the little COSU Flotilla passed them it did not seem possible that they would be in a fit state to fight when they got to France. No one dwelt on their problem. Everyone on board was too busy preparing for a rough night.

As the port of Newhaven receded and the ship began heaving in the long swell the skipper gathered everyone abaft the bridge and read the message from General Eisenhower, the American-born son of an immigrant family from the German Rhineland.

" ... The eyes of the world are upon you ... In company with our brave allies and brothers-in-arms on other Fronts, you will bring about the destruction of the German war machine ... Your task will not be an easy one ... I have full confidence in your courage, devotion to duty and skill in battle ... and let us all beseech the blessing of Almighty God upon this great and noble undertaking."

The spray was already blowing over the deck and everyone had much to think about as sealed instructions were about to be opened and followed regarding the coming operation. Sam had expected something along the lines of Henry V's exhortation before Agincourt and he wondered if in years to come

" ... gentlemen in England now abed
Shall think themselves accursed they were not here."

He dismissed the thought just as he had already decided it was not "Dulce et decorum" - sweet and becoming - to die for one's country: it was bloody and awful, as he had witnessed with his own young eyes. Yet with the supreme confidence of a twenty-year-old pushing twenty-one, he knew he would get back home to his beloved Cornwall and one day tell his children what happened - which is the purpose of this book. So, he turned to his instructions and learned, among other things, that the "cages" now suspended beneath the balloons carried by the little ships were in reality "tetrahedral reflectors with simulative response over a wide band of frequencies approximating to a 5,000-ton ship". In other words, as he had suspected, they were to be sitting ducks and each HDML would give the Germans the impression that warships the size of light cruisers were approaching the coast at the head of an invasion force of landing craft loaded with invasion troops. The American Sergeant was playing his part in between bouts of puking noisily into a bucket which had been provided by a thoughtful sailor. On paper, or rather "on air", a whole brigade had been moved from the north of England to the south coast. It was known that the Germans were monitoring army radio messages so a script was prepared purporting to be the wireless traffic generated by the movement of a large number of troops as they travelled to the coast in preparation for a landing in the Pas de Calais area. All it needed was a radio van and a dozen or so operators. The American Sergeant was one of these and that is why he had been chosen to come aboard and continue sending the bogus messages as the "invasion force" headed towards the beaches of the Pas de Calais. The Germans would recognise his voice and with the tetrahedral reflectors playing their part and COSU sound waves being heard by enemy sentries on the French shore, it was hoped that the German High Command would move troops and ships to repel the "invaders" while the real invasion took place on the beaches near Caen. Sam learned later that the RAF played their part by dropping "windows" to render the radar stations on the coast useless, and even miniature model parachutists were scattered over the target area. The mannikins were primed to explode on impact with the ground to simulate small arms fire. It was indeed a brilliant plan and when he knew the full extent of the operation Sam was forced to eat his words and agree that it had all been well worth while. He did not exactly agree with that as they turned eastwards off Dungeness and headed for a spot between Cap Gris Nez and Boulogne into the heavy seas - but that was then and in a different context! Sam was to learn much later that there had indeed been a plan as part of Operation Overlord to attack the very place where they went to make a simulated landing and the suggested date was June 1st 1944. It was felt that the Allies would have air superiority in that area and it had the shortest possible sea crossing. This bridgehead would be followed by the main landing in early autumn of the same year. It was probably wise to abandon that plan but it was evident that it was hoped the German High Command would think along similar lines and thus Operation Glimmer, which was part of Operation Fortitude, which was part of Operation Neptune, which was part of Operation Overlord, was conceived! It was truly a case of -

"O what a tangled web we weave
When first we practise to deceive."

As the little flotilla approached the coast towards the end of the Middle Watch there were hundreds of bombers passing overhead on their way to blast the German fortifications. The sailors were all glad not to be on the receiving end of that lot, but it was time to start the decoy operation. The loudspeakers were uncovered and soon the amplifiers were blasting at full volume to give credibility to the blips from the "cages" now appearing on the German coastal radar screens and the bogus army chatter which the American continued to read out. He had stopped being seasick and was very confident in his broadcasts.

As the HDML approached the appointed spot off the enemy coast, which could now be seen, the boat was lit up by the beam of a powerful searchlight. Sam instinctively ducked as he had done when an E boat had illuminated *Pathfinder* off the island of Pantellaria. Everyone was expecting a hail of bullets, or worse still, a shell to come screaming at them. Nothing happened. It was an unnerving moment. The hull was made of wood and the only protection was a collection of splinter mats placed round the tiny bridge. The craft carried on towards the coast with the smoke canisters on the stern now spewing forth white, acrid smoke to disguise the fact that the vessel was a Harbour Launch, not a light cruiser about to open fire on the German shore batteries. It had dawned on Sam's skipper that the enemy searchlight crew could not see the boat but was training the light along the radar bearing. Then came the sound of powerful engines approaching and Sam saw in the distance what appeared to be a German destroyer heading straight for them. She soon became hidden in their smoke trail which was lying low over the water astern. Contrary to expectations the warship did not come through the smoke but evidently turned and made off at high speed in the direction of the other HDMLs. Whether it was because of the shallow depth of water or because she was receiving false echoes from two other "cruisers" and suspected a trap was never discovered. Perhaps the captain had decided he would shadow the "invasion" fleet and report its movements. Nothing was recorded in documents which were captured at a later date.

The little flotilla, shaken but undaunted, completed its scheduled tasks and thankfully began the voyage back to Newhaven, sailing independently so as to avoid unwanted attention from German reconnaissance aircraft and surface vessels. Sam's vessel was indeed spotted by a Messerschmitt which came down low over her but did not open fire. Presumably the pilot was taking photographs. The gunners did not open fire as the plane swooped down from low cloud and had disappeared before the sailors could train their Oerlikons. As another sailor put it, "Someone up there is looking after us!" The rest of the trip back passed without further incidents and the tired and thankful crew tied up in the now almost deserted harbour just as it was getting dark. Even the "bolshy" pongoes manning the guns on the bluff above the harbour accepted the entry code first time, allowing them to steam straight in through the harbour mouth without having to wallow in the waves while the officer in charge looked up the password!

No one from the little flotilla needed any rocking that night. Sam turned in "all standing" as he used to do on *Pathfinder* and slept so soundly he even missed breakfast the following morning, so he strolled along the jetty from the London and Paris Hotel in the hope of being invited aboard one of the MLs for a bite. He was surprised to see a group of sailors being photographed on the jetty. They were the usual "skates" who were serving a punishment for some minor misdemeanour by sweeping the walkways and tidying the place up. Sam was informed a few days later that those individuals were described in a daily newspaper as "sailors on the jetty at Newhaven, relaxing after returning from the beaches of Normandy" - or words to that effect. It was a salutary lesson in not believing everything you read in the newspapers! The remainder of the day was spent in making everything shipshape and ready for sea again, after reports had been given to CC regarding the operation. That evening after dinner in the Ward Room, Sam phoned his parents. He wanted to let them know he was all right. He knew he could not say what he had been doing so when Mary asked him, he replied he had been making sandcastles on the beach. His mother said rather icily, "You had better talk to your father." As she handed George the phone, Sam heard her say, "It's Sam. I think he's drunk!" George came on and asked Sam what he was playing at. Sam repeated his previous statement and George said gravely, "Did it go well?" Sam said that it had indeed so George said meaningfully, "I am delighted to hear it. Goodbye, Sam," and hung up. Of course, Sam knew then that his father had understood what he was saying and wanted to tell his mother what the strange message meant. Little did Sam know at that point that he would be repeating the message again in another ten days or so.

As he was walking along the jetty the morning after returning from D Day, in search of a breakfast, Sam was asked by an acquaintance of his if he would go as an extra officer on an LCIL (Landing Craft Infantry, Large). Sam knew there would be no COSU operation in the immediate future, so after clearing it with Hugo he agreed to go and the next day left Newhaven for the invasion beaches. The American-built craft had a landing ramp for foot soldiers each side of the bow which was as near conventional as it was possible for a landing craft. She was quite speedy when all the engines were running. On long trips it was possible to steam along on one engine on each propeller shaft so they went along steadily on the long swell which was the aftermath of the storm which had postponed the main landing by twenty-four hours. Sam's first task was to check the troop deck. They were carrying Canadian troops. Each one had a bicycle which had been "folded" for the voyage across the Channel. The troops were calm and friendly and it was clear they were well disciplined so Sam left them to their own devices when it was time to take the middle watch. The LCIL officers were extremely tired after their first landing and as they were steaming in company it was a fairly routine job. They went westwards as far as Portsmouth, then crossed by the swept Channel which was pretty crowded and a bit tricky as the ships were all steaming without lights, except for their white stern lights which enabled them to keep station on the ship ahead.

The LCIL was scheduled to land on Juno Beach which was at Courseulles. The Canadians were going to carry their bikes up the beach, move as swiftly as possible through the narrow lanes rather than the main roads and attack from the rear the Germans repelling the main landing. On approaching land through the dawn haze Sam could see a low cloud of black smoke above the invasion beach. On they went past merchant ships unloading stores and ammunition into landing craft for ferrying to the beaches. Sam discovered later that his cousin, James Rickard, had sailed from Tilbury for Normandy on a cargo ship laden with stores of war and that they must have been within a mile or so of each other at that particular time. Beyond the line of merchant men the battleship *Anson* could be seen at anchor. She began firing salvoes at targets beyond the front line shortly after the LCIL went by and Sam felt pleased he was not on the receiving end as the shells whistled overhead. By now, of course, everyone was at Action Stations and the soldiers were quietly waiting in the troop deck as the LCIL made for Bernières. Tracers were sparking overhead and tin hats were donned, just in case. On the signal from the Beach Master, the skipper took the landing craft towards the allotted space and gave the order to drop the kedge anchor just as Sam felt he might have forgotten in the heat of the moment! At that very instant a buzz bomb came careering across the beach apparently headed straight for their craft and everyone ducked. Fortunately it landed astern and exploded harmlessly as the ramps were lowered and the Canadians dashed down the steps into the cold sea which came up to their chests as they waded ashore, holding their bikes up out of the water. Not for the first time was Sam glad he had not joined the Army as the soldiers ran up the beach, crouching as low as they could because of the danger of being struck by the odd stray bullet. They had been warned that German planes were liable to make a quick sortie across the beach despite claims that the Allies had command of the air. All foot soldiers were known as the PBI - Poor Bloody Infantry. In a quiet moment, much later, Sam pondered over the common service designation and thought that in future he would privately think of those Canadian soldiers as Purposeful, Bold Infantry. They were that, absolutely.

As soon as the Canadians had disembarked the skipper gave the order to haul on the kedge anchor so that room could be made for another landing craft to come on to the beach. Nothing happened. The wire cable

Canadian Infantry landing with bicycles on Juno Beach at Courseulles, June 1944

(Photo Le Goubey & Archives Nationales du Canada)

took the strain but the anchor was not holding; it began tripping on the bottom and finally the cable parted. The engines were going "flank" (full) astern - the American-built craft naturally had American engine-room telegraphs - but still the craft did not budge. They were well and truly aground. Another LCIL ploughed in alongside and after the infantry had dashed up the beach in the wake of the Canadians, she managed to get off the beach and the skipper promised he would arrange for a clearance team to come and help as the Beach Master had moved off and was obviously unaware of the dilemma.

While they were waiting for deliverance, so to speak, the LCIL crew had the opportunity to observe the scene surrounding them. Courseulles Plage did not really look like a beach at all, nor did it sound like one. Every now and again a German plane would streak across, firing in the hope that some damage would be done, and at regular intervals the shells from *Anson* rushed overhead, sounding rather like an express train in the distance, then would come the crump of the explosion when the shells landed and more black smoke rose into the sky inland. The sandy shingle of the beach was all but hidden by military equipment, stores awaiting removal, abandoned vehicles and even a few bodies still waiting attention. It was ordered chaos. Everyone on the beach had an appointed task and carried it out, ignoring the presence of other people. It was a truly remarkable sight, one which Sam was never to forget. Despite his experience in Liverpool where he had handled many types of landing craft arriving from the USA, there were types in evidence that he had never heard of, let alone seen. Standing off from the beach were LCRs (Landing Craft Rockets) which he learned had the fire power of a cruiser but could not fire continuously because of the need to reload rockets after a launch. There were also LCGs (Landing Craft Guns) which could deliver a broadside equivalent to a capital ship but of course could not manoeuvre. It was simply a floating gun battery in effect and purpose-built. The LCKs were very popular. They were Landing Craft Kitchens and their job was to provide meals for beach parties organising the landings and soldiers and sailors who were stranded or waiting to move off. These landing craft were bristling with the familiar H-shaped chimneys and drew hungry servicemen like magnets. At the same time DUKWs, or Ducks as these amphibious vehicles had become known, were coming on to the beaches and driving up the sand laden with stores and ammunition etc., and on towards the fighting line. They had dual rear axles and could drive the wheels at 50 mph on land and a propeller at 5 knots on water, carrying up to 50 men or a load of equipment. In addition, of course, Assault Landing Craft were still bringing in troops as were the LCILs and LCPs (Personnel). The sea-borne traffic was controlled by HQ landing craft anchored off and, as mentioned earlier, by Naval Commando Beach Parties on shore. They had landed ahead of the assault troops.

Assault Landing Craft on Courseulles Plage, 1978
(Photograph by David Hart)

Sam never did get off the beach in his temporary LCIL. After a long wait he decided he had better try to get back to Newhaven as he was only expected to be away three or four days at the outside. After a word with the skipper he flashed another LCIL which he had seen in Newhaven and the captain agreed he could work his passage back. A seaman was told off to row him across the water to the waiting ship. Unfortunately the chap was not very good at managing the oars so Sam volunteered to row into the onshore wind and told him it would be easier on the return journey! He wondered afterwards how many people would be able to boast having rowed across the invasion beaches in 1944. Not many, he suspected.

As soon as he got on board the LCIL up-anchored and went in on the beach. Sod's Law was at work again. They had been ordered to load German POWs and take them to Newhaven. While loading was in progress a German fighter came over and fired at the boats on the beach. The British Military Police had already learned to shout "Raus, raus!" to get their prisoners to hurry. They needed no second bidding at that particular point, especially as the MPs were gesticulating with their fixed bayonets. Sam was asked to go below and check on the troop decks when they had kedged successfully off the beach and he was struck by the stench of men who had not washed for days due to the fighting. They were obviously very tired and hungry as well and there was a crowd trying to get into the ship's heads to have a drink and a quick wash. They seemed in no fit state to want to take over the ship so Sam told the sailors guarding them to let the German NCOs organise the troop deck but stand clear of them and not turn their backs. When he revisited the troop deck a couple of hours later, it was quiet and most of the men were fast asleep.

When they went alongside in Newhaven early the following morning the prisoners were marched along the jetty to the train which was to take them to a Prisoner of War Camp. They had to run the gauntlet of the French sailors whose craft were moored alongside. The sailors jeered and threw rubbish at the Germans and some emptied dustbins over them. Sam felt sorry for the Germans but understood why the French were behaving in such a manner. He knew he would have probably reacted in the same way if his country had been overrun and people he knew carted off to concentration camps. After thanking his fellow officers for the lift back home, Sam trudged wearily along the jetty to the London and Paris Hotel and climbed slowly to his room on the top floor which he shared with Joss, who was delighted to see him and announced that Hugo had panicked when he did not return as planned and had ordered his kit to be packed prior to being posted missing! It took quite a while for Sam to live down that little episode of service life. He found that a few rounds of drinks on him to celebrate his safe return helped considerably. That evening he rang his parents once more and gave the same message about playing sandcastles. This time Mary understood where he had been and laughed out loud, adding she hoped he didn't get wet feet. If only she knew that it had been a near thing, thought Sam. But then, there are some things a man does not tell his mother!

When Sam began to study in earnest after the war he paid particular attention to the details of the Norman invasion of England. He learned that William landed from the Mora in Pevensey on the 28th September 1066 after having had to wait for a favourable wind in St. Valéry. Even so some of his ships foundered during the crossing, but he made a successful and practically unopposed landing, complete with wooden castles which had been constructed in France and dismantled for the channel crossing. His troops dug an earthen mound and reassembled the structures, forming a base from which to operate and defend the landing beach. Harold had been led to believe William was going to land on the Isle of Wight and was waiting there to oppose the assault. Sam could not help but smile at the medieval equivalent of Operation Fortitude and the prefabrication of engines of war prior to the invasion. It was a striking illustration of the French dictum, "Plus ça change, c'est la même chose" - there's nothing new in spite of changing times. No doubt Eisenhower and his planners had knowledge of the assault heralding the Norman Conquest of England!

There was a distinct feeling of deflation after the return from Normandy. Sam began to wonder how they would be able to keep the "troops" happy as their existence was lacking in purpose. They did carry out a few exercises to ensure a state of readiness. In late June there was a flurry of activity when it was decided to add some confusion for the benefit of the German troops defending Caen. Intelligence sources had reported that the Germans were still convinced there would be another landing. It was a very simple "plain" exercise, creating lots of sounds from seawards to cause a diversion of troops on shore to meet a simulated waterborne threat. It was believed that the Light Scout Car Company from Laggan House was also in action on land but there was no confirmation of this at the time. Not long afterwards in early July 1944, the long-awaited surrender of Caen was announced on the wireless. There had been heavy losses among the Canadian and British troops and Sam wondered how the bicycle company had fared. Naturally no one knew if what turned out to be the "swan song" of COSU in Europe had been a success or not. It was one of the penalties of being involved in covert operations.

As summer turned into Autumn some changes in personnel were made. Lieutenant Lawton, a jovial Yorkshireman, was appointed as Electronics Officer to COSU. He proved to be an invaluable member of the team and in due course became a good friend to Sam. At last there was someone who really understood electronics! Flex, as the newcomer quickly became known, was a Science graduate and had been involved in degaussing, which was a means of neutralising a ship's magnetic field so that it would not set off the magnetic mines the Germans were laying on the seabed.

He was also a sportsman and had played hockey for Yorkshire. That went down well with the young sailors. It did not take Flex long to get all the equipment in good order and the mechanics responded well to his friendly way of getting things done. In October they were alerted for a possible operation and got everything "on the top line". For once, Sod's Law worked in their favour. Sound equipment was placed on board a Fairmile ML. She was a lovely, sleek-looking craft in comparison with the squat HDs and Sam enjoyed going to sea in her. Unfortunately the craft developed serious engine trouble which would take a while to repair so Hugo sent Sam and his unit on leave, liable to recall. While Sam was enjoying the delights of Coverack after a quick visit north to see Grace, there was a landing in the Scheldt Estuary which involved quite heavy loss of life among Combined Operations personnel and ML crews. Although nothing official was said it was understood that COSU would have been involved if there had not been problems with the ML.

There was little time for reflection. A signal arrived announcing that the acoustic equipment was to be prepared forthwith in readiness for operations in the tropics. Flex began showing his mechanics how to wax the delicate wiring, and generally made ready. He had special wooden trunks made, complete with dessicators housed in the hinged lids to prevent the high humidity from ruining the circuits. He regaled Sam and his colleagues with tales of tropical termites which could munch their way through the rubber protecting the sophisticated wiring systems. That is why he had airtight seals fastened round the lids of the trunks. It was almost certain that in operations in the Far East, the equipment would be transported in landing craft which could penetrate the shallow rivers and so every option had to be explored when making ready. Mindful of the need for secrecy, each trunk was fitted with two stout brass padlocks to prevent prying eyes from finding out about the contents.

While all this was going on the sailors were sent in relays on embarkation leave and on their return the base Medical Officer vaccinated them against smallpox, cholera and yellow fever. There was no doubt in anyone's mind that COSU was bound for the Far East! Sam went back to Austin Reid in Brighton to get his tropical whites and other necessary kit. His sister Emily wheedled some khaki tropical shirts from the Quarter-master of her Anti-Aircraft Battery to try and save Sam some money. He was delighted but when he subsequently unpacked them in Ceylon he found they were women's shirts! He decided he couldn't just throw them away and wore them as working shirts on board ship.

It was some time before his friend Joss said to him one day, "Sam, what sort of shirt are you wearing?"

"Why do you ask ?" said Sam, casually.

"Well," said Joss, "it's different, but I don't know what it is."

Sam laughed. then told him the story of the shirts. The two friends had to wait some while before someone else got round to asking the same question about Sam's ATS shirts.

In late November, Sam took his embarkation leave. In response to the usual questions from his friends and relatives in Coverack he was suitably vague, not that he knew exactly where he was going, but mindful of the need for security he stated he thought he was going "foreign" again, and no one pressed him further. A few Coverack men had already been lost at sea and everyone knew the possible consequences of careless talk, so no one pressed him for an answer.

The second half of Sam's foreign service leave was spent at Grace's home. The two young people were now allowed the privilege of staying up late in the lounge. Sam met Grace outside her office on most evenings and they enjoyed a quiet coffee together in the Kardomah before catching the bus back home. Sam told Grace about the system of letter writing which had been adopted by sailors serving abroad and she agreed to number her letters so that when a batch of four or five arrived at the same time, Sam would be able to open them in the right sequence. He promised Grace he would remain true to her and told her once more to ignore the reputation that sailors had of having a girl in every port. To his delight Grace said she had always remained true to him since he went to Scotland and would continue to do so. In their innocence that assurance went some way to ease the pain of parting when Sam found himself once more waving wildly to the diminutive figure on the platform of Preston Station as the train started on its journey to Euston.

At last everything had been made ready for the departure of COSU for the Far East. Parties were held on the MLs, the equipment carefully packed and made ready for the long journey in the hold of a merchant ship. The group was now to be known as Naval Party 2450, c/o GPO, Reading, just like all His Majesty's Ships. Christmas was fast approaching and everyone began secretly hoping the departure would now be delayed until the New Year and that Christmas could be spent at home. It was too much to hope for. Hugo solemnly declared at Divisions one morning in mid-December that they would be leaving Newhaven on Boxing Day. Shortly afterwards he announced, on Christmas Eve, to the officers that he would meet them at 2230 at Euston Station on the Glasgow platform. He then swiftly disappeared. It was one of the privileges of being the Commanding Officer. No one was surprised. He had done that sort of thing before. Sam had even gone to sea without him on one occasion when he was on one of his mysterious "excursions". Christmas Day in HMS *Aggressive* came and went swiftly and companionably in a haze of over-indulgence of food and alcohol. The problems of impending departure were, as if by common consent, not mentioned.

The train was scheduled to leave Newhaven Harbour Station at midday on Boxing Day. Hugo had designated Sam to be in charge of the draft with Joss as second in charge. The other officers were to make their way independently. Sam diplomatically failed to inform the draft that they were to travel the few miles to Lewes and change, then there would be a two-hour wait before catching the train to Victoria. When they had all assembled on the platform at Lewes, Sam announced they had an hour and a half to spare and that they could go down the road to the pub for a drink. He added in the time-honoured phrase that if anyone went adrift he would "have his bollocks for a necklace". Sam did not often revert to the lower deck language he had learned as a seaman so he knew that his warning would be heeded. Petty Officer Dick Chard then told off three half hour relays of baggage parties. The guards were instructed to sit on the trunks containing the Sonic Equipment which were in front of the kit bags and hammocks piled on the platform.

Much to Sam's relief the enforced delay at Lewes passed off smoothly. No one went adrift and Naval Party 2450 was soon speeding towards Victoria, where, half unexpectedly, the RTO denied all knowledge of a prearranged order for a couple of three-tonners to take the party to Euston. Sam persisted, showing the Army Lieutenant a copy of the original signal; eventually the lorries were summoned and the party was travelling swiftly through the strangely quiet London streets. On arrival at Euston the baggage parties were organised once more and the sailors were free to spend the subsistence money they had been given for the journey. Petty Officer Chard reiterated Sam's warning when telling them to muster for roll call at 2230 on the Glasgow platform.

Sam and Joss then made their way to the station restaurant where an ancient, sullen-looking waiter declared solemnly that there was only jugged hare on the menu. The friends looked at each other and burst out laughing as they had already guessed the restaurant manager would fall back on the good old railway standby for a Boxing Day dinner. Their mirth softened up the old boy and when he came to arrange the table he told the sailors that as a special favour he could manage a couple of mince pies for dessert! The jugged hare turned out to be quite palatable when washed down with Devonshire cider, and the mince pies and thin custard made with water were more fruity than expected. It may have seemed that way to the two young men because they were very hungry, having had only a liquid lunch at Lewes. The waiter was duly paid and rewarded for his "special favour", and then Sam and Joss went out to the cold platform to commiserate with the "troops" who had gathered rather disconsolately well before the appointed time as the bar had run out of beer on Boxing Day of all days. "After all, there is a war on," a hapless barman reminded the lads, provoking a chorus of catcalls and naval expletives, just as, at 2230 as promised, a hatless Hugo was passing the bar, seated on a suitcase which was on a station trolley being pulled by an elderly porter. The trolley was followed by a gorgeous smiling blonde, tottering on high-heeled shoes, holding Hugo's peaked cap in one hand and balancing what appeared to be half a glass of champagne in the other. On seeing Hugo making his grand entrance to Euston Station, the sailors' jeers turned to cheers and a merry sailor called out, "Hello, Sir, have you had a good Christmas?" "What do you think, lads?" replied Hugo, grinning from ear to ear and waving his hand towards his beautiful companion. That raised an even louder cheer. Hugo then turned to the row of officers on the platform and called out, "Good evening gentlemen, is all well?" "All present and correct, Sir," said Sam, who was the first to find his tongue, and at that very moment the Glasgow train rolled slowly into the station. Petty Officer Chard shouted orders and the luggage was quickly loaded in the Guard's van. Lieutenant Flex Lawton chose two mechanics to remain, for the first watch, guarding the precious trunks which were securely locked in a wire cage with other valuable items.

Sam and Joss found their reserved two-berth sleeping compartment, which was in a sleeping car next to the carriage carrying the sailors, and settled down for the long night journey northwards. They chatted quietly for a while, sipping Duty Free Gin from their regulation tin mugs which were standard issue for Combined Operations personnel. The incongruity did not strike them: they didn't mind not having dainty glasses as used in Ward Rooms for G. and T. They were young and looking forward to a new adventure and not at all maudlin despite consuming large tots of neat "Mothers' Ruin". Before long they were climbing into the narrow bunks, laughing loudly as they had been going over the day's events, culminating in Hugo's dramatic arrival. They both agreed that he was just the man to lead their "Fred Karno Outfit". Aided by the gin they slipped into a dreamless sleep, regardless of the fact that it was their last night in the UK. There was no anxious thought for the morrow. That could wait.

Sam, circa 1943

CHAPTER SEVENTEEN

EAST OF ADEN

In the early morning, about half an hour before the train was due to arrive in Glasgow Central, the sleeper steward knocked at the door and placed two cups of tea and two McVitie and Price Rich Tea biscuits on the shelf by the window of the sleeping compartment. This was luxury indeed and Sam's favourite biscuits as well. The young officers had not travelled by First Class sleeper before and were pleasantly surprised. There was no time to muse over their good fortune. They just managed to wash and shave, being disappointed that the First Class water was cold! The train stopped and the draft was mustered on the platform. All the kit and the wooden trunks were loaded on trolleys and the men made their way to the exit. This time the RTO had organised lorries and they were soon on their way to Girvan, there being no suitable train connection.

When the sailors arrived at the quayside, they went straight aboard the SS *Mahanada* and began settling in their temporary quarters for the voyage to Ceylon. An obliging dockie had confided the name of their destination to one of the matelots and the buzz spread like wildfire. The buzz was confirmed when Hugo reported to the Captain.

The *Mahanada* turned out to be a Liverpool-registered ship of about 8,000 gross tons. (1 gross ton = 100 cubic feet of enclosed space - which means earning space in commercial terms.) She had steam turbines and had been built in 1943 for the Brocklebank Line. The passenger accommodation was luxurious compared with Royal Navy ships and everyone was pleased. It went a little way to compensate for having to leave the UK at Christmas. Sam had noted as he went aboard that the ship was flying International Flag B, denoting that there were explosives in the cargo, but refrained from commenting to the sailors though doubtless some of the more experienced ones were also aware of the fact. Sam's only experience of accommodation on merchant ships was when he had visited tankers in Falmouth Docks as a young lad. His uncles Alexander Trengilly and James Rickard were British Tanker Bosuns and were entitled to invite family members on board when they were in harbour. Sam used to go with his cousins Horace Trengilly and James Rickard and their mothers. The *Mahanada* was an Intermediate boat, carrying a limited number of passengers as well as general cargo, which in this instance turned out to be mainly bombs and torpedo warheads. There was nothing anyone could do about that so Sam put the possibility of being hit by a German or Jap torpedo at the back of his mind. Of course he could not dismiss it but he determined not to let it interfere with what promised to be an interesting voyage. It was not too difficult for one so young and he reasoned he had already had experience of the possibility of being blown up and it had not bothered him unduly because like all young people he didn't think it applied to him.

The accommodation had been adapted to carry about twice the normal complement of passengers but the members of COSU, or NP 2450 as they were now called, considered it luxurious and not at all cramped, though one or two of the civilian passengers grumbled about it. They were mainly members of the Colonial Service and included also an Egyptian gentleman who had a fund of colourful stories which he recounted to the young officers at dinner each evening. Hugo was convinced the man was being deported but there was no way of verifying his theory before the Egyptian left the ship at Port Said. Mr. Guest, a senior officer of the Colonial Service, supported Hugo in his theory but he assured everyone it was pure conjecture on his part and not because of any privileged information he had been given.

There was not a great deal to do on board ship. Sam had been asked to detail men to double up on the *Mahanada*'s defensive armament. It consisted of four Oerlikons to be used against low-flying aircraft. He divided the men into watches and asked the DEMS gunners to instruct the seamen regarding keeping a lookout, aircraft recognition, loading and firing the guns. It was fortunate that Sam was familiar with the 20 mm guns and demonstrated how to load the magazine, which contained 60 rounds, and fire, and changing the drum when emptied of live rounds which were held in place under a 49lb. spring pressure. DEMS were Royal Navy gunners who sailed on Defensively Equipped Merchant Ships, hence the name. The merchant fleet had been put under Admiralty control for the duration, so most ships were fitted with light defensive armaments. RN seamen and Royal Artillery soldiers were men chosen for their skill as gunners and who had proved to have the necessary initiative to decide when to open fire on attacking planes, surface ships or submarines. Naturally the ship's captain could override the decision of the gunners, who were sometimes assisted by the merchant sailors on board. The *Mahanada* was capable of steaming steadily at 14 knots and was in the category of ships which did not have to sail in convoy. In theory she could outpace a U-boat and thus did not have heavy armament as a U-boat would find it difficult to successfully aim and launch a torpedo at her when she was going at her maximum speed. The DEMS gunners were experienced hands and Sam felt they could pass on valuable knowledge to the young COSU seamen. Some had never been to sea before in a big ship and could do with a "sea daddy" to advise and instruct them. Conversely the Royal Navy gunners were pleased to have some help and to show off their knowledge.

As the ship steamed steadily south, lifting to the Atlantic swell, some of the sailors succumbed to sea sickness. They did not really have enough to do to take their minds off their plight and felt sorry for themselves. Sam thought of the time when after climbing through the lubber's hole on *Pathfinder* to gain access to the crow's nest for Action Stations, he was sick for only the second time in his life. He blessed his parents for giving him the kind of constitution which was not seriously affected by what Flex, who had also been affected, termed "mal de mer".

Sam was in effect still a schoolboy sailor. He knew he would have to get proper qualifications when he left the navy and in anticipation of having some spare time on board the merchant ship, he had brought George Macaulay Trevelyan's *History of England* with him so that he could spend his spare time profitably and pass slowly out of the schoolboy stage. Of course, he did not know what he would do when the war ended. He toyed with the idea of remaining in the Royal Navy, if offered the opportunity, but he was mindful of what had happened to his uncle Seth Exelby, who had remained in the Navy after the First World War, then came the Geddes "Axe" and officers were made redundant, resulting in Seth going to New Zealand as an officer in the Merchant Navy and eventually remaining there, sending for his family in the 1920s. Sam's grandmother Catherine never really got over the separation from her middle son and talked about him endlessly. Sam determined to wait and see what happened and in the mean time he would try to prepare for obtaining further qualifications. He had at one time been interested in the job of Radio Officer on a merchant ship and had indeed sent for the details of training but he abandoned the idea when he learned he would have to pay fees to enter the Wireless School. While on board the *Mahanada* he made the acquaintance of the Radio Officer, who offered to take back some of Sam's "blues" such as his greatcoat and post them to his mother when the *Mahanada* got back to the UK. Sam learned quite a bit about the conditions of service in the MN and was surprised to discover that seamen were only paid £10 a month "danger money", termed officially "War Risk Bonus", in addition to their pay, which was stopped immediately if their ship was sunk or the crew taken prisoner by an armed raider. Of course, "Sparks" lost no time in pointing out that American merchant seamen were paid more than twice the £12 that British Able Seamen were paid per month and they received 100% extra for service in the North Atlantic and Mediterranean and 80% for the Pacific and Indian Ocean. Sam had always admired the way in which the merchant ships had performed in the convoys he had escorted on *Pathfinder* and now that he was sailing with merchant seamen he began to appreciate the role of a non-combatant even more, losing no time in passing on details of the merchant sailor's conditions of pay and service to his fellow Royal Navy shipmates when an appropriate occasion arose.

Apart from the usual rough weather in the Bay of Biscay, the voyage to the Mediterranean turned out to be uneventful and everyone slipped into the easy-going routine with little difficulty. Sam had words with the purser who produced the rum ration at noon each day. He had noted that the purser was not careful when measuring the precious grog. Sam pointed out that "Up spirits" was probably the most important moment of the day for many sailors and if they suspected they were not getting the right amount there would be hell to pay. Sam added that "Jack Dustys" responsible for the rum had sustained mysterious injuries on runs ashore after being under suspicion. That implied warning sufficed to ensure the measures were henceforth accurately applied.

The *Mahanada* sailed serenely through the Straits of Gibraltar and made the first port of call at Port Said. Sam was thankful to arrive there in one piece, remembering his last voyage in the Mediterranean in 1942. Everyone went eagerly ashore to sample the dubious delights of Port Said. On stepping on dry land there was the usual horde of street vendors offering everything from packs of "feelthy" postcards of dubious origin and subjects to an introduction to a "pretty girl - you like my sister very much". There were also the usual young lads showing conjuring tricks with live, day-old chicks which they could make disappear and reappear with astonishing sleight of hand. Of course, their accomplices were jostling in the crowd, waiting for an opportunity to pick the pockets of the foreigners. Sam and Joss pushed their way unceremoniously through the noisy locals towards the docks exit, using threatening gestures and loudly shouting "Imshi" repeatedly, which had a better effect than "Bugger off", which is what it means, roughly, in Arabic. The two young officers walked briskly along the relatively quiet streets until they came to the Memorial Hall Services Club which was run by the Missions to Seamen and after a pleasant cup of tea accompanied by some home-made cakes, they set out to view the town, which was served by noisy old buses carrying what seemed to be hundreds of non-fare-paying passengers clinging to the sides. Some had even clambered up the outside of the back of the buses and were sitting on the roofs. There was only time for a brief tour of the colourful shops before they had to make their way back to the docks again as the *Mahanada* was due to set sail for Suez. Sam would have liked to explore further. There were some very fine buildings which were obviously influenced in design by European architecture and seemed to be used as posh Gentlemen's Clubs or private hotels patronised by rich Egyptians and Europeans.

When they got back on board, Sam and Geoff made the acquaintance of another civilian who had taken the place of the Egyptian gentleman. It transpired that Bill had been living in the East for the last twenty years or so and was on his way to take up a new appointment in Bombay. He replaced the Egyptian as unofficial raconteur and each evening he would invite his listeners to stub out their cigarettes on his forearm, which was covered in white scars made by the cigarettes of previous listeners. Sam and his colleagues politely declined the offer each night, so he would extinguish his own cigarette on his arm, saying it was "good" to learn to put up with a little pain. Hugo's comment, when Bill was not around, was that the poor bloke had been in the sun too long. Sam and Joss were inclined to agree! They were learning much about their fellow man on the voyage.

The Suez Canal lived up to expectations. Sam thought it was quite eerie to glide along the narrow channel, which to his surprise later on proved to be quite wide when passing through the Bitter Lakes and to have some quite sharp bends in it. They were under the safe command of an Egyptian pilot. The oppressive heat made him feel glad he did not have to do any real work, and Bill, who had come up on deck and stood next to Sam, reminded him of the origin of the word "posh", which referred to the side on which affluent passengers booked their cabins - **P**ort Side on the way **O**ut to the Far East and **S**tarboard Side on the way **H**ome, so that the cabin was on the side away from the sun. Of course, Sam's shared cabin was on the wrong side but he didn't think it would be prudent to complain even though the temperature did reach nearly 100° F. at one point. For a while, the ship was accompanied by some Egyptian soldiers riding camels and trotting along the bank of the canal. The sailors on deck shouted unprintable comments to the grinning soldiers, who appeared to reply in like vein. After dropping the pilot at Port Tufic, on completing the 100-plus miles of waterway, the *Mahanada* continued down the Red Sea. Sam was reminded of the Exodus when the Red Sea was supposed to have parted to allow the fleeing Israelites to cross. It had seemed a pretty tall story when it was told by Josiah Barker in the Wesleyan Sunday School at Coverack and now that he was actually entering the Red Sea he was inclined to remain sceptical. His scepticism was justified when some time later he read about some research into the happenings during the 13th century BC. It stated that in all probability the fleeing slaves reached a fresh-water lake known as the Sea of Reeds, not the Red Sea. The Reeds were papyrus, which only grew in fresh-water marshes. It was suggested that a strong east wind pushed the water back enabling them to cross on the bed of the lake. The pursuing Egyptian soldiers followed them and their chariots got bogged down in the marshy land, so when the wind dropped and the waters returned to cover the lake bed the Egyptians were trapped and many drowned, being unable to escape the rising water. At this point the pursuit was called off, the Egyptian leaders interpreting the phenomenon as an act of the Israelites' God, against whom they were powerless to resist.

The ship ploughed on through the Gulf of Aden into the Arabian Sea, making for Bombay. One evening as the sun sank swiftly below the horizon a vessel was spotted which with a little imagination could have been a submarine. Taking no chances the Captain went to Action Stations and piled on the speed to avoid contact. Fortunately nothing came of it and the *Mahanada* went serenely on her way. The episode did serve to remind everyone that they were at war and it was not just a cruise in the tropics. Not long afterwards, the *Mahanada* came alongside in Bombay to unload some cargo before proceeding to Colombo. Sam and Joss lost no time in giving out leave passes to the liberty men and going ashore themselves. Walking through the grim dock area it seemed that they were on the trail of someone who had recently had some teeth extracted and was bleeding profusely. They discovered in due course that Indians had a liking for betel nuts which they chewed incessantly, spitting out the red juice as they walked along. This lack of standards of hygiene practised by the locals was no doubt in part due to the shortcomings of the education provided by the British Raj. It was the lads' elementary lesson in the truth about British rule over the Empire "on which the sun never sets".

Bombay was in many respects a copy of a large British port. From seawards it was impressive, having been built on seven islands with a backdrop of the Western Ghats Mountains which gave a purple hue as they appeared to rise out of the sea. Sam learned from a book in the ship's minuscule library that the town itself had been handed to the British as part of the marriage settlement of Catherine of Braganza when the Portuguese Roman Catholic Princess became betrothed to Charles II. The government subsequently handed the town to the safe keeping of the East India Company and the port itself became the centre of the Indian cotton market which took off after the opening of the Suez Canal in 1957. Sam was to remember the rather high-handed way in which the town had been treated by the British government when he returned to Bombay just after the Japanese surrender and found a strong political movement agitating for the end of British rule. As Sam and Joss wandered through the busy streets they were struck by the familiarity of the buildings, especially the Victorian railway station, which was a magnificent copy of St. Pancras Station in London.

Sam was horrified to see, while walking with Joss through the shopping centre, a one-eyed leper sitting on a pile of rags, holding out a begging bowl while cuddling a healthy baby in her arms which were covered in the characteristic reddish white lesions, and a couple of fingers of one hand appeared to have dropped off. Sam was taken back to his Sunday School days in Coverack when they studied the book of Leviticus and were made to realise that all the laws of the Levi priests regarding the cleansing of lepers were quite ineffective through ignorance of the nature of the disease, and here he was, some three thousand years later, witnessing continued misunderstanding of the scourge. Joss was similarly taken aback and hurriedly threw some coins into the bowl. Sam did likewise and they walked on, not knowing what to think about the situation they had just witnessed. They could still hear the woman's anguished cries of "Baksheesh, Baksheesh", as they turned the corner into another street. They learned subsequently that young mothers, desperately poor, hired out their healthy babies to the lepers while they went to work. It did not take much imagination to divine what often happened after exposure to the dread disease. The two friends realised they were being followed by a few beggars. They had been warned of the consequences of being "soft" enough to give money to paupers and practised the word "joow" which was the equivalent of the Arabic "imshi". The people backed off as a red-helmeted policeman directing the traffic at the corner heard what was being said and waved his lathi at the beggars in a menacing manner. In due course the sailors were to witness Indian policemen beating beggars who were making a nuisance of themselves, the officers being oblivious to the fact that the poor people were covered in sores, probably caused by malnutrition.

The next day, Sam fulfilled a request his mother had made before he left Coverack. One of her WAAF friends named Pat had a sister stationed in Bombay and Sam had promised that if he ever went to Bombay he would look her up and give her news of Pat, whom Sam had met a few times when she came to the house for a cup of tea and a chat. The girl was a Dental Nurse in the WAAF and after making contact at the RAF clinic, Sam asked her to go to the pictures with him, in the time-honoured custom of matelots ashore. She gained grudging permission from her boss and they went to see a Danny Kaye film which was the first one in Technicolor he had seen. In addition, the cinema was air conditioned - another first - and Sam enjoyed the cool contrast with the smelly heat of the streets. The two conversed over a snack after the film and Sam brought Jean up to date with gossip from her sister. Jean had never been to Coverack so Sam lost no time in telling her about his lovely village and gave her a potted history of events dating back a couple of hundred years. He returned the WAAF to her barracks at the agreed time to find the dentist hanging about the entrance gate. Jean then revealed that she was engaged to him. Fortunately Sam had a clear conscience regarding his evening out! When Sam got back on board the *Mahanada* and gave an account of his run ashore, Joss commented drily, "The end of another beautiful friendship." Sam agreed but was pleased that he had done his duty and received his mother's thanks for making the effort, in due course!

The *Mahanada* was due to sail on the evening tide of the following day so he went ashore once more with Joss to do some shopping now that they had got the lie of the land, so to speak. They were well fed on board but Joss suggested it would be interesting to try out some Indian food. They duly entered a hotel, ordered a curry and sat sipping ice cold lime juice while they waited. The punkah wallah was operating the cooling system and they were fascinated to see the barefoot Indian sitting on the floor of the dining room with his back against the wall and one knee crossed over the other. Attached to the big toe of the upper leg was a cord which led to a rectangular board covered in raffia which was suspended from the ceiling by a couple of ropes. By raising and lowering his foot rhythmically, the punkah moved to and fro, creating a pleasant draught of relatively cool air above the heads of the diners. The coolie had got the gentle fanning movement off to a fine art and clearly expended as little energy as possible in the execution of his duties. The other diners totally ignored the actions of the coolie, being accustomed to receiving such a service, but Joss and Sam remained transfixed until served with a bowl of steaming curry with its accompaniment of rice and a delicious assortment of cool fruit which was intended to take the heat out of the main dish. To their surprise the highly seasoned beef curry turned out to be most palatable and the chapattis and iced water helped to keep the temperature down. They had fresh mango for dessert and both declared it was the most delightful fruit they had ever tasted. After lunch they did some shopping for cheap, non-bulky souvenirs and Sam bought a copy of Palgrave's *Golden Treasury* for 1 Rupee 14. It had been his poetry text book when at school and he felt some of the poems might mean more to him now that he was officially an adult. His English teacher Miss Naytor in Helston would have been proud of him as he had always learned the poems she set with reluctance. It was the done thing for adolescent boys to treat such "soppy stuff" with disdain. Sam kept the book to hand throughout his naval service and indeed it became a treasured part of his library when he returned to civilian life. After all, Miss Naytor had been at pains to tell her class that the book had been dedicated to Lord Tennyson and the two had discussed the contents while "traversing the wild scenery of Treryn Dinas" during a walking tour in Cornwall.

When they got back on board in the late afternoon the crew were making preparations for the evening departure. It was an unaccustomed luxury not to be involved in the hundred and one tasks which have to be performed before leaving harbour. Before long they were steaming out to sea with the wonderful backdrop of Bombay harbour slowly getting smaller and smaller. They were well and truly on the last leg of their long journey and there was a general feeling of relief and anticipation. They were not in convoy and hoped there would be no trouble from enemy submarines. They were left alone. The voyage to Colombo was almost idyllic, calm seas and flying fish skimming the surface as they avoided the ship's bow wave. These fish used to land sometimes on the iron deck, which was only a few feet above the waterline of *Pathfinder,* so Sam was quite familiar with the sight, which fascinated some of the younger sailors. He explained that the fish did not have wings, but extended fins which enabled them to sail through the air when they jumped out of the sea to avoid predators, and added that they had tried cooking the fish but found them to be not very pleasant so they were thrown back in the sea when they landed on board.

In seemingly no time at all COSU were put ashore in Colombo and immediately plunged into chaos. The staff of the SNO (Senior Naval Officer) were not used to dealing with Combined Operations personnel so the party was bundled off to a holding camp about five miles outside the town. Sam was reminded of an essay he once had to write when in the fifth form which was entitled, "To travel hopefully is a better thing than to arrive." Never having been further than the port of Falmouth, he was not really inspired by Robert Louis Stevenson's dictum, and he wrote a couple of pages of not very convincing argument. At that Colombo stage in his globe-trotting he felt he was finally equipped to deal with such an essay. Fortunately he was beyond the clutches of Miss Naytor but it did occur to him he might set himself the essay as an exercise in his preparation for obtaining better qualifications when he left the Navy. Of course, he never did get round to it!

When they arrived at the jungle camp they found similar groups all wandering about, not knowing what to do, bored out of their minds and wondering if they were to be forgotten by the powers that be. Sam and Joss were quartered in a basha, which was a straw-thatch-roofed hut with a concrete floor and block dwarf walls surmounted by woven cane panels from window height, strengthened by stout wooden poles at regular intervals. They slept uneasily on their first night ashore. There were all kinds of unidentifiable sounds emanating from the four corners of the basha. Every time they shone a torch the scratchings would stop, then continue as soon as the light was extinguished. Eventually they both dropped off to sleep and were awakened early the next day by a smiling Sinhalese steward who lifted Sam's mosquito net and held out his shorts for him to step into. Sam waved him away and began dressing himself. Joss did likewise. They soon discovered what the mysterious night noises were. The bone buttons of their clothes had all been gnawed away by rats and they had to fish out fresh pairs of shorts from their sea chests. The only buttons left on their uniforms were the brass ones. Joss reminded Sam of the warning they had received the previous evening so they picked up their shoes, holding them by the toes, and tapped them smartly on the floor before putting them on. Fortunately no wandering scorpion had decided to shelter for the night in them.

Their first jungle camp breakfast was the usual naval fare with the addition of paw paws, which were long, slim, marrow-like fruits of the custard apple family. They were delicious and the two newcomers rather unwisely made pigs of themselves on their first day. They were to regret their innocent gluttony later on.

Contrary to what he had been told to expect, Sam was called to the camp office and told he was assigned to the Censorship room. There were about a dozen officers there, each one busy dealing with a pile of letters. Sam was given a chair and a pile of letters which he was expected to read and censor with a thick blue crayon. No one gave him any instructions so he began to read. He assumed he was looking out for any information which could prove useful if the letter fell into enemy hands, or which, if passed on to a third party within earshot of an agent, could be transmitted to Germany and acted upon. Of course, the letters were all about family or full of endearments for the eyes of a girlfriend and there was nothing of any import except the occasional reference to a ship's name, which Sam duly obliterated. It was a pretty pointless task as Sam learned later that it was possible to go into Colombo and post a letter in the usual way and send back whatever information one chose. Naturally sailors knew only too well the consequences of the enemy finding out about convoy movements so in their own interests there was little likelihood of their disobeying the regulations regarding censorship. In any case, letters marked "On Active Service" were sent free of charge through the Fleet Mail Office. That was an added incentive to obey for men earning two shillings and sixpence a day.

The unit did not stay in Colombo very long but the unusual conditions of the jungle camp had their compensations. From time to time the personnel were allowed a day in the port, depending on the usual "exigencies of the service". It was not possible to do any real training due to the confidential nature of the equipment, but it was unpacked by the mechanics and kept in good order. The long sea journey did not appear to have done it any lasting harm. The seamen were employed on camp guard duties which they did not like very much. They grumbled that they would rather be on watch at sea than in the jungle. When allowed into Colombo most people went to Mount Lavinia where there was a lovely beach. Sam and Joss used to walk there, across the magnificent seafront, and do an afternoon's surfing. They didn't have boards so they copied other people and learned to body surf. It was a wonderful sensation being carried shorewards at speed but sometimes they paid the penalty of learners and scraped the skin off their chests as they skidded to a halt on the sharp sand. They envied the local lads who simply used palm branches as boards and rode in the waves standing up, grinning as if to say, "I bet you wish you could do this." After an hour or two in the surf, Joss and Sam used to go to the Galle Face Hotel and have a long, cool drink to alleviate the heat in their bodies caused by having to dress on the hot beach. There was a good swimming pool in the hotel with an entrance from the beach which was laid out like a large grand piano, with keys used as steps. They sometimes went straight to the pool and swam steadily up and down to keep up their fitness, and there was the added attraction of young ladies in swimming costumes sitting at tables, sipping iced drinks.

After three weeks of relative idleness it was announced that they were to leave the following weekend for Vizagapatam so the two friends decided they had better make the most of the last few days in Colombo. They decided on their next free day that they would forgo swimming and see what the town had to offer.

It was in Colombo that Sam felt the strange sensation of having been there before. He was walking with Joss towards the Grand Oriental Hotel which they had gleaned was a sort of rendezvous for Navy types, when a man in civilian clothes approached them and asked the way to the main Post Office. Sam found himself giving directions. The European thanked him and went off up the road. Joss then asked Sam how he knew where the Post Office was as he had never been there before. Sam could not explain so they decided to test Sam's description of the route. To their amazement they discovered the Post Office was indeed where Sam said it would be. They both decided it was something to do with the fabled "mystic East" and left it at that. In actual fact they were both to witness other strange happenings while they were east of Aden. One night when they were in the bungalow they rented at Waltair on the outskirts of Vizag., as they called Vizagapatam for short, they were having an evening meal after being out at sea all day and found they could hardly hear what was being said because of the howling of jackals just outside the compound. The Head Bearer was asked if he could do anything about it. Up to that point he did not seem to have noticed the noise, just as Sam and his friends tended to ignore the noise of seagulls when they were in harbour. However, Johnny was always anxious to be of service so he said he would try. He instructed Sam to take off his sandals and put them on the floor in the shape of a diagonal cross, one over the other. Sam complied, then Johnny asked him to point the centre of the V shape made by the toes of the crossed slippers towards the sounds being made by the jackals. Sam did so. It was a magical moment. Some would say a mystical moment.

The howls ceased abruptly. There followed a stunned silence, then they all began talking at once and a broadly grinning Johnny carried on serving the meal. The event was truly unaccountable: Johnny was not the archetypal Eastern guru type of person. He had worked in London for one of the local Indian Civil Service officers and was a pragmatic sort of fellow. On another occasion he was asked if he could rid the room of flies which were swarming over the dining table. There was no mystery about his response. He fetched a bucket of water and held it up close to the swarm round the light bulb. Seeing the reflection most of the flies obligingly dived into the bucket and Johnny calmly walked off with the drowning flies and no doubt a few mosquitoes as well. The solution worked every time the sailors tried it, as did the method of silencing the jackal, even when Johnny was not there. Perhaps it was pure faith in the ways of the East.

Vizag. proved to be a bit of a hell hole as well as the centre for Combined Operations. It was a small, deep-water port in the Bay of Bengal, roughly half way between Madras and Calcutta. After India got its independence it reverted to its original name of Vishakhapatnam. There were not many docking facilities. Indeed a floating dock arrived from the UK while COSU was stationed there and it proved most useful for patrol vessels and Combined Operations craft as well as the Coastal Forces MLs.

Italian prisoners of war worked in the dockyard. They were on the whole a cheerful and obliging lot and Sam felt sorry for them having to work in the oppressive heat. They were supervised by a token force of armed guards who were on friendly terms with them. There was nowhere for them to escape, so like their guards they were just waiting for the war to end so that they could go home.

The town itself was very much an Indian one, a fascinating place which seemed, unfortunately, to harbour more than its fair share of flies and mosquitoes, as well as a number of white cows which persisted in blocking the road, much to Sam's annoyance when he had to go through the town on his Norton motor bike. It was not done to give the cow blocking his path a whack on the rump as he would have done in Coverack. Cows were revered and untouchable in a holy sort of way as Sam discovered when he saw them wandering unhindered through the ground floor of the local hospital. In time he learned a few phrases of the local Telegu language and though he would not hesitate to castigate a workman he would not dare address a cow! He longed to be able to call, "Co, co, co!" as he did when working on the farm at Pednavounder. It had the almost instant effect of getting cows on their feet to come to the yard to be milked and fed.

COSU had a workshop in the dock area which was efficiently policed so there was no problem regarding security. Such windows as there were had stout vertical iron bars spaced quite close together so that even a small boy would have difficulty in getting through them. Many of the private houses were protected in the same way and often had no glass because of the daytime heat.

Three B Class Fairmile MLs were assigned to Combined Operations. In due course the little flotilla settled down to carrying out exercises in much the same manner as in Newhaven. The crews were somewhat bemused at first but saw the advantages to be gained by deception as they were quite experienced in covert operations against the Japanese. One skipper, Jack Ewe, had even slipped ashore when up a chaung as he could hear a noisy party going on and reasoned the Japs would not be keeping a good lookout. He had spied what appeared to be an empty basha in a clearing about a hundred yards from the river bank and crept up to it, accompanied by a couple of crew members. There was no one there, fortunately, but Jack picked up a briefcase and brought it back with him for intelligence to examine. Of course, he was warned about repeating such a foolhardy escapade, but apparently the papers provided important information regarding troop positions. Jack was a buccaneer type of person and laughed off his reprimand. He often declared that if his fellow officers could get him drunk enough they could shave off his beard. One night after celebrating the return from a few days' exercises in the Bay of Bengal, Jack did fall asleep during the party so it was decided to teach him a lesson, but instead of shaving off all his beard only one side was done. His comments the next morning were loud and unprintable! Nevertheless, Sam was glad Jack was on his side and looked forward to going on operations with him.

Joss and Sam had both requisitioned motor bikes from the army stores in Vizag. and used them to "recce" suitable beaches up the coast for practice landings. The bikes were very necessary as coastal roads were little more than dirt tracks and frequently they had to cross paddy fields in order to get to the spot they had chosen on the chart. They had the impression that some of the workers in the fields were not used to seeing Europeans as they stopped work when the bikes appeared and stared them out of sight before bending to their labours again. Many of the women had babies strapped to their backs. It was a precarious position to be in when the mothers bent down to work the soil but obviously the infants were accustomed to it and even slept through the morning's work while being tossed about. On one occasion Sam ran out of petrol when returning from a beach. Joss had gone on ahead and could not be of any help so Sam just sat astride the machine in the hope that someone would turn up. In seemingly no time at all a small crowd of locals gathered round, smiling and gesticulating. They were friendly, and Sam indicated by sign language what had happened. His Urdu did not run to complicated sentences and in any case they probably spoke Telegu and wouldn't understand Urdu. After about an hour, much to Sam's relief, a petrol bowser came along, driven by a naval rating. Sam flagged him down and he was given a tankful of petrol. The locals were all smiles and waved him off but Sam knew that if he had abandoned his machine there it would have been stripped of all possible reusable bits and pieces. After all, it was just what his fellow villagers in Coverack would have done if something interesting was washed ashore!

The Bay of Bengal is a huge expanse of water and was used by merchants trading with modern day Burma and Malaya. It was claimed that Vasco da Gama was the first European to sail across from west to east. COSU arrived during the monsoon season. The torrential rain soon filled the six-foot-deep monsoon ditches in the base camp but they were well drained and left an unpleasant smell when the sun shone as locals used them when empty for other purposes. The bad weather meant that the MLs were often confined to port for extended periods, which did not help dispel the feelings of discontent at not getting on with the training. No sooner had the monsoon ceased than temperatures rose even higher and more monsoon winds arrived, this time from the south west. It was not all doom and gloom as at least there was no shortage of water and everyone took advantage of the warm rain to shower in the open air on deck. Curiously this provoked a signal from the NOIC to the effect that female clerks in the docks offices had complained about naked sailors on deck. Naturally the matelots retaliated by telling their officers to tell the girls to get on with their work and not look out of the office windows. No one had the courage to send a signal to the NOIC to that effect! It was a pity, because during the monsoon season the heat was so intense below deck that one broke out in a sweat putting on one's clothes after a shower. The officers were pleased that they had had the good sense to hire the bungalow at Waltair, which, being on a height, caught what little cool wind was going.

Usually the little flotilla went north on exercises. There were few restrictions regarding movements round the shallow coast. The rivers Ganges and Hoogli presumably brought rich deposits down the delta and fishermen tended to congregate in the shallows where fish were plentiful. Sam was astonished when one morning he saw men standing up hauling nets when they were out of sight of land. The fishermen found it less tiring to haul with both feet on the bottom than from their wooden craft which were very buoyant and bobbed about like corks in the swell. Of course the MLs gave them a wide berth because of the shallow soundings but it was a sight which Sam was to remember and recount to his fishermen friends in Coverack, whose first reaction was to say, "Giss on with 'ee, Sam, 'tidn true." Sam retorted with, "Yes 'tis, my 'andsome, God's honour!" - then they knew it was not a leg pull. They had all been brought up in the Wesleyan Sunday School tradition and though they might swear and curse a bit, no one dared "take the name of the Lord in vain". They were all adults but Sunday School teacher Joseph Barker was still a power to be reckoned with and in addition they knew Sam would not risk his grandfather Henry Exelby finding out he had been telling fibs!

The best way to achieve a high standard of efficiency is by practice, practice and more practice, according to those who know about these things. COSU certainly did that during the time spent at Vizagapatam. One consolation was that during night exercises, which were not at all popular in Newhaven, the sailors got wet but they did not freeze. Sam never forgot those nights in the Channel when despite a thick towel wrapped round his neck beneath his oilskin, the cold sea water managed to get under his collar and drip slowly down his warm back making him squirm with revulsion for he knew he would have to "grin and bear it" for hours until blessed relief came with the rum toddy as they returned to base. Of course, he still got wet, but it was a relatively warm wet, so he concluded he was more suited to tropical climes than the inhospitable Channel in winter. Finally it was declared by the powers that be that the unit had reached operational efficiency and could look forward to some action. That was all very well for the powers that be but Sam felt the phrase "look forward" was unfortunate. A visiting Admiral fresh out from the UK declared he would like to "see more blood". This, said to Royal Marines and Combined Operations sailors who were veterans of assault landings in Europe, created audible rumblings of angry dissent and the ungracious gentleman ended his pep talk rather hurriedly. Sam was told his name was Power, which seemed apt as it had obviously gone to his head. Notwithstanding, Hugo announced there was some leave being granted after six months of working-up trials. Arrangements were made and within a few days Sam and Joss had packed their blues and were on the way to Darjeeling in the Sikkim Himalayas. Sam had always called the mountain range "Him-e-lay-es" but he discovered that the received pronunciation in the exalted circles of the local club was "Him-al-yus" with the tonic accent on the second syllable. It became a private joke between him and Joss when one or the other would ask, "Where are you spending your leave this year?" Back would come the reply in a bored tone, "My dear, it'll have to be the Him-al-yus again."

The railway journey involved going to Calcutta and then to a station in the foothills. They had to spend the night in Calcutta, which seemed to be the most crowded, noisy, smelly place on earth. Sam's mother had given him the address of a distant relative on the Trengilly side, so for want of something better to do the pair decided to go to Dumdum on the outskirts of the city in search of the long-lost Cornishman named Sidney who had made India his home for the last twenty years or so. The traffic really was something to behold. The noise of revving engines and the shouts of exasperated drivers was deafening. Chaos reigned. Cars, lorries, buses, rickshaws, overladen bullock carts, cyclists and pedestrian labourers carrying large mysterious burdens on their heads all competed for the right of way and shouted insults at the lathi-wielding policemen trying vainly to keep them moving in the direction they wanted to go. It was another never-to-be-forgotten scene. To crown it all, Sidney Trengilly was not at home. He had taken to the hills to avoid the heat! The next morning it was with some relief that Joss and Sam boarded the train for the three-hundred-mile trip. They had to change to the rack and pinion mountain railway for the final leg of their journey but when they saw the tiny open carriages they decided to take a taxi instead. It was necessary to agree to a price before setting out, so after the now familiar haggling and pretending to walk away to another vehicle, they settled on a sum and began the ascent. They were not filled with confidence by the sight of the taxi driver's bare foot on the metal accelerator pedal but they were soon absorbed in the beautiful wooded slopes as they wound their way to the top. The road crisscrossed the railway track so they were treated to the sight of a train being eased back on to the track by a gang of men wielding crowbars. It made them feel they had made the right decision to go by taxi. Even so, Sam found himself closing his eyes when the car negotiated some of the more spectacular bends as the road spiralled to the top. It was all worth while. Once there it was utter bliss. They realised why Darjeeling was used as a recuperation station for servicemen. The air was clear and cool with the mountains stretching away into the blue distance and the tea plantations forming a pleasant green foreground.

After a quick shower, Sam and Joss changed into their blue uniforms and began to feel "normal" again for the first time in months, despite the feeling of breathlessness when they went out for a stroll. The hill station was all it was cracked up to be and the food in the Gymkhana Club where they were staying was as near to English style as it was possible to get. A surprise was the presence of a large roller-skating rink. Sam had never had the opportunity to learn how to skate, nor had Joss, so they both decided to learn. Of course they found it not so easy as it looked and kept falling over even when they stuck to the edge of the rink, which had a rail round it for the benefit of learners. They noticed two girls laughing at their efforts so the next time they got round to where the girls were standing, Joss asked them if they could help them master the technique. To the surprise of the two sailors the giggling girls agreed to hold their hands as they towed them round. It turned out that they were sisters, the daughters of a local tea planter, and after a rather exhausting half an hour on wheels the girls suggested having a break. They took Sam and Joss to meet Mum, who, unknown to them, had been chaperoning the girls from the spectators' gallery. After a brief conversation, Mrs. Brown invited the boys to "take tea" with them the following afternoon. Naturally the sailors accepted the opportunity of the chance of talking to the girls again. They learned that the Browns enjoyed trying to make visiting servicemen feel at home while they were on leave, so the boys decided to "come clean" and spoke of the girlfriends they had left at home. When Mum found out that Joss was a church organist he was invited to come and play at the service on the following Sunday. Sam went along with him on Saturday afternoon and eventually found himself pumping the organ by hand while Joss practised for the following day. The job of blowing was done by an Indian for payment. He kept an old alarm clock on the bellows so that he could keep tally on the time. He left promptly after the hour for which he was paid during Saturday afternoon practices, which is why Sam took over. He was quite accustomed to the job as his father played the organ in Coverack and Sam was often press-ganged into service when the caretaker was not available. The next day Sam found himself in service again as the Indian did not turn up. All went well and they were rewarded with another delicious tea with home-made cakes at the Browns'. The thrill of eating home-made cakes again made Sam think of his mother's delicious cooking, so when they went round the shops next morning Sam took the opportunity of sending a parcel home. There were certain permitted items which servicemen could send. He chose tea, salted butter and chocolate. He realised that it was a risk sending butter but he knew how tight rationing was in the UK and decided to chance it. Joss did the same. Sam also bought a souvenir kukri in the bazaar. He had become an admirer of the Ghurkas who claimed they always drew blood when they drew their traditional weapon. He learned that they usually just scratched their forearms to draw blood if there was no enemy to slash. Sam's brother, Alexander, had written to tell him how glad he was to have the Ghurkas on his side after he had witnessed the way they dealt with the Japanese in the Burmese jungle.

The highlight of the brief leave was a trek by pony to see the early morning sun shining on Kanchenjunga which at 28,169 feet, is the second highest mountain in the world. They got up just before dawn and went to the appointed place where two ponies had been saddled for them. It was another almost new experience as neither had been on horseback more than a few times. They need not have worried, because the attendant helped them mount and waved them goodbye. The animals were well trained. They climbed slowly up the steep slopes of Tiger Hill and after about three quarters of an hour the ponies obligingly halted at a view point, then calmly began munching some grass as the "intrepid" pair dismounted and beheld Kanchenjunga in the early morning sunlight. It was certainly worth the effort, and they thought they could also make out Everest in the far distance to the right. They had been told it was a possibility on an exceptionally clear day but there was no one around to confirm it, not even the ubiquitous postcard seller who usually hung about such spots. Kenchanjunga was about forty miles distant but in the lovely clear air it did not seem that far and the mountain they thought was Mount Everest did seem higher. It is about 1,000 feet higher then "K", as the English "locals" called it. After about ten minutes, the ponies stopped eating their breakfast and looked expectantly at the two sailors. They gathered it was time to go back, so after a couple of abortive attempts they managed to get aboard their mounts, who began the return journey. Back in Darjeeling, they handed over the ponies to their owner and went in to a very welcome cooked breakfast - the last they were to have for some time.

That same evening, blue uniforms were packed after dinner and in the morning after donning their tropical gear they left Darjeeling. It seemed pretty certain they would not be returning so they decided to take the rack-and-pinion train down the mountain for the experience. They reached the mainline station at the bottom with just one incident on a sharp bend when the driver and his crew had to crowbar one of the wheels back on to the rail. They settled down to the three-hundred-mile ride to Calcutta and gradually got warmer and warmer. Sam's prickly heat had disappeared while on leave, but now it returned in all its former glory. It is a rash which looks like a bad attack of measles and itches incessantly. There seemed to be no cure. When Sam went to see the Combined Ops. base medical officer he simply bared his chest and showed Sam he had exactly the same condition and gave him a bottle of lotion which purported to alleviate the itching but did not claim to be able to make it disappear. One bonus, if one could call it that, was that they did not have to spend a night in Calcutta on the return journey. They simply changed trains and settled in the second-class carriage complete with bunks and shower and began the long haul back to Vizag. Before long, out came the packs of cards and the two friends began the now familiar train journey marathon of Double Patience.

A couple of Queen Alexandra's Nursing Sisters were travelling on the train. They looked a little lost and rather vulnerable when walking up and down the platform at extended station stops so Joss asked the girls if they would like to join them for a G. and T. and a game of cards. They accepted rather hesitatingly and promised to come at the next stop. The girls were as good as their word and came along at the next station. They all spent a pleasant hour sipping gin and tonic and playing Double Patience, the only card game Sam knew apart from whist. He had tried when a youngster in Coverack to learn how to play Euchre, which was a traditional game in Cornwall, but he couldn't play well enough to show others how it was done. There were some silences when shuffling the cards, during one of which the fair-haired nurse with an exaggerated upper class accent asked, "Have you ever had your ears pierced, darling?" Her companion replied in an equally fruity manner, "Well no, I haven't Ectually." Perhaps she didn't know the word began with a letter A. Sam and Joss looked at each other then hastily began examining their cards while suppressing their mirth. Many times after that, when there was a silence on board ship, Joss would ask in high falsetto, "Have you had your ears pierced, darling?" Sam would reply in similar vein, "Well no, I haven't Ectually, darling." This little charade mystified their colleagues for some time until the two friends were prevailed on to relate the story of their trip from Calcutta to Vizag. on the way back from Darjeeling. The Q.A.s were known, in general, to be well qualified nursing sisters who came from "good" stock and held commissioned rank equivalent to Army officers, whereas the Royal Navy was served by Sick Berth Attendants and the doctors were officers.

It did not take long to slip back into the routine of patrols and exercises in the Bay of Bengal. Sam was sent inland to an Army camp where a small detachment was busily practising deception manoeuvres in readiness for an operation in Burma. A drought was in progress and the camp was situated on dry sandy soil which had more than its fair share of sand flies. To make matters worse water was rationed to one large "jerry" a day each for all purposes. Sam was given a bivouac tent to himself and was glad that he had a few skills in camping which he had learned as a Boy Scout. Not for the first time did he thank his "lucky stars" for allowing him to join the Royal Navy. His Army friends were kindness itself and he did get the services of a batman who made sure he managed to cope with life on manoeuvres. The techniques being perfected were very much like those he had learned at Ballantrae. One curious ploy was that someone had discovered the Japanese revered foxes, which apparently could take over the souls of their departed ancestors. Whether this was true or not Sam never verified but some enterprising officer had recorded the barking of foxes and the sounds played back in the stillness of the night were enough to send a shiver down one's spine. Sam hoped the Japanese would react by retreating from their forward positions when they were confronted with the sounds of their dear departed forebears calling out in the dead of night! He spent a week getting to know the company which would be the land-based counterpart of COSU and hoped desperately he would never be called on to accompany them into action.

On returning to the relative peace of the harbour at Vizagapatam, Sam reported his findings to Hugo who roared with laughter at the idea of Japs being afraid of barking foxes and promptly announced that "things" were hotting up and now Sam was being sent to Poona to liaise regarding a forthcoming operation. He wasn't quite sure what he was supposed to liaise about but Hugo brushed aside Sam's queries by saying that the Colonel in charge at Poona just wanted a naval type on hand in case they needed to co-operate "in the field". Sam didn't think he would be able to contribute much to the co-operation so Hugo said he would send Joss with him and they could conjure up something between them to keep the Army happy! It was no wonder the unit was still being called "Fred Karno's Outfit" in private. Sam looked on the bright side, however, and thought it would be an interesting experience to cross India by train; besides, the 14th Army was doing well in Burma and the Japanese were falling back, so their speciality of Sonic Warfare might prove to be useful to confuse the enemy as they retreated.

Sam went on what proved to be his final observation exercise before he left for Poona. Perhaps it was fitting that he should be held up on his way to the remote beach by one of the countless funerals he witnessed while in India. Cholera was rife in the Vizag. area and of course the effects of the Bengal famine lingered, resulting in many deaths from malnutrition. Sam needed to cross a main road on his motorbike but naturally had to wait until the funeral procession passed by on the way to the beach where he used to surf, using an old ammunition box top for a board and where the local boys would look after the bike for a few annas and even cut a juicy fruit from a pineapple plant if a rupee was waved under their noses. The corpse was carried on a bier with flowers placed on the body and round the head, which was exposed to public view as is the custom and had turned an unpleasant blue colour. Professional mourners preceded the cortège, prancing about, some making a din with drums and wind instruments and others waving smoking canisters which Sam understood were designed to ward off evil spirits. The family of the deceased were obviously reasonably affluent, as that very morning while riding through the dock area Sam had seen the now familiar sight of a couple of corpses by the road side. They evidently had no family to care for them, or the family was too poor to dispose of the bodies, so they were left there, waiting for the authorities to deal with them. Sam never did get used to these sights and mentally blamed the state of affairs on the British Raj, although he knew other Empires were ruled in a far worse fashion. When in North Africa he was advised by a cynical Frenchman to back up over an Arab if he knocked him over, just to make sure he was dead, as that was less complicated for the authorities. Fortunately he never had to face that dilemma. No sooner had the road become clear and Sam accelerated away from the scene than he came across a sacred cow in the middle of the narrow road with a stationary bullock cart on either side. Sam dismounted, quietly wheeled his machine round the obstruction and set out once more, fortunately arriving just in time to see the MLs starting their run shorewards with speakers at full blast. If it had been dark and if a Japanese sentry had been on the beach, Sam was certain he would have reported the approach of landing craft and put that in his report to Hugo when he got back to the ML.

Time passed very quickly. Soon signals had been exchanged and Joss and Sam found themselves having a special dinner in the bungalow to mark their departure for Bombay. In the bungalow lived a tame mongoose whose duty was to deal with invading scorpions or snakes. That evening Hugo was in full spate, expounding on the pleasures of living on an island off the coast of Queensland, and in so doing was waving his fork in the air to demonstrate a point. On the fork was a tasty morsel of meat which he had speared and was about to eat. This presented a great temptation to the mongoose, which had climbed on to a chair close to the dining room table. The mongoose is not a particularly agile animal, being rather like a slim badger in appearance and about one foot in length. The lure of the meat proved to be too great on that particular occasion so it took a flying leap, grabbed the meat and made off with it to the veranda while everyone burst out laughing, including Hugo. He immediately declared he would teach Rikki-tikki-tavi a lesson, so when Rikki returned to the dining room some time later, Hugo wrapped a choice piece of meat round a chilli and speared it on his fork which he then held down temptingly at arm's length about ten inches above the floor. Naturally the mongoose approached the bait with caution and quick as a flash in the way it pounced on scorpions, grabbed the meat and made off with it. Hugo then confidently declared there would be no further incidents of that nature and time proved him to be right according to reports given to Joss and Sam when they returned from Poona. Sam felt rather sorry for the mongoose in one way as he had developed a method of providing some after-dinner entertainment involving Rikki. The bungalow was plagued with scorpions and everyone adopted the habit of tapping shoes on the floor to dislodge any lurking scorpion which had hidden in the shoe. Their poison was not lethal but would give anyone a very painful time for a few days if stung. The scorpion is an insect rather like a small black four-inch lobster in design. When it catches its prey it grabs it in its pincers and its long tail comes up and forward over its body to deliver the poisonous coup de grâce to its victim. After observing the mongoose doing its job of ridding the bungalow of pests, Sam decided he would capture a scorpion and when everyone was relaxing after an evening meal, demonstrate the efficiency of the mongoose. The next time a scorpion came scurrying across the tiles, Sam laid a large tumbler horizontally on the floor with the open end facing the scorpion. It stopped, up went its tail and while it was concentrating on the object in its path, Sam spooned it into the tumbler with his right hand and quickly placed a small saucer on the top of the glass to prevent the scorpion from escaping. It was unable to climb the slippery sides of the tumbler anyway. That evening after dinner, Sam produced the captured scorpion for everyone to examine and when the mongoose approached, hoping for a titbit, Sam released the scorpion on the floor in front of Rikki. After a few minutes of wary manoeuvring, Rikki attacked and devoured the scorpion in one lightning movement to the applause of the diners. Sam was prevailed on to do his party piece a few times after that, especially when some of the ML officers were invited to dinner. After the "chilli" episode he felt he would no longer have the confidence of poor Rikki. In the event it didn't matter greatly as the days of living in the bungalow were numbered.

Naturally Sam and Geoff came in for a lot of leg pulling when it was learned they were off to Poona. Their colleagues in the MLs used the phoney accents army officers are reputed to use when talking about the Mecca of the British Army in India. Their departure was delayed for a couple of weeks as Sam came down with malaria. He had resisted the bug when dosed with quinine in West Africa but the new wonder drug called Mepacrine did not protect him. He spent a few days in the hospital at Vizag. where, when he had stopped being delirious, he made the acquaintance of some French-speaking nuns. He was pleasantly surprised that he was able to communicate with them without too much difficulty. He was quite appalled at the way in which the cows and even "pie" dogs (mongrel strays) wandered through the ground floor corridors, and he was equally amazed to see whole families camping out in the grounds while their loved ones were receiving treatment. Apparently it was quite normal for desperately poor families to do this, especially when it was the breadwinner who was ill. The Swiss nuns told him that in that way they were able to get some help from the Roman Catholic missionaries who often persuaded their Indian converts to seek a cure at the hospital by paying for their treatment, which cost a fortune in relation to the pittance Indian labourers earned when they could get work. The Indian doctor, an Army Major, was reluctant to let Sam leave until he was satisfied the malaria had subsided but Hugo persuaded him that Sam was needed, so one afternoon Hugo turned up in a jeep and took Sam back to the bungalow, telling him to be packed and ready to leave for Poona the following morning as tickets had been booked and time was of the essence.

At six the following morning Joss and Sam were deposited, complete with bedrolls and kit bags, at the entrance to the station. Indian railway stations are always thronged with people. Some lived there, eking out their existence on baksheesh and what they could find or steal. Sam and Joss drove off those eager to carry their luggage and employed two official porters wearing the Brassard which gave their number so that there could be no doubt as to who they were and denoting they could be relied on. The train was about to depart and the usual non-fare-paying passengers were already standing by ready to climb on board as soon as it started. Joss and Sam had seen them before, clinging to the sides as the train thundered through the Indian countryside. The long-distance locomotives in India were huge, steaming monsters and this one looked very impressive in the early morning light. There seemed to be a tradition in India that most of the skilled railway employees were half European and half Indian, the result of mixed marriages or liaisons. These people were known, somewhat unkindly, as "chee-chees". Both Indians and Europeans gave the impression of being superior to them, which was racism at its worst for they were an essential part of the community and in general cultured, efficient, bilingual people. Many of the men were well built and good looking and the women beautiful and most attractive with their coffee-coloured skins. Perhaps it was envy or jealousy which made others consider them to be inferior. Sam and Joss duly paid off the porters their set fees for carrying the gear and after they had arranged their luggage, stood looking out of the door at the shouting, jostling people on the platform. Spot on time, after much shouting and blowing of whistles, the engine driver pulled down his goggles over his eyes, waved back to the Guard, gave a long blast on the train's hooter and the train got under way, puffing loudly as it slowly left the station. The three-day journey to Poona had begun.

They had been warned that there might be problems getting drinks en route so in addition to their standard issue water bottles they stocked up with a good number of bottles of soft drinks obtained from a vendor on the platform and put them in a cool place in the shower and toilet compartment of their reserved second-class carriage. The journey proved to be fascinating from start to finish. They were seeing the real India, not just the coastal fringes. When they stopped at small country stations the carriages occupied by Europeans and wealthy Indians were besieged by beggars asking for food and backsheesh. For the first time Joss and Sam saw Indians suffering from albinism. Their skin was an unusual pink colour, their hair was near white and the eyes reddish. They appeared to be outcasts like the untouchables and looked as if they could hardly see in the bright sunlight. It was clear they were condemned to a life of begging. The effects of the recent famine were more apparent inland. People were painfully thin, some covered in sores resulting from malnutrition. At one station a troop train came in carrying soldiers returning from Burma. These kindly men began offering some of their own rations and it was quite noticeable that despite their hunger the Indians waved away tins of bully beef which had the symbol of the cow on the outside. It was a striking example to Sam and Joss of the power of religious belief over relatively simple people.

After the first night in the train, they got out at a station to stretch their legs. They saw an Indian grinning at them and his face seemed to be familiar. Then they realised it was the man who had sold them the bottles of fruit juice and purified water when they boarded the train in Vizag. It dawned on them that the poor fellow had been clinging to the carriage all night and was waiting to get the empties back! They beckoned to him and he stood at the door of their compartment while they fetched the empties to give him. They could not imagine making the man follow them any further so they gave him some money and waved him away, indicating that the money was baksheesh and showing him the unused full bottles still in the carriage. He grinned again and walked away, presumably to get some more bottles to sell to travellers. When telling this story to more seasoned travellers on the Indian railways they learned that some of the vendors had been known to travel, illegally, right across India to get their precious empties. Sam knew Kipling drew inspiration for his writing from his experiences in India and wondered if the line "If you can wait and not be tired by waiting" had anything to do with Indian itinerant drink vendors! At least the two friends were in agreement that they did not know "how the other half lived".

Hyderabad is about half way between Vizagapatam and Bombay. On stopping there it was announced there would be time to get a lunch at the station restaurant before the train proceeded. An opulent-looking Indian gentleman heard Sam and Joss discussing whether to try out the restaurant or not and told them that while he could not offer them a cooked lunch because of the time factor, they would be welcome to go home with him and have a swim in his private pool. The friends looked at each other questioningly and decided to take the plunge on offer. The gentleman's chauffeur-driven car was waiting outside the station as he had just been on a train journey, so they were taken in style to the house which was more sumptuous than they had imagined it would be. This made them wonder momentarily if they could be candidates for the white slave traffic. However, being of the age when they would try anything for a lark they had already, when they were on the platform at Hyderabad, laughingly dismissed the idea of two sweaty sailors being wanted by anyone.

There seemed to be a small army of servants ready to do their bidding but they waved them away and donning their swimming trunks which they always kept to hand when travelling, just in case, they dived in the pool which was about the length of a cricket pitch and proceeded to do length after length while a couple of servants stood at the edge of the pool holding towels for the sahib guests of their master. After about ten minutes they were called to a light salad lunch. Their host had already eaten his and apologetically explained he had to go out on business and had to leave right away. He added that because he would be using the car he had arranged for a horse-drawn gharry to take them back to the station in a quarter of an hour's time. The two could only say how much they had enjoyed the break from the train journey and thanked him as effusively as they knew how. He dismissed their sincere thanks with a wave of the hand and said in his impeccable public school accent how much he had enjoyed his school days in England and that he was pleased to "be of service" to a couple of young people visiting his country. The "young people" never even got to know his name but often talked about their good fortune in meeting a genuine Indian anglophile whenever the conversation in the ward room turned to the current situation in India.

The ever-changing scene of inland India continued to fascinate the two friends as they viewed it from their carriage window. They became aware of their privileged position as English-born citizens, but with such huge numbers of people living in such relatively remote places it became evident to them that it was a mammoth task trying to administer such a vast country. It was not their problem, of course, but as they discussed the sights they had seen and wondered how such conditions could be allowed to continue they began, in the way of all young people, to suggest possible means of improving the lot of the inhabitants, believing that the country could have been managed in a much better way. They were forced, in the end, to admit that they could offer little in the way of solutions to the problems and began to revise their opinions of British administration, although if asked to give a comment on the lines of a school report they would have written a cryptic "Could have done better", because like teachers who despair of pupils they could only say that efforts were not good enough without enumerating the myriad deficiencies in the admin. system.

On the third evening aboard the train they realised they would be in Bombay early the following morning so they packed their belongings, which had been strewed round the compartment, and began to discuss the forthcoming meeting with the Light Scout Car Company they would be working with when they went into action. They were still rather vague as to why the Army people wanted to see them but went over all the preparations they had made in the last few months so that they could explain the naval side of the operation. It was all rather nebulous as they had no idea where they were going when they left Vizag. except that it would probably be somewhere on the coast trying to draw enemy troops away from defending Rangoon as the land forces fought their way south.

When they arrived in Bombay they had a little time to explore the magnificent station before going down to Poona. The building itself was virtually a carbon copy of St. Pancras Station in London, except that in this exotic setting it seemed larger and the architecture far more imposing in contrast to the surrounding buildings, although Joss declared the locals probably thought of it as an alien intrusion. In a strange sort of way, both Joss and Sam felt the splendour of their surroundings made them feel superior to be English but that, they concluded, was probably just inherited jingoism so they contented themselves with a quotation they had both been made to consider at school, namely, "All empire is no more than power in trust." Dryden certainly knew a thing or two about world domination and they both felt that perhaps it was time to hand back the trust to the native peoples. The journey they had just made from east to west had certainly made them more conscious than ever of the burden of empire and they both agreed once more that the "burden" could not be entrusted to a relatively small band of administrators from the "mother" country.

The journey down to Poona from Bombay was in sharp contrast to the crossing from east to west. It seemed like a trip through the prairies of Canada. When they got well away from Bombay they passed through wooded slopes and there was not much evidence of the poverty which dominated central India. On arrival at the Army camp, they were allotted a bell tent and a servant to polish shoes and do all the chores they were used to doing for themselves. It was luxury indeed. Joss remarked to Sam that he supposed it was only right and proper now that they were pukka sahibs in Poona! The mess itself was actually a temporary wooden structure and dinner that evening was a silver-service affair. They both wondered where the silver had been obtained by a regiment in tented accommodation but they kept their thoughts to themselves and concentrated on enjoying a sumptuous meal with wine to wash it down. In the Royal Navy in India they were rationed to one bottle of South African wine per month per person - as long as the monthly ship bringing supplies did not get torpedoed on the way. Now they were in Poona and sampling the high life, even if they did have to sleep in a tent.

The next day they got down to the nuts and bolts of the impending operation and both Sam and Joss began to feel it would be good to work with the men of the Light Scout Car Company. First of all they were treated to a résumé of the army operation where they were going to attract a counter attack by using sonic warfare and simultaneously COSU were going to cause another diversion further south in the hope that the Japs would despatch another lot of troops to repel a sea-borne attack, thus leaving a considerably weakened force in the "centre", allowing the main thrust of the British army to gain ground without suffering a lot of casualties. Sam and Joss were told that a naval type would join them the following day to show how it was necessary to have very accurate timing and positioning of the diversions from land and sea.

It was not to be. That very evening news came through that devices called atomic bombs had been dropped on key cities in Japan, virtually destroying them totally, forcing the Japanese to sue for peace to prevent further destruction of mainland Japan. No one had ever heard of an atomic bomb so at first the news was treated with caution until an hour or so after dinner confirmation came through that the Japanese had indeed surrendered. The war was over.

The words Nagasaki and Hiroshima did not roll easily off the tongue at first. Sam and Joss had never heard of those cities which were to be quoted ad infinitum by Peace Campaigners for decades to come as horrific examples of the effects of an atomic war. At that time everyone was involved in the arrangements for the biggest party since the beginning of the war. It was to be held in Poona. Sam and Joss had been loaned army scooters which folded neatly in two and were designed to be dropped by parachute for use by airborne soldiers. They were delightful machines and could be parked propped up against the pole of their bell tent at night so they had literally what became known as door to door transport! However, mindful of the possibility of drinking well but unwisely on such a unique occasion as the celebration of Peace, they both secured lifts to the party in a three-ton truck which was bedecked with flags for the occasion.

In retrospect, Sam found it difficult to recall much of the first real night of Peace. He and Joss came in for quite a bit of leg pulling concerning the Royal Navy's participation in the war and they replied with lighthearted anecdotes such as the one concerning "Pongoes" who always left a distinct aroma behind after unwillingly vacating landing craft on alien beaches! It was banal and in truth hid an immense feeling of relief and longing to be back home and start living a normal life. Most of the young officers, like Sam and Joss, had really never had the opportunity of being young and carefree as they had swapped the discipline of school for service discipline with no opportunity of tasting the "freedom" about which their seniors were constantly being nostalgic during the quiet hours. They all hid their emotions beneath loud laughter at the telling of well-worn risqué jokes and joining in the songs being bashed out on the piano. Joss took it in turns with a soldier to play the tunes they all knew by heart. There were two pianos in the mess. Sam was told one was for music, the other for placing beer mugs on when soldiers wished to leave the room for personal purposes. During the singing, "Bless 'em all" came in for special treatment, with the line "They say there's a troopship just leaving Bombay, bound for old Blighty's shore" being sung loudly and with feeling. Little did Sam know that before long he would be leaving Bombay once more and sailing in the opposite direction.

Since the two sailors were in a state of euphoria at the thought of the possibility of going home, the long journey back to Vizagapatam from Poona did not register permanently in their minds. Despite the brilliant sunshine and the fascinating sights and sounds of continental India it passed rather hazily in bouts of chain smoking punctuated with glasses of well-watered duty-free alcohol which induced a somewhat fanciful anticipation of the immediate future in their young minds. It goes without saying that the projected operation against the Japanese had been abandoned, so there was no report as such to be prepared on the preliminary work that had been done in Poona. On arrival, they were greeted with the news that COSU was already in the process of being disbanded and they were to await further orders from Their Lordships. Lying in his bunk that night with the mosquito net firmly tucked under the mattress to prevent insects getting in and infecting him with another malarial bug, Sam's thoughts again went back to his schooldays in Helston when he had been given the essay on "travelling hopefully". He had been told that in all probability the officers would be sent to Colombo to await their fate. Hugo had discovered this by using his rank to probe in the office of the NOIC in Vizag.

Things began to move swiftly after Sam and Joss got back from Poona. The ratings were placed in the Combined Operations "Pool" to await a draft to wherever. The MLs were paid off and their officers and crews sent to a Coastal Forces "Pool". Meanwhile Hugo was appointed to a shore job in Sydney, which suited him as he was going back to his island home off the coast of Queensland. The rest of the officers just literally sat around and awaited developments.

The servants were quite despondent as they were about to lose their relatively well-paid jobs. The current rate of pay for Indian domestics was so low as to be embarrassing, prompting the COSU officers to decide to give them almost double the going rate to salve their consciences. Gabriel, Sam's "bearer", who always had a beaming smile and worked hard to please, asked Sam if he could get him some more cloth. He was not really capable of saying what he wanted so he resorted to having a letter written for him by a local "scribe". It ran as follows.

> To The Master, RNVR Mess, Waltair.
> Honoured Sir,
> I P. Gabriel most humbly beg to bring the following few lines in to your kind consideration.
> Sir, I am in need of some white cloth I was surching for white cloth in Vizag but could not succeed therefore I request you to kindly consider this poor case and grant me six yards of white cloth in your honoures department. I will pay the money in my salary sir. I shell ever remain greatfull to you and pray for your long life and proseperty.
> Thanking you sir,
> I beg to remain honoured sir
> Yours most obedient servant
> P. Gabriel

How could Sam refuse? He was aware, of course, that he could not write a similar letter in Telegu which was Gabriel's native tongue and though he was amused by the scribe's flowery language, he was impressed by Gabriel's initiative and decided to get the cloth from naval "slops" and give it to him as a parting present. After all, it was not even half a day's pay for Sam, and the Bearer deserved it. Besides, Sam was on Indian Income Tax, being East of Suez, and was relatively affluent. In addition, when on board landing craft he was paid "hard lying" money as an extra.

Sam never thought he would be reluctant to leave Vizag. It was typical of ports all over the world but with monsoons, heat waves, cholera epidemics, smallpox outbreaks and even one minor tidal wave thrown in for good measure. On one occasion a "stray" Japanese fighter bomber put in an appearance, probably having lost its bearings when on a reconnaissance flight. Some of the ships in harbour which had recently been in action and were still in state of readiness opened up on the plane, which disappeared as quickly as it came - along with a goodly number of local dock workers who were not used to gunfire. All these attributes, if they can be called such, did not endear the place in Sam's mind, but he had a distinct feeling of not wanting to leave. He put it down to the fact that an era was over, and it was in truth not the area he would miss but his friends and colleagues.

The day dawned when they were due to leave for Ceylon via Madras and the ferry across the Falk Strait, which was virtually a causeway of coral islands between the two countries. The bearers were determined to make a show of their departure. Gabriel presented Sam with a garland of flowers which he had to drape over his neck and Johnny, as the senior servant, announced he was going to accompany the masters on the train. Of course that meant they had to stump up for his return fare but it was worth it as they had virtually home comforts until they left India for good.

When they arrived in Colombo after a tiring journey, Sam was sent to Lake Road Mess. The others went he knew not where. It was quite sudden and painless. There was no more time to come to a conclusion about the loss of COSU as a unit, just an opportunity to exchange addresses before they were sent on their separate ways. Sam was never to see Joss again but he met up briefly with Flex a few months later in Singapore.

After a couple of days with nothing to do except go swimming at Mount Lavinia, Sam was called to the office and told he was to be a temporary Naval Assistant Provost Marshal in Colombo. Of course, he didn't have a clue about what he was supposed to do but was told all would become clear when he reported to the Regulating Office in the docks. On arrival there he was delighted when a familiar voice called, "Hello, Sam, what brings you here?" It was Jack Peters, who was a Petty Officer Stoker on *Pathfinder*. They reminisced for quite a while and Sam learned that *Pathfinder* had been in action against the Japs, bombarding coastal positions and even going up chaungs and using small-arms fire to rout out Japs who were trying to escape the main thrust of the 14th Army. Finally, two Japanese Hamps attacked the ship at Ramree Island, off the Burmese mainland. They dived and dropped three bombs from almost masthead height. They damaged the port screw and smashed a hole in the stern, causing the stokers to shift the fuel oil from starboard to port tanks to compensate for the list which quickly developed. Eventually, with the help of some Army Royal Engineers, the ship was patched up sufficiently to enable her to go to Trincomalee, escorted by the destroyer *Paladin*. Typically, *Pathfinder* entered harbour flying her pennants G10 and a captured Japanese flag! Jack then told Sam that the *Pathfinder* had been so badly damaged that she was now on her way back to the UK with a reduced crew on board, hence Jack was ashore doing the duties of a Regulating Petty Officer. After hearing that story, Sam began to wish he had never left *Pathfinder*. She had proved to be what he had always thought, an exceptional ship with an exceptional crew.

However, Jack put him wise to his new duties and informed him he would be in charge of the night watches from 2000 to 0800, adding that as a former Bosun's Mate that shouldn't prove too onerous! Sam grinned and thanked Jack for giving him the short straw and asked if they could meet up and catch up on other news. Jack laughed out loud and said, "Sorry, Sam, I'm leaving for the UK tomorrow on a merchant ship in charge of a draft of stokers due for demob!" Sam never saw Jack again.

That night after dinner Sam sat by himself in the Ward Room of Lake Road, pondering on what might have been. He knew it was a fruitless exercise but he felt drawn to do it. He thought it likely that if they had arrived in Vizag. a little earlier, they could well have been operating off Ramree Island and he would have seen *Pathfinder* in action. He dismissed the idea as fanciful and asked the Sinhalese steward to bring him a John Collins to cheer him up. At that point a middle-aged Warrant Officer Shipwright came and asked if he could do with some company and introduced himself. He was David Lower and had a Devonshire accent. Sam said he would be pleased to have someone to talk to and they told each other what they had been doing in the recent past. David was a fatherly type and obviously guessed that Sam was feeling a bit isolated. He told Sam he and his wife had been in Colombo since just after the outbreak of war. They had elected to stay on when his two-year commission ended because he was due for retirement and knew he would be given a shore job if he returned to the UK. Warrant Officer Shipwrights usually only go to sea on big ships and he felt he would be more useful in the base at Colombo. It turned out that he and his wife were renting a bungalow in a street leading off the main road to Mount Lavinia and during the course of conversation David asked Sam if he would care to come for a meal one evening. Sam was quietly delighted: it seemed ages since he had been in a real home. David told him he would have a word with his wife and then they would be able to fix a date. Sam said he would be doing two nights on duty followed by two off so it would not be difficult to arrange. After more conversation when the subject turned inevitably to home, David announced it was time for him to go back to his wife, so they agreed to sort out a date in a couple of days' time.

The following evening Sam duly reported for duty at the base Regulating Office and the Petty Officer in charge of the evening patrol asked him if he would like to go on a tour of the town so as to get the lie of the land, so to speak. Sam agreed and off they went in the jeep. The PO certainly knew his beat and Sam was impressed with his efficiency. At the same time he found out more or less what he was expected to do. His duties consisted mainly of checking the foot patrols out and about in the town and being on hand in the office when liberty boats landed and left to ensure that everything was done in proper naval fashion. It really amounted to the fact that he was a "presence" in case of trouble and to be seen moving about the jetties usually ensured that comings and goings were carried out in accordance with good order and naval discipline! Sam was very grateful for being filled in on what his duties were. The PO told him he had had a string of young officers sent to him since peace had broken out as there was nothing much for them to do until a real job was found for them. Sam asked him if he knew Jack Peters and discovered that they had been ashore together on their off-duty nights so from then on Sam knew he would soon learn the ropes with Petty Officer "Chalky" White as his mentor. He had been a jaunty for about ten years and there was not much he didn't know about the antics of Jack ashore after a long period at sea.

While this discussion was taking place, Chalky had parked the jeep in a road which led to the red light district. All was quiet as it was not yet midnight. During a lull in the conversation they both heard the sound of someone trotting along the road pulling a rickshaw. What was strange was the fact that the rickshaw wallah was wearing shoes. Normally they worked in bare feet and you could hear the "slap" of the soles of the feet on the tarmac road. The two looked at each other and both decided simultaneously to get out of the jeep and see what was happening. Round the corner came a tall, tubby, capless matelot running between the shafts of a rickshaw with a grinning coolie as passenger, wearing the matelot's cap on top of his turban. Sam and Chalky couldn't suppress their mirth but nevertheless ordered the sailor to stop and asked him what he thought he was doing. The sailor, who had obviously had a few drinks, told them the coolie looked very tired and had difficulty in pulling him so they had exchanged places! Sam and Chalky looked at each other. Sam shook his head, indicating he didn't want to do anything about it, so Chalky told the sailor to pay off the rickshaw man and get in the jeep. The matelot did as he was told and asked if he was "in the rattle". Chalky replied it would be up to the Officer to decide if he was going to be charged. Then they set off for the Regulating Office in the docks. On the way, Sam wondered how on earth he would describe the conduct of the sailor. In fact, it did not really appear that he had committed an offence, so when they got to the docks the sailor was told to go and join his ship and "thank his lucky stars the Officer was in a good mood". When they got inside the office the two burst out laughing and Chalky had to admit that in all his ten years as a naval policeman he hadn't had such an experience before. It was getting near the time for the liberty boats to take the sailors back to their ships so they had a brew of tea and went outside to give a "presence" so that all would go smoothly. Fortunately, sailors under naval discipline were wary of behaving in an unseamanlike manner when returning to their ships, so despite the shouting and rolling about there were no unpleasant incidents on Sam's first night as an ANPM, although quite a few with an exaggerated rolling gait had to be assisted down the steps by members the shore patrol to prevent them falling into the "hoggin".

Sam was invited to have dinner with David Lower and his wife Lucy a week after the two men had met in the Ward Room. Initially it presented a problem for Sam as he had no idea what he could take with him as a token of his appreciation. To begin with he dismissed the idea of taking flowers as he could not recall having seen any florists' shops in Colombo. He was about to ask one of the stewards for advice when he overheard someone saying that the locals were very appreciative of gifts of a bottle of Duty-Free Gin as the local "brew" was ghastly. That settled it. Sam still had a couple of bottles left from his Vizag. days as sea-going sailors were entitled to a monthly ration of Gordons or Plymouth Gin, so he took one along and it was much appreciated. He was glad he did, for Lucy Lower was a superb cook and even offered her home-made Devonshire splits instead of rolls to eat with the fish soup which was a variation of Bouillabesse. The three spent a pleasant evening reminiscing about the Westcountry and after some friendly banter concerning the merits and demerits of Devon and Cornwall they unanimously and diplomatically concluded "the west" was the best. Sam left on foot, saying he would get a rickshaw when he reached the main road as he had seen a little knot of the tiny vehicles gathered at the turning down to the Lowers' bungalow. He assured his hosts he would be more than delighted to come again "before too long" as they put it, but of course Their Lordships had other plans for Sam and he never went back to the tranquil spot.

The following night Sam experienced another of the coincidences which sometimes happened in the Services during the war. In one respect the Royal Navy is like a large extended family because of the fact that there were not such vast numbers of men in the "Andrew" as there are in the Army for example. There were still some sailors from the US Seventh Fleet coming ashore for their last look at Colombo before going home to the States so Sam and Chalky White decided to do a tour of the docks on foot just to reassure themselves that nothing untoward was happening away from the mainstream, so to speak. As they walked along behind a group of officers in their number six uniforms, Sam thought he recognised the broad shoulders of one of the men in front, so to test himself he called out softly, "Stewart". The man turned round and it was indeed Stewart Collins from Cadgwith who had been at school with him in Helston. Both were astounded as neither one knew the other had joined the Navy. Stewart was in Coastal Forces and about to go to Rangoon. He couldn't work out why they were needed there now that the war was over but that was the order they had been given. Sam told him about COSU and learned to his horror that Stewart had heard a buzz that the MLs from Vizag. were going to be taken out to sea and sunk by gunfire as they were old and considered no longer economical to run in a peace-time Navy. Whether or not that actually happened Sam was unable to find out as when his two nights of duty were over he was informed he was being sent to Bombay. Of course, no one knew why. That is the way of the Royal Navy at times. He was to meet Stewart again in a few years when they were both in Education.

CHAPTER EIGHTEEN

SINGAPORE SWAN SONG

It didn't take long for Sam to pack his kit as he had not taken much from his sea chest. There were not many "Goodbyes" to be said, just a hurried phone call to David and Lucy Lower to thank them for their kindnesses to him and to express the hope that one day they would meet in the U.K. Sam knew that Chalky White would see a signal to the effect that Sam would no longer be on his list of ANPMs and the rest of his farewells consisted mainly of telling those he had met in the Ward Room at Lake Road that he was leaving for Bombay. In seemingly no time at all Sam found himself once more travelling by Indian train on his own. In a curious sort of way he was glad to be alone so that he could collect his thoughts concerning the immediate unknown future and ponder about the part he had played in the COSU operations. In the end he decided it was not a very productive exercise and settled down to a couple of days' idleness on the train. From time to time after he had left the navy he did wonder if there was still a sonic warfare unit hidden away somewhere from prying eyes and quite by chance he read an article in the *Sunday Express* on the 19th April 1998. It was the heading "Sound tactics from the Army with no soldiers" which caught his eye. It stated that British soldiers had used a secret weapon to keep the peace in Bosnia. It went on to describe recordings of a convoy of heavy armour were played to give guerrillas the impression the British Army was up to strength when in fact there had been a massive withdrawal of troops.

The article concluded that the "masterful deception" had kept the peace without any troops actually being there and referred to it as a "war of noise". Recognition at last! Sam was prompted at that point to see if he could make contact with Joss on the Internet but the search revealed nothing. Sam was not surprised. Sam's only tangible memory of Joss remained a post-war snap of him with his baby son, which had been sent before they lost touch.

After reaching the magnificent railway station at Bombay, Sam took the train for Deolali where there was a camp for what one sailor termed "odds and sods". He was right, of course. People wandered about rather aimlessly awaiting their fate. While there Sam was given one job to do. He had to escort a party of WRNS to the docks. There was considerable unrest in Bombay at the time due to the movement for independence and there had been some ugly street demonstrations against British rule, so RN lorries were being given armed escorts. Sam was given a Webley revolver and ammunition and he sat with two ratings armed with Lee Enfields in the back of the three-ton truck with the girls behind them, sitting on their kit. The journey passed off quietly except for one incident when the traffic was held up by a bullock cart which had shed its load in the middle of the street. The usual crowd had gathered to watch and see if there was anything worth carrying off and one or two started shouting at the occupants of the lorry which was being driven by an Indian civilian. He was leaning out of the cab shouting at the hapless bullock-cart driver to hurry up and get out of the way. This did not please the people in the street and they started shouting at the foreign occupiers in the lorry, who of course did not understand one word of their insults. Sam and his two ratings stood up so that the Indians could see they were armed, and to make it quite clear Sam tapped the holster of his revolver and tried to look as fierce as possible while he spoke to the sailors and told them to fire in the air if things started to get out of hand. Fortunately, after an uncomfortable minute or two of much shouting and blaring of horns of the traffic behind, the driver managed to move off. The return journey passed off without incident. Thus ended Sam's contact with the Indian people. Fortunately his abiding memory of them was as smiling and friendly, and he passed off the moment of unpleasantness as an understandable demonstration of their need to manage their own affairs.

One morning after breakfast, about a week later, Sam was called to the camp office and shown a signal stating that he had been promoted to Lieutenant and appointed as Flotilla Officer of 485 LCA Flotilla, Singapore. The *Highland Chieftain* was due to leave Bombay for Singapore in 48 hours. His not to reason why, though the thought did cross his mind there would be no need for a dozen assault landing craft in peacetime Singapore! There was nothing for it but to return to his tented cabin and pack. His "blues" were near the top in anticipation of a return to the UK so he buried them beneath his tropical uniforms so that they would be out of sight when he unpacked in Singapore. They would not be needed for a while.

The next morning after breakfast Sam boarded the three-ton truck which was to take him and half a dozen other officers to Bombay docks. There were no incidents this time, just the usual bumpy ride punctuated with jolting stops caused by careless pedestrians ambling across the street in the path of the lorry, despite the Indian driver's virtually constant application of the horn, accompanied by a torrent of abuse in Hindustani. On arrival at the jetty the party went aboard the *Highland Chieftain* and Sam was allocated a cabin which he had to share with a cheerful Sub. Lieutenant called William Wallace.

When William and Sam had settled in they went up to the boat deck to watch the arrival of the other passengers. They were a motley crowd of soldiers, sailors and airmen who had been selected to "hold the fort" while Singapore was getting back to normal after the Japanese occupation and to replace those who were due for demobilisation. Each person had been allocated a Group Number, the lowest numbers being given to those who had joined the service at the beginning of the war. It seemed a pretty fair system but of course there was always the risk of being held back if the "exigencies" of the service so demanded, and conversely if key personnel were needed in the UK to get the country back to normal, they were granted early repatriation. As the people walked silently up the gangplank, the expressions of resignation on their faces reminded Sam of one of his father's favourite expressions - on occasions when he came home from school, having lost a football match, or, more frequently, with a pile of extra homework to do by the next day, he would enter the house looking really downcast and that would prompt his father to shake him out of his temporary misery by stating in a loud voice, "Every picture tells a story!" More often than not his father's tactic would elicit a reluctant grin from Sam and invariably he would recover after being given one of his mother's yeast buns to tide him over until the evening meal was ready. There was no such palliative awaiting the reluctant travellers boarding the *Highland Chieftain*, but some wag did put a Gracie Fields record on the ship's public address system. It was the popular wartime song which began, "There's many a troopship just leaving Bombay, bound for old Blighty's shore." The irony of the situation was not lost on the passengers and William and Sam could see them grinning at one another. Shortly afterwards a low buzz of conversation could be heard as the troops began searching for their billets. "Perhaps it's not going to be such a bad trip after all," thought Sam.

That evening after dinner, one of the cargo hatches was cleared and arc lights were rigged up on the derricks in readiness for an ENSA concert. The troops gathered round and sat on the deck, ready for an evening's entertainment. After the usual fare of popular songs, dances and comedy sketches, it was announced that Elsie and Doris Waters were going to perform one of their double acts. Sam had first seen them in the more sedate surroundings of the Chapel at Lancing College when they attended as guests of the Ward Room of HMS *King Alfred*. This time they were much less inhibited and gave a performance which Sam's cabin companion described as "rather risqué". The troops stamped and cheered and applauded in their usual exuberant fashion but Sam had the distinct impression that the men did not wholeheartedly approve of two middle-aged ladies telling questionable jokes which were clearly not part of their radio repertoire. After all, the sisters were about the same age as the mothers of some of the young servicemen. He decided not to give a detailed account of the performance to his mother as Elsie and Doris were among her favourite radio entertainers and he didn't want to disillusion her. The evening ended with the community singing of wartime songs. The last one was the one which had been played as the troops were embarking but the men sang, "There's many a troopship leaving Bombay, bound for old Singapore" and sang it again with gusto for good measure.

The ship cast off early the next morning and Sam went up on deck to enjoy what he correctly assumed would be his last view of the Ghats mountains. He found it difficult to believe that well over a year ago at Christmas he was leaving "old Blighty's shore". In some ways it seemed an age and in others "just like yesterday", and now he was settling down to spend another Christmas at sea. Fortunately the ship was not crowded. The *Highland Chieftain* had not been permanently adapted to carry troops and was still a comfortable ship. Officers had the boat deck as their exercise area and Sam resorted to his usual shipboard routine of keeping fit by skipping with a length of cod line for twenty minutes minimum every morning and evening. He always skipped as fast as he could and the exertion helped considerably to use up his surplus energy as he had little else to do and no duties to perform. He continued reading History and began brushing up his French. He had always enjoyed both subjects and felt the need to further his knowledge.

One morning Sam awoke in his upper-tier bunk to find William sitting cross-legged on the deck below, holding a small prismatic compass in his hand. Sam refrained from comment and closed his eyes to hide his embarrassment. Later that day, to Sam's surprise, when the two were walking up and down the boat deck chatting idly, William revealed that he had been converted to Islam. This gave Sam an opportunity to let William know he had seen him orientating the compass that morning.

William grinned and said he wanted to face Mecca as all true Muslims do when at their devotions. He had guessed Sam had noticed what he was doing so he thought he ought to explain. Sam then told him about the trip on the *Mahanada* when he used a compass to work out the ship's position by dead reckoning, adding that all good sailors should carry a compass in wartime, just in case. William reminded Sam that the war was over now so he might as well put his compass to good use!

Now that the conflict was over the atmosphere on the *Highland Chieftain* was more relaxed than it had been on ships during the war at sea. Sam enjoyed reading G.M. Trevelyan's *History of England* and, realising his education was rather basic, wondered if he would be accepted for further training in a college of some sort. While contemplating his future he thought it would be a good idea to try his hand at some writing to see if he could make a sustained effort after such a long time doing little in the way of academic activity. He remembered being set an exercise by Miss Naytor when she asked the class to write a parody on Thomas Gray's "Elegy Written in a Country Churchyard". His effort was one which he would rather forget but a boy named Hichens composed an amusing parody, changing the line, "The lowing herd wind slowly o'er the lea" to "The motor racing swiftly o'er the lea". Sam thought at the time that it was a brilliant idea and he realised that his effort was mediocre as did Miss Naytor, who didn't choose to read it out. In view of this Sam set himself the task of doing a parody of W.H. Davies' "School's out".

Jack's Out!

Friendly Jack's ashore at last.
This news always travels fast.
Pub doors are left open wide
To lure matelots in their stride,
As they joyfully make way
To the town just for a day,
Their familiar rolling gait
Witness to rough seas of late.
Now they're eager for some sport
In another friendly port!

Sam read his first effort to William, who thought it "Ti kai". Sam was not exactly encouraged by the OK in Hindustani but at least William had not gone out of his way to give a convoluted but meaningless reply in order not to hurt Sam's feelings. He put it down in his mind as "Satisfactory, but could do better", and resolved to get a textbook of some sort when an opportunity arose.

Christmas was drawing ever closer, and the Naval Chaplain on board began rehearsing a volunteer choir in readiness. Sam didn't join. Although he had sung the odd solo for Sunday School anniversaries in Coverack he was well aware that he was no singer and in any case he couldn't read music and he knew that there wouldn't be any of his favourite Thomas Merritt's Cornish Carols such as "Hark the glad sound, the Saviour comes" or "Hail, sacred day, auspicious morn". He smiled to himself when he thought of the latter as there was a certain lady in the choir at Coverack who always sang "hauspicious morn" to the delight of the youngsters in the congregation. Sam wondered if he would be lucky enough to hear her sing that at Christmas 1946. He also doubted if the ship's choir would sing "While shepherds watched their flocks by night" to the tune Lingham, which was a "must" for all good Cornishmen, but that didn't prevent him from looking forward to the carol concert with eager anticipation, especially after he went along to listen to a rehearsal and knew he was in for a treat as there were some very good singers in the choir.

One afternoon after listening to a rehearsal Sam went up on the boat deck to do his skipping exercise and as he was temporarily tucking his shirt under one of the ship's life-rafts lashed to the deck, he fancied he could smell burning. It was not the usual smell of heated fuel oil emanating from the funnel so he decided to track down the source. When he got to the false after-funnel he could see a wisp of smoke coming from under the door in base of the funnel. He opened it gingerly and found a splinter mat smouldering away. He shut the door quickly and ran to the fire hose coupling which had two red buckets filled with sand beside it. He grabbed the buckets and dashed back to the funnel which was used as an upper deck ready-use locker and smothered the end of the splinter mat with the sand. Fortunately the smoke stopped and it became clear after a couple of minutes that the fire was out. Sam pulled the mat out of the funnel, closed the door and went to the bridge to report. The Second Officer came aft with him to the funnel to inspect the mat and satisfy himself the fire was indeed out and there was no further danger. He explained to Sam that during the forenoon the now redundant splinter mats which had been protecting the bridge were unshipped and stowed in the funnel space. He declared that it was almost certain one of the seamen told off for the job had taken the opportunity to have a "crafty fag" while sitting on one of the mats. He assured Sam that there would be a general "rollicking" delivered to the forenoon watch deck party when they next assembled for allocation of jobs, and regretted that as it was a dry ship he couldn't offer Sam a drink as a "thank you" gesture. Sam told him not to worry, adding that as there was no one around the incident could well be omitted from the ship's log as he certainly wouldn't publicise it.

The days passed slowly but pleasantly, with Sam enjoying the unaccustomed leisure and lack of responsibility. He began to enjoy his serious reading, punctuating it with short periods of letter writing. He recounted to his parents and to Grace what had happened to him since VJ day, and with tongue in cheek assured them that despite going further away from the UK it would not be too long before he would be on his way home. There being no censorship, he was delighted to be able to tell them his whereabouts for the first time since he had gone to sea.

Christmas Morning, 1946. They were approaching the Malacca Straits. After breakfast Sam went up to the boat deck to be alone with his thoughts, taking his skipping rope with him despite the fact that the evening before he had thought of giving himself a day free of exercise. It was a beautiful day with a stiff breeze whipping up the sea. Quite suddenly the ship altered course to starboard and began to lean over, taking everyone by surprise. Sam dashed to the port side and looked over to see a drifting mine floating harmlessly astern. Clearly it had been spotted at the last minute in the choppy sea by the Officer of the Watch who had no doubt taken the Quartermaster by surprise by the unexpected wheel order, "Hard a Starboard!" Nevertheless the QM executed the order at once as QMs do, and avoided a catastrophe. It was a dramatic reminder that although the war was officially over the dangers hadn't passed. Of course, having been born in Coverack and coming from a lifeboat-orientated family, Sam was well aware that at sea one should always expect the unexpected - or pay the price. As he watched the mine drift away in the choppy sea he uttered a silent prayer of thanks as he had done on many occasions before. Later, on that memorable Christmas Day, the Carol Concert on deck ended, uncharacteristically, with the singing of

> "Eternal Father, strong to save,
> Whose arm doth bind the restless wave ..."

Sam sang as lustily as he knew how the last two lines -

> "And ever let there rise to Thee
> Glad hymns of praise from land and sea."

During the forenoon that day, Sam wondered how the day would be celebrated on a "dry ship" without the usual Christmas cheer. Of course, the only "cheer" at his home in Coverack had always been his father's annual quaffing of Ginger Wine but Sam had been "corrupted" by his time in the Navy and felt the need to celebrate in true naval fashion. It gradually dawned on him that Naval Chaplains were resourceful chaps and that it might pay him to make a courtesy call at the Chaplain's cabin to wish him a Merry Christmas. To give himself confidence he asked William Wallace to accompany him. Despite his recent conversion to the Muslim faith, William was enthusiastic about the idea. He was no doubt remembering past Christmas Days with his family and wanted to share in the shipboard jollifications, though he told Sam he would not go back on his word and accept alcohol. As they made their way towards the Chaplain's cabin, Sam described briefly the sort of Christmas Day he used to spend in Coverack and playfully commented that Methodists and Muslims were two of a kind in that the consumption of alcohol by adherents was frowned upon by the former and forbidden by the latter but William was not to be drawn and merely nodded assent as they walked along the companion way. Sam admitted to William that he had found drinking to be a pleasant social habit but also that abstinence, when funds did not allow it, did not seriously inhibit social intercourse. As they approached the small stateroom which was the padre's cabin they could hear a buzz of animated conversation and on coming through the open door of the stateroom found a dozen or so junior officers, all with glasses in their hands, chatting amiably. The padre greeted William and Sam by saying, "Merry Christmas, boys. Go over and help yourselves to a drink." Sam surprised himself by choosing an orange juice to keep William company and they joined in the conversation which was, predictably, focused on Christmas past and "... this time next year". They spent a pleasant half hour getting to know shipboard people they hadn't come across before, then the padre announced it was nearly lunch time and offered up a prayer for the "loved ones we would all like to be with on this special day of the celebration of the Saviour's birth", and concluded with a prayer of thanks for deliverance from the drifting mine which had come so close to the ship. It was a fitting end to the forenoon, and after thanking the padre for his hospitality they all strolled soberly to the dining saloon.

They had a splendid meal of "poultry". It didn't taste like chicken, nor turkey. A wag suggested, in a loud voice, that it was vulture - an old joke to people serving in the Far East. Sam never did find out exactly what it was but it was much enjoyed and heavily disguised with rashers of bacon and succulent stuffing. It was followed by an oblong of Christmas pudding. Sam recognised it as having been extracted from packs of American K Rations. He was quite familiar with the block, which was packed solid with raisins, currants, sultanas, chopped nuts etc. Landing craft crews often had these packs when away from base and they were much appreciated when it was not possible to have hot meals.

After Christmas lunch, William and Sam retreated to the boat deck once more. Their cabin was stiflingly hot so they chose a shady spot beneath one of the lifeboats and sat chatting contentedly until William succumbed to sleep, and Sam followed suit after a few minutes. They awoke just as the short tropical twilight began, accompanied by a cooling shower which often occurred in those latitudes. They hurriedly went below and after putting on their shirts made their way to the Carol Concert which was to be held on the cargo hatch which had served as a stage for the ENSA entertainment in Bombay harbour. It was an unaccustomed luxury to be steaming along with arc lights blazing and the pianist playing Christmas music while people gathered expectantly and found vantage points just as they had on their last night in India.

The Carol Concert was introduced by the Naval Chaplain. It began with a couple of items by the newly formed *Highland Chieftain* Choir, and then several carols were sung in unison, interspersed with solos by men who were obviously talented musicians. The padre delivered a short Christmas homily before the final hymn which was "Eternal Father", then the audience dispersed quietly and those who felt in need of a snack were invited to go to the saloon before turning in. Contrary to his original expectations, in retrospect Sam found it was indeed a Christmas Day which he would remember for decades to come when he described his last Christmas Day in the Royal Navy to a captive family audience after the Queen's speech and before the children were finally "released" and left to their own devices.

Boxing Day came and went in a haze. No one felt inclined to make a special day of it but in the afternoon an enthusiastic Army type organised an inter-services Tug of War contest and Sam was inveigled into being one of the Royal Navy team. Not surprisingly the sailors won and were awarded a trophy which was an old tin mug inscribed with the words "Top T.O.W. team" painted in black by an unsteady hand. Thus ended the Christmas celebrations aboard the *Highland Chieftain*. The ship was due to dock the following morning. Packing had to be done and there was much speculation as to what conditions would be like in Singapore. Official news bulletins from SEAC (South East Asia Command) did not reflect what life was like for the "ordinary" service personnel so rumour was rife. Sam was already hardened to the effect that buzzes could have on him so he again decided to follow Asquith's dictum and "Wait and see." He had the distinct feeling that Sod's Law would be in operation. He was not far wrong. Two distinct impressions remained in Sam's mind regarding his landing in Singapore. One was the embarrassing spectacle of Japanese POWs bowing when they came face to face with him - one or two even went on their knees in the dock area when they saw his bits of gold braid on his shoulders. The other horrendous sight was watching British troops who had been POWs taken aboard UK-bound ships. They were virtually yellow-skinned skeletons. Some managed to walk up the gangplank, others made it with the aid of a crude crutch or the helping hand of a sailor. Many, if not most, were carried. It created a well of anger inside Sam. He had not been warned about it and he discovered that in this instance he could not forgive his enemies, despite his Sunday School upbringing. He thought of friends who he knew had been taken prisoner, and wondered how they had fared. He was to learn later that Frank had been drowned by the Japanese by being taken out to sea on an old ship which was full of prisoners and then sunk. Jack survived and returned to Coverack only to go blind after a few years due to malnutrition. Billy came home physically unscathed, though a walking skeleton. He remained in the navy and eventually drew his pension.

While on the *Highland Chieftain* Sam had wondered how he would cope as Officer in Charge of 485 Landing Craft Assault Flotilla. He could see "no rhyme nor reason" in the appointment, so on reporting his arrival he was not in the least surprised to learn that 485 Flotilla had already been disbanded. He was once more "surplus to requirements" and spent a few days in a Combined Operations Holding Unit Camp. It was camping out with a difference in that he had a bell tent to himself and a Japanese POW steward to look after him. The Jap turned out to be quite a resourceful chap. By sign language Sam made him understand he did not like sleeping in his bedroll on the hard-baked ground. Somehow the Jap managed to purloin half a dozen very comfortable oblong sheets of rubber. Sam indicated his pleasure by giving him a cigarette, for which he showed his gratitude by bowing repeatedly until Sam told him to stop. A couple of days later Sam was given a berth aboard LCT 1329. The skipper had just been demobbed so there was just one officer on board. Jim Knight proved to be a very pleasant fellow and despite being somewhat of an interloper on a small ship with a crew that had been together for some time, Sam was made to feel at home.

There was one incident on board 1329 of which Sam was not proud. It occurred when some POWs were sent to unload stores. Sam saw a crew member offer one of the POWs a cigarette and, losing his temper, Sam gave the kindly crew member a severe dressing down - for committing the very act he himself had done in the Holding Camp. Sam told the sailor that had their roles been reversed the Jap would probably have pulled out his finger nails one by one rather than give him a cigarette. The surprised sailor apologised but was clearly annoyed with Sam, who was annoyed with himself. In mitigation, Sam had seen a signal a few minutes before, warning sailors to be on their guard as a POW had been caught emptying harmful chemicals in a ship's water supply when working on board, so he called the sailor back and explained why he had got angry. The sailor told him not to worry, he understood. Later that day when the contents of the signal were made known to the crew they could be heard expressing their feelings in the usual flowery language and Sam felt slightly vindicated but nevertheless remained annoyed with himself for having let fly.

Time passed slowly. The ship was just swinging round the buoy and there wasn't enough work to keep the crew occupied. There's a limit to what you can do on a stationary Tank Landing Craft. One forenoon a signal marked Immediate arrived for Sam, instructing him to report to the NOIC's office forthwith. He put on some clean "whites" and proceeded as instructed. He did not see the Naval Officer in Charge but was directed to an office where a WRNS officer told him he was being offered a chance to remain in the Royal Navy as a regular officer. Sam fleetingly had visions of going back to the UK at once for retraining at Dartmouth but he had sense enough to ask outright if it meant just that. The Wren smiled knowingly and explained that it would happen "in due course" but meanwhile he would remain in the Far East for what she termed the foreseeable future. Sam decided not to burn his boats at once and told her he would think about the offer and make his decision "in due course". In actual fact by the time he had reached the door of the spacious office he had virtually made up his mind. Firstly, he wanted to go home, secondly he thought he could be put on the beach in a few years' time when politicians might decide to get voted in again by making economies in the Royal Navy and operate a Geddes axe as they did after the First World War. His father had told him that was why his uncle, Seth Exelby, had emigrated to New Zealand when he was "axed". The next time he went ashore, Sam had made up his mind and went back to the NOIC's office, told the Wren he would prefer to be demobbed, and asked when Group 43 would be going home. Of course, she didn't know but thought it wouldn't be too long.

Ten Dollar Note issued by the Japanese when occupying Malaya
After the surrender the notes were valueless and some were found abandoned on the jetty in Singapore.

There were all kinds of rackets in Singapore at this unsettled time. At night a Guard Boat patrolled the harbour to deter the local Chinese from trying to buy "spare" stores from ships at anchor. One night at about 2100 during the First Watch, 1329 was hailed by the Guard Boat. There was a bit of a party going on to say farewell to an Able Seaman. Sam and Jim were sitting in the minuscule cabin enjoying a John Collins and pretending they couldn't hear the noise being made on the Mess Deck. They didn't hear the Guard Boat's "What ship?" but they did hear the reply, which was not "LCT 1329" but the phrase, "Effin 'ardship, mate. Why don't you f... off?" In practically no time at the Guard Boat had come alongside and an irate Sub Lieutenant confronted Sam and Jim who had come out of their cabin. They both invited him to their Ward Room and there apologised profusely, assuring the Sub. they would find the culprit and sort him out, adding that all the crew was due to go home shortly and that it would be a pity at this stage to spoil the good record of anyone for making such a stupid remark during a farewell party. Meanwhile Jim had poured out a large Gin and Tonic and offered it to the Sub, saying, "Here, old boy, get outside that before you cast off. You've earned it." The Sub hesitated, then said, "Well, all right, just the one." Meanwhile the Coxswain had invited the stoker and Leading Seaman off the Guard Boat to have "sippers" with the crew. Not many sailors can resist the offer of a free drink of rum saved from the daily ration, so they both accepted. Twenty minutes later they all left 1329 amid shouts from her crew saying, "Come aboard again, mate!" and as the boat drew out of earshot, other less polite invitations.

Time dragged on. LCT 1329's cargo of naval stores in the tank space were gradually taken ashore when required by the Base Stores Officer until just a few drums of grey paint were left. Frustrated by this state of affairs, Sam went ashore to see if he could bring the paint to the jetty as he had been told the ship was being sold to a Chinese firm of traders and that she would be handed over as soon as the stores had been discharged. A friendly Supplies Warrant Officer took Sam on one side and told him to "ditch them". A couple of nights later, after the Guard Boat had passed by, there was a flurry of movement aboard 1329, followed by some distinct splashes after some heavy objects were trundled to the lowered ramp and given a shove. After a decent interval of a couple of days, Sam sent a signal by Aldis lamp to NOIC stating quite truthfully that all cargo had been discharged. There followed three days of anxiety until the long-awaited signal was received ordering 1329 to be brought alongside for paying off. Sam did so, managing to carry away a couple of guard rails on the jetty in the process because he had misjudged the amount of way as he came alongside. He felt bad about having to pollute the harbour but desperate times require desperate measures and the crew were desperate to get home. Thus ended Sam's Singapore Swan Song.

While he was waiting in the Combined Ops. Holding Camp for repatriation, a large parade was held in Singapore at which Admiral Lord Louis Mountbatten took the salute. It was a splendid occasion and Sam enjoyed being part of it. As he had no duties to perform he started going sightseeing, ending one trip in the Raffles Hotel, which he had heard so much about. He also spent a day at a war crimes trial. It was a sobering experience. A Japanese Sergeant Major was accused of murdering two Chinese civilians who had been caught helping a British soldier. The Jap admitted torturing the men before killing them. Asked to explain what he did, he described, through an interpreter, that he put match heads under their finger nails then lit the match sticks so that they would ignite when the flame reached the match heads. The prisoner's face was impassive as he admitted what he had done and sat waiting for the interpreter to tell the court. One day in that building was enough for Sam. He subsequently learned that the Sergeant Major had been sentenced to death for his crimes committed in Changi gaol.

Another pleasant excursion while waiting to go home was an evening in the Garrison Theatre where the well-known pianist Solomon was giving a recital. There were some Dutch ladies in Singapore who had been interned by the Japanese in Java. The ladies were lodged in a hotel while waiting for repatriation and Naval Officers were invited to help in their rehabilitation by escorting them on evenings out. Sam volunteered. He called at the hotel at the appointed time and was amused at having to sign for the smiling, fair-haired lady who was to be his companion for the evening. Gerda appeared to be quite a few years older than Sam and fortunately spoke reasonable English as most Dutch people seem to be able to do. Sam had expected her to be emaciated after her ordeal but she was what his mother would describe as "painfully thin" and he knew Mary's remedy for that would be "a few pasties to fill her out a bit". Sam had been warned not to ask about her treatment by the Japanese, so after a few false starts - one cannot discuss the weather in Singapore as it is so predictable - Sam told her all about his beloved Cornwall in general and Coverack in particular. She seemed to be quite interested as she said she had never been to England. Of course, Sam was at pains to tell her that Cornwall was a very special and separate part of the UK which used to have its own language. Before he could expound on the subject they had arrived at the theatre and Sam turned his conversation to the evening ahead. He admitted to Gerda that he didn't know very much about music but said he was a keen listener and had heard Solomon on the wireless, adding that he wanted to go to the concert so that he would be able to write and tell his parents about it as they were lovers of good music and his father was a chapel organist. He was pleased he had thought of telling Gerda about that because as each piece was performed she gave him a little résumé before it began and that made it all the more enjoyable.

After signing Gerda back in the hotel, Sam made his way back to the camp and the following morning he was told to pack as he would be going home on the *Indomitable* the following day. It was true! Sod's Law did not operate. He boarded an LCM with a couple of dozen other naval people and was ferried to the aircraft carrier, which he had last seen in

1942 when she was in the Mediterranean. Once aboard he was informed he would be working his passage back as a second watch officer. He was relieved in a strange sort of way as he could not envisage being a passenger on a Royal Navy ship.

The "Sons of Heaven" going into the Municipal Buildings, Singapore, to sign the surrender, January 1946

CHAPTER NINETEEN

ENGLAND, HOME AND BEAUTY

It took Sam some time before he could find his way round *Indomitable.* One of his duties when on the First Watch from 2000 to midnight was to conduct "rounds". This entailed being taken by the duty Buffer round the ship to ensure that all was well. The sailors stood to attention when rounds were called as they hurried through the mess decks. It is a tradition in the Royal Navy for an officer to keep his cap on when entering the crew's quarters on duty. At all other times the cap was carried under the arm to signify there was no need for anyone to acknowledge his presence. Sam had known the drill since his days as a Bosun's Mate on *Pathfinder*. He remembered it was the custom to point out any object which had not been stowed away properly. As he progressed Sam would espy what he considered to be the deliberate mistake and tell the Petty Officer to get it stowed properly without stopping to find out who was responsible. That way satisfied everyone and no one got in trouble. Actually there was a very good reason for keeping the lower decks tidy as in an emergency when men had to run to their stations as fast as they could, someone tripping over an unexpected object lying in his path could fall down and those following close behind could in turn fall on top of him, creating a real hazard which could result in endangering the ship, especially if, as often happens in an emergency the lights failed, leaving only the faint blue "police lights" to cast a faint glow on the scene. So, each night when Sam had the First Watch he would point out something to be put right and carry on the tour, which included a visit to the ship's cells to see if the prisoners were all right by asking each one in turn and of course he checked that the guards were doing their duty correctly - while he was there, at least. One evening Sam saw a familiar stocky figure approaching as he marched through the corridor. It was Herbert Sobey, a fellow pupil from Helston School who lived at Garras. He had joined the "Andrew" as a Writer a while before Sam. When he was stopped by the Duty Officer, Herbert did not know what to say until Sam said "'Ow 'ee doin' an boy?" Herbert took a look at Sam and laughed, then they had a quick exchange of news from their part of Cornwall while the Buffer waited to continue the rounds. Sam did not come across Herbert again for some thirty years or more, when they discovered they had been living within a few miles

Officers at Divisions on the Flight Deck of HMS *Indomitable* in the Bay of Biscay, 1946

Sam is fifth from right on the front row.
Inset: HMS *Indomitable* from the air

of each other for most of that time. They then optimistically made a pact to meet again in another thirty years!

Keeping watch on such a large ship as the *Indomitable* was a new experience for Sam. The course was set by the "Pilot" or Navigator, and the Watch Officers had the responsibility of seeing the course was maintained and any deviation necessary to assure the safety of the ship duly recorded in the log, as was the ship's position, which was checked at regular intervals. They did not encounter many ships on the way to Aden and no large alterations of course were needed to avoid ships whose bearings remained constant as they approached. During one watch when there was not a great deal to be done except the routine duties, Sam counted a dozen telephones on the bridge. They were used mainly for routine reports from vital parts of the ship such as the Engine Room and were easily dealt with during a quiet watch but Sam knew that when in action it must have been different story and he was glad he had done most of his service on small ships. He was amused one forenoon when a rather officious OOW spent some time looking at sailor-passengers through binoculars as they strolled about the Flight Deck. After a while the OOW sent a bridge messenger to bring a couple of sailors wearing jungle green up to the bridge. When they arrived the Officer of the Watch gave the two bewildered men a dressing down for not having shaved that morning. The rest of the bridge party, including Sam, found it necessary to concentrate hard on what they were doing at the moment as it was extremely difficult not to laugh out loud. One imagined those two unfortunate matelots would not be applying to remain in the Royal Navy when they got back to the UK! When they had left the bridge the OOW turned to Sam and asked if he knew why on earth those men were dressed in jungle green. Sam explained as gently as he could, but loud enough for everyone to hear, that the sailors were almost certainly members of a Combined Operations Unit and that wearing tropical whites when on a landing craft carrying infantry up a chaung to attack a Japanese position was tantamount to committing suicide. There ensued what might be termed "an awkward silence" after Sam's explanation; then the OOW announced he was going to check the ship's position on the chart. The broad grins on the faces of Sam's companions told their own story.

Officer-Passengers were only required to do one watch in every twenty four hours so there was plenty of spare time. Sam continued his reading and joined one of the ship's hockey teams which were assembled on an ad hoc basis depending on who was available at the time. It was a novel experience playing on the Flight Deck at sea and he was glad he had managed to adopt some of the techniques which Flex had passed on to him when they played matches in COSU. During one match Sam received such a whack on his right hand that he had to go to the Sick Bay for treatment. The Doc. examined the hand and asked Sam how long he had had a row of warts on the back of his hand. Sam explained that the warts, or whatever they were, had appeared three or four months previously after he grazed his knuckles when trying to start up an Onan generator on board one of the MLs in Vizag. The Doc. then told Sam it was probably some kind of dermatological reaction and that if he could come to the Sick Bay during the following forenoon he would try to get rid of them.

He was as good as his word and bound up Sam's hand after putting some kind of chemical on the warts. Nevertheless Sam continued playing hockey when he could and by the time the ship reached Portsmouth most of the warts had disappeared, for which Sam was truly thankful.

By the time *Indomitable* got to Aden Sam was ready for a run ashore. He was not particularly interested in combing the bazaar for presents as he already had a royal blue Indian sari for Grace and in Malaya he had bought one of the new-fangled bikinis. Of course the latter garment was purchased with the idea of giving Sam pleasure, if he could persuade Grace to wear it when they went swimming in Coverack. He had a ring from Ceylon for his mother which had an opal in the centre and five white diamonds around it, and a briar pipe for his father (probably made in Brum). He also intended giving his father a couple of half-pound tins of pusser's pipe tobacco to go with it. There was a silver bracelet for Emily. He had already sent a carpet by sea for Alexander and his wife Pat who would be setting up home with their baby daughter Wynn, whom Alexander had yet to see. He had been sent by hospital ship to Johannesburg from Burma for special treatment of some kind of tropical illness which he had caught in the jungle. Sam was pleased when his cabin companion suggested he might like to accompany him on a trip to see the Queen of Sheba's wells, which were in the foothills behind Aden.

The pair set off in their Red Sea rig of blue trousers and white shirt. After a brief visit to the bazaar, where Sam bought a lighter to replace the inscribed one which he had been given by his crew when he left Preston - unfortunately he must have dropped it somewhere in Colombo - the pair took a taxi up to the wells. There they felt the searing heat of the Yemen afternoon as they marvelled at the construction which had been laid down about a thousand years before the birth of Christ. There was no sign of any water. Presumably it was underground but Len and Sam were back on board before either one thought of asking about it and it was too late then. Sam never did find out.

The *Indomitable* left Aden early the next morning. Sam was not on duty when they went through the Suez Canal. After the relatively broad passage through the Bitter Lakes it seemed the massive ship would never negotiate the narrow ribbon of water but of course she did, proceeding at a sort of majestic slow march speed. The Egyptian pilot sat on a specially constructed high platform chair amidships. It was similar in design to the ones used by tennis umpires at Wimbledon but much, much larger, and was connected by a telephone line to the navigating bridge on the island, which was on the starboard side and did not provide a practical viewpoint for the precise navigation needed to negotiate the narrow confines of the canal. The experience was quite a contrast compared with the outward passage on the merchant ship *Mahanada*. There was no shore leave at Port Said. No one minded. Everyone wanted to get home. Calm seas greeted them to the Mediterranean. It was a pleasure to be on board ship.

Sam had a wonderful view when he was on duty, high up on the navigating bridge. One day he was taking a bearing of an oil tanker which was crossing their path in order to make sure they were not on a collision course when the OOW said, "That's a Shell tanker." She was still painted in wartime grey with no distinctive funnel markings.

Sam took another look through his binoculars and said, "I think it's a BP tanker."

The OOW replied, "OK, I bet you half a crown it's a Shell boat."

"You're on," said Sam.

When they got closer, the OOW told the bunting tosser to flash the tanker and ask, "What ship?"

Back came the reply in slow speed which Sam was able to read - "British Engineer". He was already smiling when the signalman told the OOW her name. "Don't worry," said Sam. "I'll let you off lightly. Buy me a G. and T. in the Ward Room later on."

Gin, being Duty Free, was only 3d. a glass, the same price as orange squash. Sam had seen British tankers going in and out of Falmouth since he was a child and knew their silhouette as well as he knew those of the Coverack fishing boats. He admitted this later when chatting to the OOW over his prize G. and T.

When they reached Gibraltar, Sam was pleased to go ashore. Previously he had never managed to get beyond the dock area due to shortage of time. He slipped ashore with Len Toms and they did the round of the shops which did not appear to be suffering from the shortages like those of the UK. They didn't have time to make their way to the summit. It was good to see British Bobbies in their uniforms, though many had unmistakably Spanish features. Sam bought a Heath's *French Grammar* in Malin's Book Shop. It was to stand him in good stead when he went to college.

Anticipation was evident as they left Gibraltar. Everyone knew the next port of call would be Pompey, then, "Home is the sailor, home from the sea!" It was a saying Sam had heard many times. Fortunately at that stage in his education he was unaware it was a saying which R.L.

Stevenson thought appropriate as an epitaph for a seaman. As the homecoming excitement grew on board ship, someone had the brilliant idea of organising a sweepstake as to the exact time the ship would pass Nab Tower before entering Portsmouth. Sam didn't take part as he already knew the ETA through his duties on the bridge and the actual time wouldn't be far off that, all things being well. He was looking forward to going up through the English Channel after making The Lizard and leaving Coverack on the port beam. In the event they passed his home village after dark and he wasn't on duty anyway but his disappointment was only momentary. There were much more exciting rendezvous to think about.

Passing through the Bay of Biscay on an aircraft carrier doing fifteen knots is not quite the same as rolling around on a destroyer in the Bay, escorting a convoy doing all of nine knots, so on this last voyage Sam was scarcely aware of the rough seas in the Gulf of Gascony as the French call it, though he did recall it was one of the two places where he had been seasick. It is strange how the English call the channel the English Channel and the French lay claim to the Bay when both stretches of water are in reality international. Mercifully Sam was asleep in his bunk when they left Coverack abeam after making The Lizard so he didn't spend any time speculating about what was happening at home as the ship went up-Channel. It was, of course, not possible to let the villagers know that a Coverack man was on board by giving three blasts on the siren. Coverack men serving on merchant ships had been known to persuade their captain to do this in pre-war days when names and dates when ships were expected to pass The Lizard were published in a weekly Shipping News and villagers with relatives on board kept a look out.

The final day on board *Indomitable* dawned at last. Sam and Len were in the last stages of packing when it was announced that Nab Tower was abeam and the name of the lucky winner of the sweepstake would be given out shortly. By the time their cabin was made shipshape once more and their kit ready to be taken to the disembarkation point, Sam and Len heard the name of the winner announced and that he would receive a prize of just over £200, which was a small fortune at that time. Soon afterwards the Customs Officers came aboard and began interviewing the homecoming passengers as they queued to get off the ship. When Sam's turn came he reeled off the names of the "rabbits" he was bringing home as presents and souvenirs from a list he had prepared the night before. He had forgotten about the tobacco and cigarettes so when he was reminded he admitted he had the maximum amount of each, at which the Customs man said, "OK, off you go. Enjoy your demob leave." It was as simple as that, no bands playing on the quayside, just a scramble to get his kit together and make for the train to London. Len got swallowed up in the crowd and he never saw him again but they had already wished each other well in civilian life so it was just a case of "ships that pass in the night" as Len had put it when they said "Goodbye".

Travelling in a happy daze over a familiar route, it was not long before Sam found himself waiting on Euston Station with a crowd of other Combined Ops. types, all bound for Roseneath. He bundled into a compartment when the train came in, slung his case in the rack and happily settled down in readiness for a night in the train, keeping his greatcoat on for comfort as he did not feel very warm. The other sun-tanned occupants of the carriage did likewise and after the usual exchange of servicemen's information regarding old ships, home towns and so on, the compartment went quiet and as if by common consent everyone was soon asleep.

The next morning the people bound for the demob. centre were collected from the station and when they arrived they were given breakfast and told the process of leaving the Royal Navy would start at eleven o'clock, when they would have had time to settle down in their allotted cabins. When Sam gave his name to the PO on the reception desk, he was told a letter had been waiting for him since about mid April. Puzzled, Sam opened it and found a brief note from Peter Fell who had passed that way some time before. He had enclosed an official receipt for a chronometer which had been used in COSU on operations. Peter somehow found it in his kit and knowing that Sam had signed for it, he had taken the watch to stores and got a signature for it in Sam's name because he was afraid Sam might be charged for it and chronometers were worth "an enormous amount." Sam was delighted and took it as a sign that all was going to go well. That night, after phoning home, he wrote a note of thanks to Peter, addressing it to his Chelsea home, thanking him for the receipt and giving a brief résumé of his activities since leaving Vizazgapatam.

The actual demobilisation process remained a bit of a blur in Sam's memory. He passed through a succession of offices, answering questions and filling out forms. Everyone was most kind and as he left each room he was wished, "Good luck in civvy street, Mr. Exelby!" He had never been called Mr. Exelby before: he had always been Sixth Former Sam Exelby. He began to warm to the idea.

Sam's last day in the Royal Navy dawned and after being given another hearty breakfast, despite rationing, he collected his civilian ration book and a First Class travel warrant to Helston and was informed he would have to collect his demob. suit at St. Budeaux before going home. The Pay Master told him his final pay, including Foreign Service leave pay and subsistence allowance, would be paid into his bank in the normal manner. He added that there no real hurry regarding the collection of his box of civilian clothes and he could go there when convenient. Sam was delighted to hear that and before leaving to catch the train he sent Grace a telegram saying he would be arriving in Preston in the late afternoon. He had not seen her for eighteen months but he just knew she would be as lovely as ever.

Sam was right. He was not disappointed. He was given a wonderful reception by the whole family and despite arriving almost without warning, was told he could stay as long as he liked. Greatly daring, he announced he would be expected at home quite soon and his parents had asked him to invite Grace to come to Cornwall with him for a holiday. To his surprise and delight, Mr. and Mrs. Predin agreed. The next day, Grace was granted some leave from her office job and a couple of days after that, the pair found themselves alone at last, in the train, on the way to St. Budeaux.

There was not a great deal of choice available when it came to choosing a mass-produced suit. It was governed by the sizes and colours available at that particular time. Sam got a sober green-coloured affair with a very faint pale orange pinstripe running through it. The only headgear available in his size was a trilby. When he tried it on he felt he looked like a staid old man and Grace thought the same, being unable to repress a giggle when Sam stood in front of her. At that point Sam determined he would keep the hat in reserve for rainy days and possibly funerals as it gave him a sombre air. In fact, he kept it out of sight until he went to study in Paris for a year. There it marked him out as an Englishman and provoked cries of "Chapeau!" when he stood in the queue for meals at the Lycée Sainte Barbe in the Latin Quarter.

The pair made their way back to Plymouth North Road Station after Sam had been kitted out and soon they were crossing the Tamar on Brunel's Bridge, which fortunately had escaped the blitz. There was no doubt about it: once more Sam felt a kind of indescribable physical change in his being as they chugged into Cornwall. Grace was looking at him and remarked quietly, "I can see that now you feel you are really at home,

Sam. In a strange sort of way it affects me as well, which is strange for a Lancashire lass who has only been to Cornwall with you once before." The "magic" that is Cornwall was at work. At that point an old fellow sitting in the corner seat of the compartment turned to Sam and said, "Your little maid is right, my 'andsome. 'Tis always like this when you're back 'ome. 'Tis something in the (h)air!" Everyone laughed and settled down to enjoy the "magic". In years to come, Sam was to savour the delightful experience of re-entering Cornwall many times, when bringing his pupils back home. They would open the windows of the carriage when half way across the bridge and shout, "Oggy, oggy, oggy, oi, oi, oi!" Non-local passengers would look askance at Sam, wondering why the "master" did nothing about what appeared to them to be rowdy behaviour. In reply, Sam would just smile as the children closed the windows and settled down again. The war had been fought so that those kids could have the freedom to show their love for their native land. After all, it was better than their being made to shout, "Sieg heil", which could have been the order of the day if the war had not been won.

In retrospect, Sam likened the bridge experience to the familiar photos printed on the wrapper of a bar of his favourite Five Boys Chocolate. There were five different facial expressions portrayed, beginning with one of a lad with an eager expression on his face, entitled "anticipation" and ending with a boy with a beaming smile entitled "realisation". The bridge was merely "anticipation" and he determined nothing was going to spoil the "realisation" of arriving back in Coverack. Nothing did. Even the villager who called out, rather cynically, "Home again, Sam?" implying he was frequently coming on leave, could not divert him from his feeling of total pleasure. He meekly replied, "Ess, I b'lieve," which was the stock reply to silly questions in Coverack, and continued unhurriedly up the steep hill towards Sunny Cove, savouring every step of the way, with Grace bringing up the rear, carrying the familiar cardboard box containing his demob suit.

Sam's mother, ever a model of politeness, greeted Grace first with her usual "smacker" followed by a bear hug, then after eyeing Sam up and down, said,"You've gone some thin, boy," and gave him her special "smacker" as the tears of relief flowed down her rosy cheeks. Everyone laughed at the expected comment, then she said, "Come on in. The pasties are ready. We'll soon feed you up, the pair of you." Sam was lost for words and blurted out the sentence he had heard quoted many times on the *Indomitable* during his final voyage - "Home is the sailor, home from the sea," before turning to his father who in his inimitable fashion had remained quietly in the background while his beloved Mary took the centre stage. The two men shook hands and George said quietly, "She's all right now, my son. She've got her baby back home, the last of the three, and there's some great licker of a pasty waiting for 'ee."

Sam's war was over.

C.W.712/R.A.

ADMIRALTY,

S.W.1.

10th May, 1946

Sir,

On the occasion of your release from Naval Service, I am commanded by My Lords Commissioners of the Admiralty to convey to you an expression of their recognition of your services in the Royal Navy during the war.

The good wishes of Their Lordships go with you on your return to civil life.

I am, Sir,

Your obedient Servant,

Sam's final message from the "Lords Commissioners of the Admiralty"

(Photograph: Dr David Hutson)